Workers' Guide
to Health and Safety

by Todd Jailer
Miriam Lara-Meloy
and Maggie Robbins

hesperian
health guides

Berkeley, California, USA

hesperian
health guides

Hesperian Health Guides
1919 Addison St. #304
Berkeley, California 94704 USA
www.hesperian.org

Credits

Editorial oversight
Todd Jailer
Sarah Shannon

Editorial management
Catherine Doe
Miriam Lara-Meloy
Kathleen Vickery

Additional writing and research
Kathleen Bubriski
Diane Bush
Aryn Faur
Michele Gonzalez Arroyo
Yelena Ionova
Michelle Loya-Talamantes
Tara Mathur
Tom O'Connor
Suzanne Teran

Indexing
Victoria Baker

Cover design
Kathleen Tandy

Design and production
Iñaki Fernandez
Shu Ping Guan
Kathleen Tandy

Art Coordination
Catherine Doe
Miriam Lara-Meloy

Community review coordination
Catherine Doe
Todd Jailer
Miriam Lara-Meloy
Maggie Robbins

Technical review
Garrett Brown
Tom Gassert
Enrique Medina
Rory O'Neill

Project support
Catherine Doe
Yelena Ionova

Additional project support
Kathleen Bubriski
Lilian Chen
Amber Collins
Kate Dube
Alison Hamburg
Sa Liu
Lila Marshall
Patricia Navarro
Candace O'Bryann
Sana Patel
Maria Rosales
Michaela Simmons
Nainwant Singh

Proofreading
Sunah Cherwin

Cover photography
Andrew Biraj/Reuters (Rana Plaza, Bangladesh)
Institute for Global Labour and Human Rights (sleeping worker, China)
Miriam Lara-Meloy (shoe factory, Indonesia)
Marco Longari/AFP/Getty Images (garment worker, Africa)
R. B. Reed (wires)
Andy Shapiro (thread)
Richard Vogel/AP Photo (shoe worker, Vietnam)
Bobby Yip/Reuters (electronics worker, China)
Joseph Younis (shoelaces)

For their kind permission, we thank
the Solidarity Center and
the International Labour Organization
for the use of their illustrations.

Art
Roberto "Galo" Arroyo
Heidi Broner
Gil Corral
Regina Doyle
Sandy Frank
Shu Ping Guan
Jesse Hamm
Haris Ichwan
Lori Nadaskay
Mabel Negrete
Chengyu Song
Yoly Stroeve
Ryan Sweere
Kathleen Tandy
Christine Wong
Kevin Wood
Mary Ann Zapalac

Field testing

Australia:
Oxfam - Australia

Bangladesh:
Karmojibiu Nari - KN
Nari Uddug Kendra - NUK

Chile:
Centro de Capacitación para la Mujer
    Trabajadora - CECAM

China:
China Labor Support Network
Chinese Working Women's Network
    - CWWN
Female Migrant Workers' Training
    Project
Guangzhou Occupational Health and
    Occupational Rehabilitation Resource
    Center
Institute of Contemporary Observation
    - ICO

Costa Rica:
Asociación Servicio Pro-Laboral
    - ASEPROLA

Denmark:
Misión Dinamarca/PRODECA

Dominican Republic:
Centro de Investigación para la Acción
    Femenina - CIPAF
Federación Dominicana de
    Trabajadores de Zonas Francas
    y Afines y Project Alta Gracia
    - FEDOTRAZONAS

El Salvador:
Movimiento de Mujeres Mélida Anaya
    Montes - MAM
Centro de Estudios y Apoyo Laboral
    - CEAL

Ghana:
Industrial and Commercial Workers
    Union - ICU

Guatemala:
Centro de Acción Legal en Derechos
    Humanos - CALDH

Comisión de Verificación de Códigos de
    Conducta - COVERCO
STITCH
UNSITRAGUA

Honduras:
Comunicación Comunitaria - COMUN
Equipo de Reflexión, Investigación y
    Comunicación - ERIC
Centro de Derechos de Mujeres - CDM
Central General de Trabajadores - CGT
Equipo de Monitoreo Independiente de
    Honduras - EMIH
International Textile, Garment and
    Leather Workers' Federation
    - ITGLWF

Hong Kong:
Asia Monitor Resource Center - AMRC
Hong Kong Workers' Health Centre
    - HKWHC

India:
Initiatives for Social and Health
    Advancement - ISHA
Self-Employed Women's Association
    - SEWA

Indonesia:
Social Information and Legal Guidance
    Foundation - Yayasan Sisbikum
    - SISBIKUM
Local Initiatives for OSH Network
    - LION

Kenya:
Kenya Women Workers Organization
    - KEWWO

Korea:
Social Programme for Action and
    Research in Korea - SPARK

Malaysia:
Women's Development Collective
    - WDC

Mexico:
Servicio, Desarrollo y Paz, A.C.
    - SEDEPAC
Alianza Fronteriza de Obreras - ALFO
Casa Amiga

Centro de Apoyo al Trabajador - CAT
Comité Fronterizo de Obreras - CFO
Centro de Información para
   Trabajadores, A.C. - CITTAC
Colectivo de Obreras Insumisas
La Mujer Obrera
SITEMEX

Namibia
Labor Resource and Research Institute
   - LaRRI

Nicaragua
Movimiento de Mujeres Trabajadoras y
   Desempleadas "Maria Elena Cuadra"
   - MEC

Pakistan
Working Women Organization - WWO

Philippines
Institute for Occupational Health and
   Safety Development - IOHSAD

Kilusan Ng Manggagawang
Labor Education and Research Network
   – LEARN
Resource Center for People's
   Development - RCPD
Trade Union Congress of the Philippines

South Africa
Development Institute for Training,
   Support & Education for Labour
   - DITSELA
Community Health Global Network

Sri Lanka
Free Trade Zone and General Services
   Employee Union - FTZ & CSEU

United States
Environmental Health Coalition - EHC
ENLACE
Garment Worker Center
Madre
Mujeres Unidas y Activas

Special thanks to the following individuals and organizations:

Garrett Brown is the godfather of this project. It would never have been completed without his patient advice, tireless support, and relentless networking through the Maquiladora Health and Safety Solidarity Network. Tom Gassert gave generously of his time and expertise, as did Jeong-ok Kong and members of KILSH and SHARPS, and Ted Smith and Mandy Hawes of ICRT; we couldn't have produced the electronics section without them. Rory O'Neill of *Hazards Magazine* was a constant fount of information, resources, and networking connections. Apo Leong, Sanjiv Pandita, Omana George, Sally Choi, and others at the Asia Monitor Resource Center have accompanied this book since its start and we are thankful for all their support throughout the years. Jagdish Patel, Noel Colina, Melody Kemp, and Darisman Man were among the many in the Asian Network for the Rights of Occupational and Environmental Victims (ANROEV) who, alongside Julia Quiñones at the Comité Fronterizo de Obreras in Mexico, shared their experience and knowledge with us, reminding us often why we were developing this book. Lynda Yanz, Ana Enriquez, and Kevin Thomas of the Canadian Maquila Solidarity Network provided essential connections and resources. Providing help in a myriad of ways from popular education techniques to hazard mitigation, we appreciate Suzanne Teran, Betty Szudy, Laura Stock, Diane Bush, Valeria Velazquez, Robin Dewey, and others at UC Berkeley's Labor and Occupational Health Program, Katie Quan of UC Berkeley's Labor Center, and Linda Delp, Deogracia Cornelio, Sarah Jacobs and others at UCLA's Labor and Occupational Safety and Health program. Finally, our coworkers at Hesperian, past and present, provided personal and collective support to this project through its many iterations, and to them we give our heartfelt thanks.

A million thanks for their assistance to:

Suvechha Adhikari
Sarah Adler-Milstein
Lupita Aguila
Nasimul Ahsan
Babul Akhter
Shirin Akhter
Kalpona Akter
Donald Aleman
Nelly Amaya
Karen Andrews
Evangelina Argueta
Nina Ascoly
Syed Asif
Nasir Ateeq
Jeff Ballinger
Jordan Barab
Jorge Barajas
Sherry Baron
Irene Barrientos
Enrique Barrios
Dinorah Barton-Antonio
Nikki Bas
Lucrecia Bautista
Mary Bellman
María de la Paz Benavides
   Hernández
Blanca Blanco
Megan Bobier
Suchada Boonchoo
Tim Brady
David Bronkema
Jim Brophy
Earl Brown
Marianne Brown
Lorena Patricia
   Cabanillas
Sonia Cano Narvaez
Silvana Cappuccio
Martha Lorena Cárdenas
Teresa Casertano
Ariel Castro
Carla Castro
Jean-Marc Caudron
Magdalena Cerda
Martha Cervantes
Serapina Cha Mi-Kyung
Jackie Chan

Ka Wai Chan
Amber Channer
Mirai Chatterjee
Esther Chavez Cano
Helen Chen
Debby Cheng Yi Yi
Maria Chin Abdullah
Suetwah Choi
Edwin Christiawan
Soon-ok Chun
Suki Chung
Kirsten Clodius
Stephen Coats
Niza Concepcion
Floridalma Contreras
Dick Crosbie
Andrew Cutz
Melona Daclan
Glorene Das
Enrique Davalos
Caoimhe de Barra
Cindy de Erazo
Leonardo de Leon
Carmen Manuela Del Cid
Nelly Del Cid
Abdulhalim Demir
Kelly Dent
Blanca Velázquez Díaz
Leonor Dionne
Tess Dioquino
Alejandra Domenzain
Peter Dooley
Phil Drew
Jonathan Eaton
Daniel Edralin
David Egilman
Howard Ehrman
Jill Esbenshade
Rosa Marina Escobar
Steve Faulker
Catherine Feingold
Bridget Fellini
Maria Antonia Flores
Luzviminda Fortuna
Virginia Franco
Hannah Fritsch
Eric Frumin

Bartolo Fuentes
Homero Fuentes
Sugio Furuya
Simmi Gandhi
Gilberto García
Irene Garza
Leslie Gates
Olimpia Gatica
Pilar Gonzalez
Gino Govender
Jay Govender
Ariane Grau Crespo
Elizabeth Grossman
Rubenia Guadalupe
Marina Gutierrez
Catalina Guzmán
Catherine Muthoni
David Harrington
Robert Harrison
Katja Hemmerich
Nick Henwood
Jeff Hermanson
Eugenia Hernández
Ricardo Hernández
Rodrigo Hernández
Ygnacio Hernández
Josefina Hernández Ponce
Hannah Higginson
David Hornung
M. Delowar Hossain
Jim Howe
Emily Ilag
Janice Jacobson
Lily Jahan
Harsh Jaitli
Rubina Jamil
Herbert Jauch
Nityanand Jayaraman
Lucia Jayaseelan
Ana Jimenes
Richard Hirsh Jordi
Edwin Jurig
Rusti Jutajulu
Aanchal Kapur
Elizabeth Katz
Amarjeet Kaur
Margaret Keith

Naira Khan
Heiner Koehnen
Athit Kong
Mariano Kramer
Eva Kreisler
Andre Kriel
Yuling Ku
Jennifer Kuhlman
Evelina Kurki
Laura Kurre
Joe La Dou
Luisa Lange
Bill Lankford
Bjarne Larsen
Ka Mei Lau
Kimi Lee
Alberto Legall
Amparo Lennarduzzi
Michael Lesli
Parry Leung
Chuck Levenstein
Pedro Reyes Linares
Karen Lo Hui Yu Ling
Zhang Ling
Belinda Liu
Kaiming Liu
Joann Lo
Rene Loewenson
Sandra Lopez
Maria Teresa Loyola
Pheara Ly
Sam Maher
Pia Markkanen
José Amado Mancía Leiva
Margaret Mandago
Nasir Mansoor
Anton Marcus
Gladis Marroquín
Genevieve Martinez
Ramon Martinez
Rolando Fúnez Mateo
Lisa McGowan
Ilona Medrikat
Racheal Meiers
Fred Millar
John Miller
Nanette Miranda
Frank Mirer
Sujata Mody

Norma Molina
Karla Montalvo
Dunia Montoya Medina
Lisa Moore
Gemma J. Moraga
Dominique Muller
Karen Mulloy
Marcela Muñoz
Robin Munro
Beth Myers
Abby Nájera
Dulceamor Navarette
Sheikh Nazma
Jesper Neilson
Neil Newman
Nguyen Ngoc Nga
Pun Ngai
Qu Ning
Ganesh Nochur
Huberto Juárez Nuñez
Patricia Nyman Apollis
Dennis O'Brien
Liz O'Connor
Tom O'Connor
Martha Ojeda
Juliana Omale
Abed Onn
Surama Orantes
Dara O'Rourke
Lida Orta
Elisa Ortega
Miriam Ortega

Pedro Ortega Méndez
Mina Palacios
Hilda Palmer
Madhavi Panda
Lourdes Pantaleon
Pola Pantoja
John Pape
Luis Paredes
Maritza Paredes
Alison Paul
José Nelson Paz Velásquez
Robert Perillo
Sonia Pernillo
Gary Phillips
Magaly Pineda
Au Mei Po
Laura Podolsky
Jackie Pollock
Dimu Pratama
Malee Pruekpongsawalee
Patty Quinlan
Carolina Quinteros
Richard Rabin
Peter Rabinowitz
Saeed Rahimi
M. Mofizur Rahman
Reyna Ramirez Sanchez
Sandra Ramos
Rey Rasing
María Luisa Regalado
Marina Ríos
Beti Robles-Ortega

Yadira Minero Rodas
Lumi Rodríguez
Rita Isabel Romero
Sirajul Rony
Mila Rosenthal
Shakh Rumana
Monica Ruwanpathirana
Lilibeth Sabado
Omar Salazar
Albert Sales
Arnel Salvador
Raquel Sancho
Ratan Sarkin
Mary Sayupa
Peter Scholz
Yoem Seda
Ashling Seely
Mónica Segobia Moscoso
Dharmesh Shah
Mashuda Khatun Shefali
Janet Shenk
Ruth Sherer
Young Shin
Carolina Sierra
Arist Merdeka Sirait

Darius D. Sivin
Juliana So
Sim Socheata
Luis Solano
Chun Soon-ok
Juliana Soon-ok
Stan Sprague
Ashwini Sukthankar
Emiliana Tapia
Dorothy Tegeler
Michael Terry
Wanee Thitiprasert
Trina Tocco
Zernan Toledo
Anna Torriente
Sreyneath Touch
Marion Traub-Werner
Wilhelmina Trout
Rachel True
Cecilia Tuico
Marco Tulio Juárez
Juan Miguel Tumi
Laura Turiano
Jane Turner
Carmen Valadez Perez

Jim Vannoy
Clara Velasquez
Roberto Vivar
A. Viyakulamary
Etienne Vlok
Norbert Wagner
Chan Ka Wai
Cathy Walker
Phan Wanabriboon
Hsing-Chi Wang
Deborah Weinstock
Wyger Wentholt
Heather White
Sarah Widmer
Dorothy Wigmore
Michael Wilson
May Wong
Monina Wong
Michael Wright
Emelia Yanti
Cheryl Yip
Jim Young
Chan Yu
Wilber Zavala

FUNDERS

We gratefully acknowledge the generous support of:

Amnesty International - Ireland
Berger-Marks Foundation
California Wellness Foundation
Church of Sweden Youth
Dominican Sisters of Springfield, Illinois
Egilman Family
Ford Foundation
General Service Foundation
Grousbeck Family Foundation/ Lakeshore Foundation
He-Shan World Fund
Jadetree Foundation Trust
Kazan, McClain, Satterley & Greenwood, PLC
Lawson Valentine Foundation
Left Tilt Fund

Levi Strauss Foundation
Maquila Health and Safety Solidarity Network
Moriah Fund
Panta Rhea Foundation
Partnership Foundation
Public Welfare Foundation
Rockefeller Foundation
Sidney Stern Memorial Trust
Sisters of Charity of the Incarnate Word
Solidarité Mondiale
Solifonds
United Methodist Church - Women's Division
West Foundation
Women Working Worldwide

We also thank the many individuals who contributed financially to make this book posible.

Contents

PART 4: Social Dangers and Solutions

Where to find

Workers' rights

**First
Aid**

Activities

How to

PART 1

Organizing for Safe and Fair Workplaces

1 Working for a living and living well

Work should be safe, dignified, and fair, and should not harm our health nor the planet. But for millions of factory workers around the world, dangerous jobs harm their health. And after working long, hard days, they still may not earn enough to live on.

This book describes the safety and health problems workers in export factories face and some of the solutions they have tried. It shows how workers have organized — sometimes with and sometimes against their bosses — to improve conditions, do away with poverty wages, install safer equipment, and use fewer and safer chemicals. The examples in this book focus on export factories, but the problems and concerns are common to other factories and jobs as well.

The industries covered in this book — garment, shoes, and electronics — produce enough profits to improve conditions for workers. Companies that have invested in making work safer and better have found significant benefits: healthier, happier employees work better and stay in their jobs longer, and factories with worker representation produce better products, dispose of less waste, and create more equal workplaces.

The global factory system

Global companies contract factories all over the world, especially in poor nations, to make their products. These companies — well-known "brands" such as Gap, Walmart, Apple, Adidas, and others — tell the factories exactly what to produce. In this system, the brands don't have the responsibility to actually build or run any of the factories themselves. But because their orders are so large, they can dictate the terms of the contract (price, quality, schedule) that the factory must meet if it wants the job.

These global companies also bargain with the governments of poor countries in order to get low or no taxes, low wages, weak laws protecting workers' and environmental rights, and inexpensive facilities, electricity, communications, and roads. These conditions usually guarantee low costs for factory owners who are providing jobs, and especially for the brands who can sell the products for many times what it cost to have the factories make them.

Around the world, export factories compete with each other to offer the lowest prices in order to win contracts from the global companies. This has been called a "race to the bottom" as the brands bargain with the next factory in the next country to offer its workers at lower wages and accept its pollution with fewer rules about paying for clean-up.

This "race to the bottom" has created the conditions that have made jobs in the global factory unhealthy, unsafe, and unfair for workers.

Who designed the factories and the jobs?

Someone planned the factory you work in and decided what machines, chemicals, tools, and materials you combine in the products you make. Your boss may have made these decisions, or maybe it was the factory owner, or the company that buys your products. These same people can also decide to make jobs and workplaces less harmful, more fair, and more successful — especially by asking the workers to share their knowledge and ideas about how to do it.

It is the responsibility of the factory owner to make sure the workplace is safe, and that all jobs are safe jobs. If the boss does not have the expertise to do that (and most do not), he can hire occupational safety and health (OSH) professionals to oversee conditions in the workplace. Many factories have health and safety departments, and labor and management safety committees, to constantly monitor and hopefully improve workplace conditions. When the people in these positions are committed to protecting worker health, they can be a huge force for change.

But the global companies who contract the factories have already won the "race to the bottom." They usually do not leave local factory owners a lot of room to improve conditions, increase wages, or make changes. The brands have an iron grip on the global factory system. That is why it is so important for workers to make alliances with consumers who want a fair and sustainable system, and with governments and occupational safety and health professionals who want to protect peoples' health and safety.

People can work together — or against each other — to make a better workplace.

Who can improve job safety and working conditions?

Your factory owner: The employer is responsible for providing workers with a healthy and safe workplace. It is the boss's responsibility to find and fix problems. A conscientious boss can make a big difference.

The factory that buys your factory's products: If another factory subcontracts work to your factory, your working conditions — what you produce, what chemicals or materials you use, at what price your factory owner can sell the product, and so on — may be determined outside your factory. The contracting factory is like your boss's boss.

The brands: The brands design "their" product — what it does, how it looks, what is inside it, what processes you use to make it, etc. Their decisions determine how work is done. If they ignore workers' health and well-being while designing the product, brands help create the harmful conditions affecting workers in the factories they contract to produce it. Brands must take responsibility for work processes and conditions.

The government's labor inspectors: Most countries have labor laws and labor inspectors charged with investigating working conditions and taking actions to improve conditions in the factory. Unfortunately, usually there are few inspectors and they earn very little, creating fertile ground for corruption: inspectors are often bribed not to apply the law, and good inspectors are often treated badly or fired when they try to enforce labor standards.

Independent monitors and codes of conduct: Health and safety inspectors or "social auditors" are hired by brands and factory owners to inspect factories. Since the auditors are hired and paid by the people they are inspecting, it is not surprising that they often find few problems. When they do, the owners often ignore them. Instead of improving work conditions, their efforts often just support public relations.

The International Labour Organization (ILO) and the ILO Better Work program: The ILO sets standards for work conditions and rights internationally. Their decisions have moral authority, but no enforcement authority. The ILO Better Work program is a public-private partnership, now in 7 countries, in which international funds are used to improve conditions in garment factories.

Unions, worker organizations, and community organizations: While an organized workforce and community may not be enough to win every struggle to improve conditions on the job, experience shows that lasting improvements will be made only if people are organized. Organized workplaces are overwhelmingly safer and healthier workplaces.

Chakriya's story

Chakriya moved from the countryside into Phnom Penh, Cambodia's capital city, to work in a garment factory. She quickly found a job at Song Industrial, a company that makes clothes for international brands. She and her baby son moved in with Veasna, a woman from her village, in a tiny room in the Canadia slum near the factory. The minimum wage Chakriya earned was barely enough to pay for food and rent. To send money to her parents and sisters, she had to work lots of overtime.

The minimum wage in Cambodia is not enough to live with health or dignity. This makes life very hard for workers and their families, but it is why the brands come to countries like Cambodia in the first place. International companies contract with Cambodian factories because they are the cheapest. When factories compete to offer the lowest price, rarely do they invest in protecting workers' health and safety.

The factory where Chakriya worked was very hot. The air felt like an oppressive, steamy cloud that never moved. One day in a very busy week, Chakriya noticed a sweet, sickly chemical smell that made her head spin. Then she fainted. A truck took her and 2 dozen other workers who had fainted to the hospital. More than 2,400 Cambodian garment workers faint at work each year, but the industry says they don't know why.

The factory owners blame the mass fainting spells on the workers, saying they are hysterical women who feed off each other's mental health problems. But Chakriya doesn't think the problem is in her mind. "We work too many hours and we are just too tired. Our salaries are not enough to buy food. And if we buy food, we cannot pay our children's school fees. And there's nothing left to send home to our parents."

Increasing the minimum wage would not harm profits.

Higher wages would send the brands to other, cheaper countries.

We have no control over factory wages.

We support a fair wage but can't be the only ones paying fairly.

ILO   Factory owner   Brand sourcing department   Brand social responsibility department

One day, the boss called the workers together. Some foreigners spoke about how the ILO Better Work program had made an agreement with their factory to improve conditions. Soon the lighting and ventilation were improved, but the wages stayed the same. That was the last time Chakriya heard of Better Work and the only time the factory got any better.

Chakriya had joined a union at her factory hoping that by acting together the workers could get higher wages and better conditions. The union joined a general strike over wages in 2010, and 68,000 workers stopped work for a week. The company immediately fired 160 active union members. The union organized workers to work slower, to refuse overtime, and to complain about the condition of their machines until the company rehired the union members. After 5 months, the fired workers got their jobs back. But the factory still didn't increase wages.

At the end of 2013, the workers couldn't take any more. They demanded that the minimum wage double, from $80 to $160 a month, a basic "living wage" that would let workers pay rent, eat nutritious food, and care for their families. But the government, pressured by the factory owners, only raised salaries to $95 – not enough! The workers walked out in a general strike that lasted almost a month.

This time the government responded violently. Police attacked workers, and killed 4. Many people fled to their villages because they were scared. Finally, hunger and repression drove the workers back to their jobs. 23 protesters were jailed for 5 months.

We were not expecting violence because we came with empty hands. We were only demanding an increase of the minimum wage. We did not expect such cruel treatment.

The struggle of Cambodian garment workers did not go unnoticed. International unions, the ILO, NGOs from Europe and the US, and even some responsible brands began to pressure the Cambodian government and factory owners to improve conditions. Most important, the Cambodian workers stayed united and strong, and in November 2014 they won another increase to the minimum wage.

Chakriya still earns too little and works too hard in bad conditions. But the gains she has made with her union, and the alliances her union has made internationally, have shown that getting organized and working together for change is necessary to make things improve.

Solve health and safety problems at work

This book can help you identify and correct problems in your workplace, and to become a worker health promoter (see chapter 2: Learning and teaching about health at work). Because everyone in the factory is exposed to problems, everyone has a stake in improving conditions. Some approaches to solving problems are more effective than others.

Strategies that do not protect workers

Making the workplace safe is the responsibility of the factory owner. But when faced with dangers in the workplace, bosses respond in different ways. Often they put the blame on workers for complaining unreasonably or for not following the rules already in place. If they do admit there is a problem, they look for the "solution" that costs less, not the one that most effectively promotes health and safety.

"Do Nothing" strategy

The boss may deny the work is dangerous and do nothing. When a worker becomes injured or ill, he will get rid of her and hire someone else. He will not keep records or will hide records of worker illness or injury.

The boss yells at me to work faster but this cleaner makes me so sick!

I'm so hot and uncomfortable now. It's too hard to work like this.

"Change the Worker" strategy

The boss may try to change the worker by making her do the work differently or forcing her to wear uncomfortable safety equipment. And when she cannot do the work like that, he blames her for being lazy and causing her own injuries or illnesses. "Change the worker" often just means "blame the worker."

Strategies that make work safer

With the help of OSH professionals, an employer committed to the health and safety of workers will ask: what dangers do workers really face and how dangerous are they? A good boss will change the workplace by fixing or replacing equipment, tools, and processes to eliminate dangers and make the work safer. Knowing that the workers are the real experts about their jobs, a good boss will involve workers in all steps of making work safer. Health and safety committees that include management and workers are necessary to make work safer, and they function best when everyone can ask OSH professionals for help in finding solutions.

"Change the Workplace" strategy

Prevent the harm that work dangers can cause.

Eliminate the danger.
Improved machines and products are being developed all the time to make work safer. They might cost more, but if they prevent a cancer or save one life they are well worth it. It is also important to train workers in the new processes, and in how to use warning systems and alarms.

This new ventilation system changes everything! And the brush cleans better!

Enclose the danger, remove it, or protect the worker from it. Install enclosures, barriers, separate work areas, machine guards, ventilation, and whatever else is needed.

Change the organization of work. Reduce the amount of time individual workers are exposed to dangerous work. Make work less boring. Interesting and fulfilling jobs tend to lead to fewer accidents.

Provide safety equipment when necessary. When the 3 previous steps are successful, there should be no need for Personal Protective Equipment (PPE, see chapter 18). But if work dangers still remain, PPE can be used to make work safer as long as the workplace has a program to ensure that PPE:

- fits each worker using it.
- is the right kind for the dangers faced in each job.
- is cleaned or replaced as often as needed.

Make work safer by removing social dangers

Workplace problems are not only caused by chemical exposures, electrical problems, unguarded machines, and other dangers that can be fixed by repairs or better equipment. Workplace problems are also caused by discrimination against women, racism, and other attitudes, customs, behaviors, and conditions that deny workers their rights and dignity. Most of these social dangers reflect the power relations in our communities and may be harder to see than work dangers. When communities are not fair and just, workplaces will not be either. It is necessary to change these conditions for a healthy and safe workplace, and sometimes it may even be easier to begin to undo poverty, discrimination, racism, and sexism in the workplace than in the larger community.

Organizing for better jobs

One worker alone can make small changes to improve her job, such as adding a cushion to pad the seat of her chair or support her back. But a single worker cannot change the most important problems harming the health of factory workers, such as what chemical to use as a cleaner, whether to enclose a dangerous machine, or how to make sure that no worker or group of workers is always stuck with a particularly dangerous, dirty, or boring job. By working together with others who want to see improvements in the factory, workers can decide what changes they want to make and organize campaigns to convince or pressure the boss to make these changes.

Workers' rights

Every country has laws meant to protect workers from unsafe and unfair work conditions. Find out more about them by asking a labor lawyer, a government official, a union, or another worker or community organization, or by doing research online.

Basic labor laws usually cover minimum wage, time off, maternity leave, health insurance, and health and safety at work. Most laws also include information about how they can be enforced: who can inspect the factories, how to file a complaint with the government, and how the government will resolve the problem. Some countries have very good laws on paper, but all too often the governments do not do their best to enforce them.

International laws on workers' rights

 The United Nations (UN) brings together almost all the governments of the world to promote positive relations and international cooperation to solve economic, social, cultural, and humanitarian problems. UN conventions (international laws) that guarantee human rights and freedoms are referenced throughout this book in boxes like this one that include the UN symbol.

 The **UN Convention on the Elimination of All Forms of Discrimination against Women (CEDAW)** is a powerful organizing tool for creating more equal and fair conditions for women at work and in their communities.

 The **International Labour Organization (ILO)** is the part of the United Nations that promotes labor rights and sets international standards for workers' rights, working conditions, and worker health. The ILO also promotes the development of independent, democratic worker organizations and unions. ILO standards, adopted by many governments of the world, are referenced throughout this book in boxes like this one that include the ILO symbol. The ILO sponsors a program in many countries called Better Work, a public-private partnership to improve conditions in garment factories.

For more information about ILO conventions and how to use them, see Appendix A.
For more information about the ILO Better Work program, see page 456.

Workers' rights are also made explicit in international law, for example, in conventions created by the United Nations (UN) and International Labour Organization (ILO). Countries that are members of the UN and the ILO sign these conventions and agree to make these rights a reality in their own laws. The UN and ILO conventions say all people have the right to safe, fair jobs that pay enough for a worker and her family to live in dignity. Knowing about these conventions can help you motivate others to fight for better jobs and encourage your government to improve and enforce its labor laws. See the box on the previous page and Appendix A on page 448 for more information on the UN, ILO, and other avenues to pursue international law on workers' rights.

Women's rights

Knowing and protecting women's rights is particularly important in export factories, where women are often the majority of workers. The UN, ILO, and the laws of many countries also say that women and men have equal economic, social, and political rights. These rights include:

- equal pay for equal or similar work.
- equal training and promotions.
- freedom from discrimination as women or mothers (see pages 309 and 380).

The health needs of women, including bearing and caring for children, should be considered in the design of jobs.

Unions and workers' organizations

International law and the laws of most countries recognize a union as a worker-controlled organization with rights and responsibilities to defend its members' rights. An employer must negotiate work issues with the union chosen by the employees. The union has the right and responsibility to negotiate pay, safety and health, working hours, and fair and equal treatment of workers. Some unions also negotiate how work is organized. Employers and governments are prohibited from harassing or intimidating workers for being union members.

The right to organize: Workers fought for years in many countries to win the legal right to form a union, but there are still countries where it is illegal for workers to organize unions. Even where unions are legal, workers organizing for better conditions may face threats, violence, and discrimination from their bosses, hired thugs, police, or soldiers. But in countries where union movements are strong, workers successfully participate in movements to improve living and working conditions and pursue social justice.

Independent, democratic unions and worker organizations: In some countries, unions are controlled by the government, employers, or corrupt "leaders" who support the interests of the bosses or companies instead of those of the workers. These unions give the appearance that a workers' organization exists, yet deliver few of the benefits of worker empowerment. In these situations, workers have formed independent, democratic unions or other types of organizations — workers' centers, injured worker groups, women's and community organizations, and others — to represent their interests.

Other worker organizations

For many years, women have formed groups to teach and learn about women's rights, and to protect and expand them. Women's groups have helped women reform their unions and gain respect. Sometimes women workers have formed their own unions when the men leading unions ignored women's needs or didn't allow them to participate as equals.

In places where unions are controlled by corporations or the government, workers have also developed different sorts of groups to fight for changes that their unions will not take on. For instance, when unions do not support compensation for workers hurt by their jobs, workers have organized as "accident victims" to win justice and compensation for injured workers and their families. When unions do not oppose the pollution caused by factories, workers have formed environmental groups to fight for cleaner forms of energy and manufacturing.

Workers have also formed groups based on ethnicity, culture, language, or national background for support and solidarity. These groups educate their members and others about their rights and how to protect themselves in the community and at work. They also help keep alive their traditions and connections to their home villages and countries.

Workers often form coalitions with other groups to increase the power of their organizing. A coalition may form around a specific campaign or may come together for a longer time around broad political and organizing goals. These coalitions may include unions, religious organizations, women's groups, human rights groups, political parties, students, retirees, and other kinds of community and worker groups.

Employer organizations

Companies often join together to promote their interests. They organize to lower their taxes and promote laws, working conditions, local development and international trade agreements that make their companies more stable and profitable. Often their desires to increase profits drive them to lobby against or ignore UN and ILO conventions, and national labor and environmental regulations, and to oppose the interests of workers.

Some companies have developed Codes of Conduct for employers and workers in the factories that make their products. The codes say the company will only work with factories and contractors that respect specific labor and human rights standards. These codes may be weaker than the standards set by the ILO and UN for decent jobs and protecting workers' rights, but may be an improvement over common conditions in an industry.

For example, the codes usually require employers to pay workers at least the local minimum wage and obey local working hour laws. But in many countries, the legal minimum wage for export factories is very low and legal working time very long. So even when employers follow these laws, workers may still be exhausted by work and living in poverty.

Many people question why multinational companies create these weaker codes instead of using the international standards agreed on by the UN and ILO. Nonetheless, sometimes the codes lead to improvements that workers can use to organize for better conditions.

Some companies that are concerned about human rights, the environment, and climate change have begun to organize to help each other change sourcing and production methods. Groups such as BizNGO are working to help companies phase out harmful chemicals from their production processes, thus improving workers' health and the environment. Business for Social Responsibility sponsors the HERproject to educate working women about health issues. The Institute for Human Rights and Business works on human rights both in the workplace and at a policy level, on the rights of migrant workers, threats from digital surveillance of workers, and other issues.

When corporations accept and value international norms on human, workers', and women's rights, they can bring a game-changing array of resources to our struggles for safe workplaces and a sustainable world.

Organizing wins changes

Workers in almost every country have organized to build effective, representative unions, win better working conditions, and create long-lasting organizations to defend their victories. Over many years, unions have won higher wages, limits on working hours, safer workplaces, health care programs, and social insurance for disabled, ill, and retired workers. Sometimes unions have also helped to change governments in the interests of workers.

Chinese workers develop new ways to organize

Conditions in factories in China are often very bad: low wages, forced overtime, swing shifts, harassment and violence, and few guarantees of health and safety. Workers who have migrated to cities to work in export factories have no political rights and no access to services. Although a government-run union might exist, workers have little power to organize collectively to change working conditions. Strikes are illegal, and repression is constant. Workers in China are pushed to work as much as is physically possible, to never complain, to move to an equally bad factory when work in their current factory becomes unbearable, and to go back to their home villages when they physically or mentally break down.

But as a famous Chinese leader used to say, "Where there is oppression, there is resistance," and workers are finding ways to resist. Every year, workers carry out tens of thousands of actions, expressing their anger and demanding improvements. "Wildcat" strikes — strikes that happen suddenly, like a pot boiling over — have been a very useful tool for workers.

The disruptions caused by wildcat strikes have also helped workers see how their work is connected to work done in other factories. When a factory making batteries does not finish its order because workers are striking, then the factory waiting for those batteries cannot finish theirs. Workers in electronics assembly factories are beginning to use these "supply chain" connections to raise their demands more broadly and more effectively.

New forms of organizing among Chinese workers are beginning to rise. Since their official unions are an instrument of their oppression, they have formed worker centers. Since they cannot organize openly, they connect invisibly through social media or their phones. While wildcat strikes continue to happen, more strikes are well-strategized and well-organized. The workers' demands are comprehensive and explicit. Workers are moving beyond reacting to bad conditions to becoming leaders of their own health and futures.

2 Learning and teaching about health at work

Everyone can learn to recognize the ways work can harm our health and to identify the changes necessary to make work safer, healthier, and fairer. And because it is necessary to involve others in making these changes, it is important to learn to help others learn.

This book gives you tools to do that and to become a worker health promoter. It will enable you to:

- identify health and safety problems in your factory.
- understand the causes of worker health problems in your factory.
- think about and implement short-term solutions to work problems.
- plan and organize to achieve long-term solutions to work problems.

How factory work can harm your health

There are often many dangers to workers' health in a factory. In this book, the word "danger" means a condition in the workplace (or the community) that can harm you. Not all workers will be injured, made ill, or affected by a danger they experience, but some will. The health problem (usually an injury or illness) may affect workers immediately or may not affect them until many years in the future. For example, a worker may have a skin rash now that is caused by contact with chemicals. Another worker may become sick with cancer many years after he was exposed to chemicals.

Some problems caused by work may not show up until after work has ended, so you may not think of them as a health problem caused by work. For example, some chemicals lessen a person's desire for sex or their ability to enjoy sex. Other dangers at work are also common dangers in our communities. For example, unsafe drinking water or air pollution.

Some health problems are caused by **"work dangers."** These dangers are often easy to see and may be fairly easy to control. Some work dangers are:

- repetitive movements
- factory fires
- chemical exposures
- poor ventilation
- spoiled food, unsafe water, and lack of access to clean bathrooms

Some health problems are caused by **"social dangers,"** the unfair and unjust social conditions inside and outside the factory. Some social dangers are:

- low wages
- working shifts that change from week to week and working nights
- threats or harassment from your boss or another worker
- too many working hours
- discrimination based on gender, ethnicity, sexuality, or religion, for example
- working multiple jobs

While we feel the effects of work dangers and social dangers as individuals, these worker health problems are not individual problems. The problems harm us as a group, as workers in a factory doing our jobs together. More than almost any other area of health, worker health and safety can only be improved when workers organize to collectively confront and resolve the conditions of work that injure us and make us sick.

Worker health problems have many causes

Workplace problems have many causes. By observing and discussing the problems, you can identify some immediate causes, but you may have to dig deeper to find the underlying causes.

Imagine a polluted river that carries waste into the ocean. You go upstream and find a person dumping plastic bottles and cans into the river. Maybe he is the cause of the pollution. After you show him how to recycle and compost, there is less waste but the river is still polluted. You go further upstream and you find a family piping their wash water and toilet waste into the river. Maybe they are the cause of the pollution. After you help them build a composting toilet and a leach field, there is less waste but the river is still polluted. You go further upstream and you find a factory discharging waste directly into the river. When they change to safe production methods, respect their neighbors and environment, and begin to value their workers' health, the pollution stops.

Workplace problems are often like that river. Work dangers, like the man dumping his trash, are among the causes that are easier to see and to change. However, as you keep following the river upstream you find causes which are more complex. To solve workplace problems we must address the social, political, and economic issues that cause them: companies that favor profit more than people, social problems such as racism, discrimination and violence against women, and structures of power and government in our countries and communities.

Juanita's story

Juanita was a sewing machine operator for 5 years. In the factory, her hands moved lightning-fast as she repeatedly sewed seams about 800 times each day.

As she sewed, her fingers and hands grasped, pinched, twisted, pushed, and pulled clothing parts, bundles, bins, and tools. She worked 10 hours each day, 6 days each week, sometimes more. Although the pace of work was already fast, her supervisors constantly pushed her to do more.

Her wrists and forearms had been sore for several years, but since she could still work, she did not worry. She knew the pain came from her work because on holidays when she took time off to visit her family, her hands began to feel better. Eventually, the pain got so bad she could not sleep. As her hands grew weaker and more painful, it became harder for her to carry water, prepare food, and do other house chores.

She knew other workers had pain like hers. No one knew what to do other than hope it would go away. When she asked to see the doctor, her supervisor said, "No. Get back to work." She finally went to a doctor after work. He told her to rest and take pills for the pain. She could not afford the pills, but she bought them anyway. The pills helped her work for 2 more months. Then the pain slowed her down so much she could not make the quota and she was fired.

Juanita does not know how she will survive. She has no other job skills besides sewing. She only went to school for a few years because in her family, only the boys stayed in school and learned other work skills. She could clean houses, but that pays even less than sewing and is hard work too. She hopes rest will heal her hands so she can return to sewing soon.

Activity   But why?

Asking "But why?" can help you see the causes of Juanita's problems and choose solutions. Asking "But why?" again and again will give a group the opportunity think of more causes than when they first hear Juanita's story.

1. **Why do Juanita's hands hurt so much?**

   Her job was designed to sew pieces of a garment as fast as possible. She had to bend, turn her hands constantly, and repeat tasks hundreds of times each day.

2. **But why was the work designed like this?**

   The boss set up the factory quickly and cheaply. He did not think about protecting workers' hands and bodies from injury. The boss paid Juanita based on how many shirts she sewed, not how many hours she worked. So Juanita worked as fast as she could for long hours to meet her quota and earn a living.

3. **But why was her pay based on how many shirts she made and not how many hours she worked?**

   The boss wanted her to produce more shirts in less time so he would get more profit. The boss competes with other factories that pay workers the same way.

4. **Why did Juanita stay at this job if it caused so much pain?**

   It was the only job she could get. She has no other training or skills. In her town, most jobs for women with little schooling are in factories.

5. **But why is this the best work Juanita can get?**

   Her family was poor and her parents did not think girls needed to go to school. The factories hire women like Juanita who need the work and won't complain because they don't want to lose their jobs.

6. **But why does the boss get away with overworking and underpaying workers?**

   He can treat workers however he wants because the government does not enforce labor laws and the workers do not have the power to stop him. Many workers want Juanita's job. Garment workers in other factories face the same conditions.

7. **But why are there not better jobs for poor people like Juanita?**

   Many poor countries try to attract foreign companies to build factories and create jobs for people like Juanita. The government builds Export Processing Zones or makes special deals to lower the taxes these businesses pay. To afford this, the government cuts spending for education, job training, and other programs that could fund better jobs and prepare Juanita for them.

Activity   Analyze the causes of worker health problems

Talking about all the causes of a problem helps workers find more ways to solve the problem and prevent it from happening again. Workers can talk about which causes are the most important, which causes they can change, and who might be their allies to help them change other causes. Different workers will ask different questions and come up with different answers. The questions and answers for your situation will grow out of your own conditions.

Group the answers to the "But why?" activity to make it easier to see the causes of Juanita's problem. For example, group causes into "work conditions," "social causes," and "political and economic causes." Create your own groups of causes.

Dangerous work conditions include toxic chemicals, frayed electrical wires, repeating the same movements many times each day, and unsafe drinking water.

Social causes of health problems for workers are attitudes, customs, and behaviors that deny workers' rights and dignity, such as low-pay, harassment, and discrimination. Women workers are especially affected by social causes.

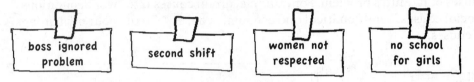

Political and economic causes of health problems for workers are actions by those who own and control land, resources, and political power in the city, region, or country. Political and economic causes include: labor laws and policies that allow bosses to pay low wages for long work hours, the practice of firing workers who do not make quota, and the prohibition of unions. Political and economic causes also include governments that do not provide people with safe water, sanitation, education, and other services, and the kinds of policies and pressures that force small farmers to search for work in the city or in factories to survive.

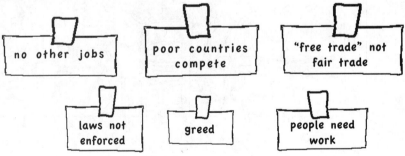

Many ways to begin to solve problems

While the problems might be clear, sometimes the solutions are not. Ask safety and health professionals for advice and reach out to health workers, union safety representatives, or others with experience. Workers often have good and practical ideas about how to make their work safer. Getting support from a range of people can help you find the most effective and realistic solutions.

Short-term solutions: Simple, low-cost changes that do not need a lot of support from your boss can be a good way to start. A good short-term solution protects workers now and can win their support for a long-term solution. Short-term solutions do not remove the boss's responsibility to protect workers in a more comprehensive way. But they do give workers the experience of taking action and winning better working conditions.

Long-term solutions: Many solutions involve finding safer chemicals, getting new equipment such as ventilation systems or safer machines, or enclosing work processes. Safety and health professionals can help design and implement these changes, which may take time to achieve. It is important to involve workers in these long-term solutions. Their knowledge can avoid costly errors in design and installation of equipment, and their pressure can ensure that the improvements happen as quickly as possible.

By actively involving workers in solving a few problems at the factory, you can begin to engage their creativity in other areas of work as well, such as improving the way work is organized and its efficiency, and the quality of what is produced. This engagement and empowerment often carries over to making positive changes in the community as well.

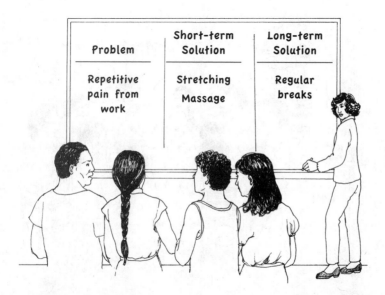

Helping workers learn about health at work

The best people to help other workers learn about and organize around health at work are the people who believe workers can work together to change their world.

A person who wants to help workers learn about health at work and organize to make work safer is called a "worker health promoter." A worker health promoter does not know everything about how work affects people's health. She does not have a solution for every problem at work, nor for every issue workers raise. But a worker health promoter can make a big difference.

A worker health promoter can be anyone who:

- workers respect and will talk to.
- has experienced and understands that health problems at work are caused by both physical and social conditions.
- knows that working conditions are designed by people and can be redesigned to protect people's health.
- believes healthy and empowered workers can build a healthy and sustainable business.
- believes that people with information, training, and the right tools can make better decisions and be safer and healthier.

Worker health promoters are usually volunteers. If there is a factory or union safety committee, they may be part of that. What makes them worker health promoters is their commitment to improve workers' lives by improving their health and safety at work.

Everybody can learn about health at work.

Your role as a worker health promoter is to:

- Know enough about health at work to guide workers towards the information and advice they need to take action.

- Teach workers how to observe their workplace, identify problems, and find the information they need to solve them.

- Build relationships with friendly OSH professionals to bring their technical support to answer questions from you and your co-workers.

- Raise workers' self-esteem by encouraging them to become active in their own health at work. Workers are their own best advocates — they are the ones who experience problems directly and will benefit the most from improving health and safety at work.

- Support workers who are ready to organize around the issues that are most relevant to them.

Worker health promoters in Mexico

Promoters who work with the Comité Fronterizo de Obreras (CFO) in Mexico talk to workers and encourage them to talk with each other about conditions at work. Often the process begins slowly, with 3 or 4 people discussing their problems and frustrations. Through this process, the workers in the groups gain self-confidence. Usually it starts with small steps, such as role playing a confrontation with a supervisor. Once she's practiced with friends, a worker has the confidence to say to her boss: "Don't yell at me. I hear you fine when you talk in a normal tone of voice." Supervisors are often shocked to find even minimal resistance, and workers learn that they have power.

We created this organization so we can share our concerns and learn about our rights. Now we can speak up at work and be heard.

A worker health promoter's principles of health and safety

1. The most important products of any factory are the health and safety of its workers. It is the employer's responsibility to design and organize production to protect workers' and community health and safety first, and meet production requirements and generate profits second.

2. All workers have the right to know about the chemicals, materials, and machinery they work with. It is the employer's responsibility to provide information, including the names, dangers, and needed protections to workers.

3. Workers have the right to refuse to work in dangerous conditions and with dangerous substances.

The labor laws say we can refuse work if it is dangerous.

We won't go back to work until you fix the problem.

4. Dangers at work are best corrected by going to the source of the problem and finding safer alternatives. The best solutions exchange dangerous substances for safer ones, dangerous machines for safer ones, enclose or guard machine or work process problems, improve ventilation, and so forth. Only use personal protective equipment as a last resort or backup.

5. Workers have the right to monitor their workplace health and safety conditions, and to get medical care and checkups. It is the employer's responsibility to monitor workplace conditions and make sure free, quality medical care is available to workers.

6. The efforts of workers and their organizations to improve health and safety in the workplace contribute to the quality of work, productivity, and health of the surrounding community. The employer must allow workers to organize freely.

7. Because workers are the most directly affected by health and safety dangers, they are also the most powerful and effective force for changing conditions to achieve a safer and healthier workplace.

Encourage workers to analyze problems and act on solutions

The human mind is the best tool a person has to understand and change the conditions that affect her and her friends, family, and co-workers. Activities you carry out with workers, even informal discussions, should encourage people to think, not just follow. Ask people, "What do you think?" and always look for something useful and positive in every answer. Make sure you listen to everyone, not just the men with the loudest voices. When someone disagrees about the cause or result of a problem, explore the issue rather than dismissing it. A contrary opinion can be an opportunity to talk about the different challenges we face in our jobs and the different ways we can act to make our work lives better.

A good worker health promoter moves:

from sharing facts	→	to learning and teaching skills
from sharing stories	→	to solving problems
from the classroom (theory)	→	to the factory (practice)

This is how we work.

How to improve bad chairs

1. Observe

2. Analyze

3. Take action

Advice from worker health promoters

Start with what workers know

Start every project, training, and discussion by asking people to share what they already know or experience. To help people think about how work conditions might hurt their health in the future, start with what they might be experiencing now. The activity Draw a body map on page 42, is an example of an activity in which people first share what they know so the promoter can then teach new information.

Even if a person has worked at a factory for many years, probably he has never been asked about how to make the factory better. More than anyone else, workers have inside knowledge about their jobs and often the best ideas about how they can be made safer, more efficient, and more satisfying. Always ask workers to offer their ideas and make time to discuss them.

Work on the big problems

Try to solve the problems that cause the most harm first. For example, you might feel the most important problem is to limit exposure to dangerous chemicals at work, while some workers might feel the most important thing is to be paid more. One solution might be to demand fewer hours of work with toxic chemicals but no decrease in pay. At the same time, you can also press for safer chemicals and better ventilation.

Focusing first on issues that can be more easily changed and improved might give workers the energy and self-esteem to push for more important changes.

Teach what is most needed

There is a lot of information available about health and safety at work. But it takes too much time to cover everything, and it can be more confusing than helpful to receive too much information at once.

Ask yourself, "What information will be most useful for our workplace?" Make the most essential information the center of your classes or trainings. Focus on what will enable workers to take action — the tools, ideas, and information that help people think critically about their situation and prepare them to find their own answers and solutions.

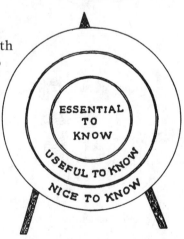

Teach what is most essential.

Use words people understand

Experts often use technical words that have an exact scientific meaning. They learn this technical language when they study, and tend to use it not only to be accurate but also to show they have gone to school and gained power and status.

But most people do not use technical language. As a worker health promoter, you can translate difficult terms into the words that people use every day, even if they are not perfect or "correct." Always invite people to ask you to stop and explain a word or idea they do not understand, or offer to talk to them separately later. People do not need to know proper technical language to improve their workplace.

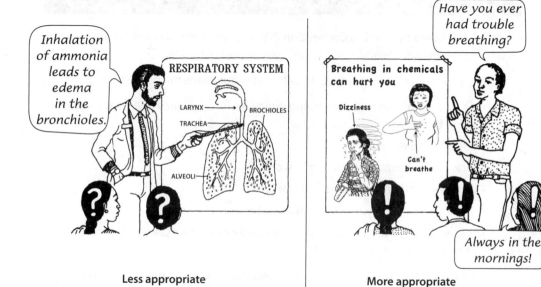

Less appropriate | More appropriate

Teach people how to learn

Everyone learns best when they get a chance to participate and do things instead of just listening to someone talk. Ask all the members of a group to give ideas about how they would solve a problem. Role plays (see page 325) between the boss and workers are fun ways of getting people involved and having them come up with arguments for and against a solution.

Worker health promoters share information and ideas, while encouraging people to come up with their own ideas. But their most important job is to teach people how to look for information, and how to discuss it with their co-workers to see if it makes sense. When you do this, you help workers develop self-esteem and self-reliance and learn problem-solving skills, and also encourage them to take initiative.

Get help when you need it

When conditions at work are dangerous or the factory management is clearly doing things that are illegal, you and your co-workers might not feel you can safely stop work or correct the problem yourselves. The laws in your country may allow you to call the Labor Ministry, the Fire Department, or another government agency to compel the employer to correct the problem and enforce standards of safety, health, working conditions, or salary and benefits.

The right to workplace inspection

The **ILO Labor Inspection Convention (No. 81)** says that governments are responsible for establishing labor inspections as part of the law.

Inspectors can be either female or male and should have the power to:

- go into a workplace without giving notice, especially if they believe the law is being broken.
- talk to workers.
- look at any documents relating to work.
- post notices in the workplaces about laws.
- take samples of materials or substances for further testing.
- inspect workplaces as often and as thoroughly as is necessary to ensure the effective application of the law.

The **Labor Inspection Convention** also says that inspectors should be part of an inspection system that:

- reports to the government.
- enforces the laws regarding hours, wages, safety, health, child labor, and other issues.
- offers technical information and advice to employers and workers.
- reports abuses to the government, even if they are not covered by existing laws.

The roles of the UN, ILO, and other international organizations that promote workers' rights are explained in Appendix A.

Where to find information and support

There are many ways to collect information about work dangers and solutions. Many OSH professionals like to help workers — that is why they went into that area of work. Do not be afraid to ask for their help. Sometimes a person who answers a few simple questions will become an ally who will support your organizing in other ways.

Your co-workers are your best source of information about conditions at work and practical ideas to improve them. Talk with workers regularly to share ideas and information. Do not speak only with people you already know. Make it a habit to talk with new people every week.

Unions usually have information on the rights and health of workers in your country and industry. They have specific information about dangers in the industries in which their members work. Unions may also have experience solving workplace problems, organizing workers, negotiating contracts, and pressuring employers to make changes. Learning from their experience can give you many ideas for what to try or what to avoid.

Community groups can be very helpful with resources and information about laws, rights, strategies for community education and organizing, and local political conditions. Women's groups, religious groups, and political organizations are often active in campaigns for worker's rights and health. Some of these organizations have national and international connections that may be useful for collecting and sharing information for a campaign.

Government agencies can provide information about dangers in your industry, and the laws and regulations protecting workers' rights and health. They can tell you how to file a complaint when working conditions violate the law, and how the law is enforced. Before you go to the government for information or help, consider whether the official or agency has the power and political support to help you.

Safety and health professionals may be able to provide technical information about dangers and some solutions for them. They know where to buy equipment, tools, and supplies your employer may need to fix dangerous problems. They may have equipment to measure how dangerous your conditions are. They often know the laws and regulations on workplace safety and health. They can help you access reference books, other professionals, and the Internet to get more information.

Company records may contain useful information on a variety of topics: how wages and work hours are documented and paid, injuries and illnesses workers are experiencing at work, how much money the company earns and spends, what chemicals they use, or if they have measured health dangers. In some countries, the law requires the employer to give this information to workers who ask for it.

The history of your employer may contain incidents when the employer has mistreated workers or had a disaster such as a fire or chemical spill. You may find out if the factory manager or owner has helped the community or how they are connected to local government officials. Look in old newspapers or government files. Talk to current and former workers at the factory. Ask community groups about them. You will need to judge who to ask, how to ask to learn what you want to know, and how to understand the answer according to the history of the company with the person you ask. Keep in mind that two people may honestly remember the same events very differently.

Books and the Internet can be good sources of information. Look for health, chemical, industrial, and business information. You can usually find information about your country's laws on workers' rights, workplace safety, women's rights, and so on. You can also find detailed information on work dangers and the names of organizations that have more information.

Advice for occupational safety and health professionals

Each one of us has valuable knowledge and experience, but nobody "knows everything." This is true for experts too. As an OSH professional, you can help workers think critically about what they know and what they are told. When there is controversy and information from employers or experts doesn't seem right or does not correspond to their experience, encourage workers to trust their doubts, try to learn more, and challenge it if necessary. If they are mistaken, you can help them find and evaluate the information that will change their minds.

Involve workers at every step.

Talk to workers first. Ask workers about their experiences. Focus on the reality of a factory and what happens rather than the ideal conditions, book knowledge, or statistics.

Prioritize what is best for workers and the community even when it might be easier to prioritize what is cheapest or fastest, what is best for profits, or what best serves the ambitions of politicians or employers.

Pay attention to social issues such as wages or harassment. These are health and safety issues too. Health at work depends on more than machines and tools.

Be honest about prejudices. Some safety and health experts work for unions, others distrust them, even when unions are recognized as important partners by the company or government.

Share your knowledge with workers so that they can become better advocates for health and safety.

3 Organizing to improve worker health

Because problems in the workplace affect many people, often the best way to resolve them is to involve many people. A worker health promoter needs to be able to help other workers get involved, learn, and organize around health at work. Bringing a group together and keeping people motivated to improve worker health is one of the most important things you can do. It takes time and patience to encourage people to participate and keep them involved.

This chapter includes activities to help you bring people into a group to work together, identify and learn more about problems, and educate and convince your co-workers about short-term and long-term ways to improve the workplace. It also shows how forming health and safety committees can help workers, OSH professionals, and employers to make these needed changes happen more smoothly.

When choosing an activity, think about:

- Which activity is best for the kind of information you want to gather now?
- Which activity do you and your co-workers have time for?
- Which activity will create a network for communication among co-workers? Which will increase cooperation with others, including management, OSH professionals, and neighbors?
- Which activity will get workers excited about organizing for change?

What these activities can help you learn

No matter which activity you choose, the information you collect from workers through holding discussions, doing surveys, drawing maps, and comparing notebooks will be different from factory to factory. But to help identify common problems and work on successful solutions, you should always be looking to answer questions like these:

- What problems do all or most workers share?
- Do men and women mention different problems?
- Which health problems happen regularly? Which happen occasionally?
- Which problems are the most serious or can be the most harmful?
- Which problems will most workers be excited to fix?
- Which problems will most interest leaders in the community?
- Which problems can be solved quickly and easily?

Share what you learn

Share the information you collect with other workers, especially those who shared their ideas and concerns with you. Talking with your co-workers helps to keep them involved, builds support for changes, and interests them in making more changes in the future. For the same reasons, share information with allies in the community such as church groups, women's groups, or neighborhood organizations.

Talk with workers about their concerns

Find ways to talk to workers about the work conditions that bother them and that they think are important. These discussions let you "take the temperature" of the factory and learn how people feel about organizing to change conditions. It also gives your co-workers a chance to know and trust you, and to begin to build power within the workforce.

Reach out to people in your factory in informal ways at first. It might be safer and easier to talk to people outside work. Be clear and open about why you are asking questions and what you plan to do with their answers. Do not force anyone to share information if they do not feel comfortable. Be discreet when approaching people, especially in public.

When you are ready to hold a meeting, identify a small group of interested and trustworthy people in your factory. Invite them to meet at a location outside work. Meeting in small groups is best at first. Small groups can be especially useful if workers come from different cultural, language, ethnic, or immigrant groups. It may also be useful to gather men and women separately at first, so women feel free to voice their concerns. Over time, groups can develop enough trust to include workers from all backgrounds.

During conversations with workers, create lots of space and time to let people talk about what bothers them and what issues they think are important. Be tolerant of people who do not want to talk or organize, and do not discriminate against them for not participating. Some people need more time to make up their minds.

Some issues people raise might make you feel uncomfortable. Try your best to be open to their concerns and look for others to help you think through how to respond. Remember, your role is not to help solve every problem, but to help people think and find tools to solve problems themselves.

If you ask about health at work, expect people to want to talk about their whole health — health does not clock in and out of work!

Activity   Talk in small groups

One or two people can lead several small groups, or you can have several people lead one or two small groups each. This allows more people to develop leadership and lets you gather more information in less time.

Meet: Call a few workers together in a place where you all feel comfortable talking about work problems. Find a safe space that is easy to get to.

Talk about concerns: Ask what bothers people at work or mention a concern you have. Find out what conditions they think harms or might harm them.

Listen for problems and proposed solutions: Listen carefully to each person's concerns as well as for problems many workers share. Find out if different concerns affect different groups of workers. Pay special attention to the ideas of women and others from groups who are often discriminated against, such as migrant workers or people with disabilities.

Write what you learn: To help remember everything, take notes during the discussion or write your thoughts down immediately afterwards.

Summarize the results: After speaking with many workers, summarize what you have learned by answering questions such as: Which problems are common to many workers? Which problems do workers feel are the most important? Which ones have the easiest solutions?

Do you need help? OSH professionals, unions, NGOs, and others may have helpful skills and experience. Ask the group who might approach them.

Ask questions through surveys

Carrying out a survey helps you gather similar information from many people, so the answers are easier to compare. A survey can also build a relationship among the team carrying out the survey, and between each team member and the co-workers they talk with.

Surveys are less useful for collecting complex information. Those issues may be best talked about in a group where everyone participates. Topics about feelings or issues people are uncomfortable with may be best collected with one-on-one survey questions.

Tell people who you are, why you are doing the survey, and how sharing their experiences will help improve workers' lives.

Ask specific questions, for example, how many hours a person worked the past week, if people have skin rashes, or if a supervisor limits time at the toilet.

The simplest, easiest method of gathering information is always the best. If you have only a few, very simple questions, you might be able to just ask for a show of hands in the cafeteria and not need to do a survey.

Surveys with many complicated questions can be difficult to carry out and to analyze. People often want to talk about more issues than can be included in a survey. Plan to listen to people's opinions about various things, note them down, and then invite them to meetings or discussions where they can follow up on their concerns.

Keeping information private is important when doing a survey. It will protect you and the people you are surveying.

Activity	Do a survey

Meet: Ask several co-workers to help you. Meet in a place where you all feel comfortable talking about work problems.

Talk about concerns: Work with this team to make a list of questions to ask your co-workers. Start with the issues at work the group is most concerned about. From this list, choose a few common dangers or the issues you think are the most important to find out.

Write survey questions: Create a list of questions. When you ask about a specific problem at work, always ask how important that problem is to them and how much they care about improving it. If you have too many questions, think about which are most important. Questions with yes/no or multiple-choice answers are easier to summarize than open-ended questions. Do not make the options too limiting so you can find out what people really think. Try the survey first with a few co-workers who did not work on the questions. If they find the questions unclear or think there are too many, rewrite the questions and shorten the survey.

In the last month, have you had:
Rashes: Yes/No
Cuts: Yes/No
Pain: Yes/No
Breathing problems: Yes/No

Plan the survey: Decide how many workers each of you will survey and from which parts of the factory. Set a date for the team to meet and check on progress. Use role playing and other activities to prepare the team for all the things that could happen during the survey. Also plan what you might do after the survey to see if the questions will generate the information you will need.

Do the survey: As some workers may not read well, you might decide to ask the questions in person and write down the answers.

Check in with each other: When the team meets again, have each person talk about the funniest or most interesting person they surveyed, and the most difficult ones. If some team members are having difficulties, ask other members to share some of the ways they found to make surveying easier.

Summarize the results: When you have enough information, add up all the answers and categorize them. Then summarize what the team has learned by answering questions such as: What are the most common dangers people have observed or experienced? Which dangers are felt by only one group of workers? What health problems related to work are people experiencing? What do people seem to care about most? What are they willing to work to change?

Listen to what workers know

A group of us took a workshop on ergonomics. We learned how work can be designed in a way that hurts less. If we put things we need often closer to us, we reduce how much our bodies must move, which makes them hurt less later. We also learned to stretch, massage, and exercise our bodies to keep them healthy.

When the trainer talked about injuries caused by repeating the same movements over and over, we knew what she was talking about. Many of us have hand pain because of that! So when we went back to work and talked about "repetitive strain injuries," we thought people would be interested. Instead, people told us, "You are wrong! What we have is arthritis, not this repetitive strain nonsense. You get arthritis as you work more and get older, and nothing can fix that."

At the next workshop, we complained about our hard-headed co-workers in the factory. The trainer explained that every person has lots of ideas about health. Our role is to value people's ideas and then introduce new ones. If we tell people they are wrong, they probably will just stop listening. We have to find ways to help people understand new ideas, and show how a new idea is related to what people already know.

Instead of saying they were wrong about arthritis, she suggested we ask questions, such as: Where does it hurt? Do you feel tingling, tiredness, and other sensations besides pain? Does it hurt more after work?

The questions let people bring themselves to an understanding of the differences between arthritis and strain injury. And since they got there themselves, people were willing to accept the new information.

The trainer also said we could invite people to test the new ideas and see what happens. Ask some people to try to lessen their pain through small changes at their workstations, or to stretch with you during breaks, and you can show that the ideas work. After a week or so, ask them if they feel any better.

We followed her advice, and our co-workers started to learn how work was making their bodies hurt and that they could do something about it besides suffering the pain. But we learned a bigger lesson: when we help people understand instead of just telling them, we get better results and build a stronger, more active group.

Share experiences with mapping activities

Group activities that invite people to share their experiences and observations about their bodies, their work, and their communities are an opportunity to build upon people's knowledge and to create a shared understanding of work problems. Mapping activities also let workers see how common many of their problems are. This helps a group more easily agree on solutions and priorities for taking action.

Nobody knows workers' bodies or workplaces better than they do. By letting workers show where in the body they have pain, they can help us pinpoint the areas where improvements have to happen so we can help reduce their pain.

This is what an occupational doctor looks like

Map of the body: This map lets you ask, "Where does work hurt your body?" Everyone in the factory can contribute to this kind of map. A good way to start is for you to talk about where you feel body pain. That will help others feel comfortable talking about themselves and their problems at work. See an example of a map of the body on page 160.

Map of your factory: With workers comfortable talking about problems at work, make a workplace map. Label where the processes, jobs, or areas are that can harm workers, including harmful people, such as a rude supervisor. Also mark where accidents have happened. The workplace map focuses the group on specific problems in specific places in the factory. Then you can talk about specific solutions for them. See an example of a workplace map on page 253.

Map of the community: After doing the Pollution walk activity on page 443, bring together a group to map out the routes in which the problems inside the factory spill out into the community. You can map pollution by looking at where the waste goes after it leaves the factory and the health problems it causes. Showing the links between the factory and the community can help persuade neighbors and community groups to support workers' campaigns to improve factory conditions and to convince unions to support environmental causes.

Activity — Draw a map of the body

Meet: Gather a group of co-workers and have something to draw on that everyone can see. A large piece of paper and a marking pen, a chalkboard and chalk, or a smooth area of soft soil and pebbles or nuts would each work.

Draw an outline for the map: Draw the outline of a human body on the paper, chalkboard, or earth.

Mark and talk about pain: Ask people to mark the places on the drawing of the body where they feel pain from work. After people mark the map of the body, ask them to explain why they put the mark where they did. What pain do they have? What work tasks cause this pain? What dangers cause this pain? After each person does this, ask who else has the same pains.

This is how I use my body in my job as a cutter. My shoulders and back hurt so much because the blade is heavy.

Look at all the pains we have.

Discuss dangers and solutions: After everyone has spoken, discuss which dangers affect the most people, which dangers are the most serious, which might be easiest to fix, and then which the group thinks should be fixed first. Ask for ideas on how to fix these problems.

Write what you learn: Take notes about the pains people describe, the dangers that cause the pain, and the solutions they propose. Write them in a place where others can see them and add to or change them.

Options: If you have several colors of marking pens, use different colors for different kinds of problems. For example, you might decide that ergonomic problems will be red and problems caused by chemicals will be blue.
Or, have the workers from each work area use the same color to see if they share problems. Using colors might also let you see if one kind of problem is more common than another. You could also use "ouch" stickers on the map to show where there is pain.

Activity	Draw a map of your factory

Meet: Gather in a place where all feel comfortable talking about dangers at work. Lay a large piece of paper and marking pens in several colors on a table (or use a chalkboard and chalk).

Divide large groups: Divide into small groups so each can create and discuss their own map. Each group can explain their map to the others as a way to share different views of the same workplace.

Draw an outline of your factory: Ask the group to draw it as if they were looking down through the roof of the building from the sky. Each floor of the factory will need its own map. Include the walls, doors, windows, and exits. Draw in the work areas, workstations, machines, people (supervisors and co-workers), or anything else the group wants to include.

Mark and talk about dangers: Ask the group to mark the areas on this map where they have experienced or seen dangers. Use different colors. For example, use red to mark physical dangers such as fire, electrical wires, slippery floors, bad stairs, and so forth. Use blue to mark where chemicals are used or dust is created. Use orange where jobs cause strain, sprain or overuse of workers' bodies. Use yellow for biological dangers such as contaminated food and water, or dirty bathrooms. Use green where workers feel stress from threats, harassment, and unfair treatment.

Take one more look: Have the group look over the map and ask if any important dangers are missing. Add them to the map with words, colors, or a drawing. Also ask if anyone has lost their job or gone on sick leave because of work problems, and add them to the map where they used to work.

Summarize the dangers: Help summarize the dangers with questions: Which dangers are common to many workers? Which dangers are felt by only one group of workers? Which dangers cause the most serious problems?

Activity	Draw a map of your community

Bring paper and pencils, pens, or markers to draw the map. Or use stones, sticks, and other materials to make a map on the ground.

Meet: Invite workers and community members to do the Community pollution survey on page 443 where people survey community members, walk through the community, and take photographs. All of this can be used to make a map.

Draw a map: Ask people to draw a map of the community that shows the factories and the areas where people live, go to school, buy their food, and spend time. Be sure to include community water sources, bodies of water, food growing areas, and waste dumps. The size of the area represented by the map can be as large or as small as makes sense for your situation.

Mark causes and effects of pollution: Use a different color (or material) to show each kind of pollution. Show where it starts, how it moves through the community, and how it affects people's health.

- **Where pollution starts:** Are the factories in your community polluting the air, water, and land? Which ones are polluting? What does pollution look like? Mark where and how it comes out of the factory. Some kinds of pollution are not as visible as others.

- **Signs of pollution:** Where does the waste go? Are waste and chemicals dumped into the water? Can you see or smell smoke or chemicals in the air? Do people and animals in the community come in contact with factory waste? Ask people to talk about all kinds of pollution and the ways we interact with it. Be sure to include the people in your community who collect, clean up, or recycle waste.

- **People who are sick:** Mark areas where people complained about health problems such as rashes, asthma, reproductive health problems, children born with birth defects, and cancers, because these are some of the health problems caused by pollution that your survey might uncover. Look to see if a problem "clusters" in a specific area. Often you will find clusters in the communities closest to the factory. But if the factories dump chemicals or other wastes into a river, communities downstream are likely to have similar clusters.

(continued)

Activity   Draw a map of your community *(continued)*

Take one more look: Have the group look over the map and ask if any important information is missing. For example, people might want to add areas where materials get recycled in your community and talk about pollution there, too. Or talk about other important polluters in your community.

Document and summarize what you learned: If your map is on paper, take it with you; if it is drawn on the ground, take photos of it. Discuss how you will share it and its information with other workers, people in your community, government officials responsible for environmental and public health, and with social media or other kinds of media. Getting people to pay attention to the problems outside of the factory that are caused by the factory can help you bring their attention to the problems inside the factory and get support to improve them.

Keep information about work and health

Many countries have laws that require the factory to keep records about accidents and workers' health problems. These records can help you determine the most dangerous areas of your factory, whether workers from one part of the factory are getting the same illnesses, and what type of accidents happen most often. This can help you work with the factory management to lower the number of illnesses and injuries in the plant. Ask your employer to share this information with you.

Many employers will not share this information. In any case, it is a good idea to keep your own records and show other workers how to do the same. One important thing about keeping your own health notebook is that you can take it with you from one job to another. You will not lose the record of your exposures to chemicals or how many days of serious headaches you have had just because you change factories.

Keep a notebook

Keep a record of your own work and health history, including details about working conditions, chemicals used, and signs of health problems, especially when you are starting a new job. Pictures and videos of your workplace or of a rash on your body, for example, can be helpful too. This information can help a doctor find out what is happening to you. It is useful for lawyers, OSH professionals, union organizers, journalists, and others helping you. Keeping a notebook will help you understand your own body and work conditions better.

 You will see this symbol throughout the book to remind you to write work dangers and health problems in your notebook.

Your health: Keep a simple daily record of your health. At first it might be easier to write only what hurts or makes you feel sick, such as when you have a fever or a rash. But if you write something every day, you will begin to notice more about how your body feels and changes from day to day. Record information about headaches, dizziness, rashes, and breathing problems, which are problems often connected to chemicals. Include health problems that may not be related to your work as well. And if you have medical test results, save a copy, take a photo of it, or write down as much as you can remember about it.

Your jobs and employers: Every time you start a new job, write down as much information as possible about your employer. Include the name of the company, the exact address (take a picture if you can), and the names of your bosses and supervisors. If the company is sold or you get a new boss, update that information in your notebook. Also note trainings, medical checks, or certifications you received while working there. Note when chemicals are changed and new chemicals are added in your work process.

Review your notebook with other workers: Review what you have noticed about your own health and problems at work with others who may also keep notebooks. Look for common problems around common dates. What might have caused them? If you find that a change in cleaning chemicals gave everyone a headache, for instance, that can give you more reason to suggest to your boss that he find a safer and better cleaner. Sometimes a health and safety committee will collect information into a combined notebook for a work area or an entire factory.

Help measure dangers at work

You can help safety and health professionals in your factory by monitoring and measuring dangers. This is a good activity for small groups of workers in the same work area because it helps workers come up with solutions and tracks whether changes solve the problems or not.

Some dangers can only be measured by using special equipment or tests, for example, measuring how much of a chemical is in the air you breathe (see Testing for chemicals on page 156). But you can take a lot of measurements with just your senses.

These are some of the dangers you can help measure and some ways you can measure them:

Let's count how many bundles we move today.

- **Ergonomics:** Count how many hand movements you make for each part and how many parts you produce each hour, shift, or day.

- **Heat and cold:** Measure how hot or cold the air is with a thermometer.

- **Fire:** Count how many fire exit doors are in your factory and how many exit doors are locked during the work shift. (None should be locked!)

- **Discrimination:** Compare the pay of men and women workers.

- **Violence:** Count how many workers have been threatened or hit by the supervisor.

- **Access to toilets:** Count how many toilets there are in the factory, how many are unlocked, and how many are clean.

Write in your notebook any accidents at work, for example, a chemical spill or any situation that puts workers in danger. Count how many times these happen in a month, and in which areas of the factory. This will allow you to measure how dangerous an area or time period is. Write down date and time, exactly what happened, if people were injured, if police, inspectors, or ambulances were called, and any other information that might be helpful.

Organize a health and safety committee

Setting up a health and safety committee in your factory can help workers address health and safety problems and win changes. Health and safety committees can be formed in workplaces that have unions or in workplaces that lack unions. Health and safety committees usually include equal numbers of workers and management. Their job is to identify dangers, tell workers about the dangers, propose solutions to the dangers, monitor how the problems are fixed and that they stay fixed, and encourage workers to be active in their own health and safety.

Health and safety committees work well when they:

- include workers who represent the interests of the workers.
- hold elections to choose the worker representatives.
- allow workers to say what they think without fear of punishment.
- initiate changes and see them through.
- have procedures to confront dangerous problems that are not fixed.

Having a health and safety committee in your factory might be required by law. Ask a union or a lawyer about your country's labor code. If a health and safety committee is not required, try to convince your boss that a committee would allow him to find factory problems before they become dangerous to workers and expensive to fix. A committee can also help the factory win more contracts by preparing for audits and ensuring the work is safe. One limitation of health and safety committees is they tend to ignore many labor issues. For example, getting paid enough and on time, as well as limiting the number of working hours and shift work, contribute to workers' health and well-being, but health and safety committees usually do not cover these issues.

You can also organize a health and safety committee with workers only. If you cannot hold an election, look for workers who you know are responsible and committed to improving work. Informal committee meetings, without management, can allow safety committee members to discuss issues and decide how to share information with other workers. They can also help you stand up more powerfully to the boss. For example, your committee can collect all the Safety Data Sheets (SDS) for the chemicals used and then organize a training to help everyone understand them. A formal health and safety committee can do this, too. You do not need a lot of people – you just need a strong group of involved people who want to keep other workers informed and involved.

Organizing unions in export factories

When organized in unions, workers have safer workplaces, better working conditions, higher pay, and more power on the job. It is legal to organize unions in most countries, but sometimes in special export processing zones union organizing is illegal. Even where it is legal, government officials may not be willing or able to enforce labor laws and protect workers who are organizing. And when workers do succeed in forming a union, sometimes the employer refuses to recognize it or to negotiate a contract.

These are difficult conditions for organizing, but democratic, honest unions are still the best solution workers have found to improve their work and their lives. As workers gain more experience in organizing changes in the workplace, their unionizing campaigns tend to be more successful. As in struggles for health and safety, the key to effective organizing is listening to what your co-workers want to see changed, and encouraging their participation in making that change happen. Each organizing victory inspires the next campaign in your factory or a factory down the road or across the ocean.

Forming a union despite company opposition

Workers at the Yoo Yang garment factory in Honduras were tired of harassment, low pay, and bad working conditions. They decided to form a union, inspired by workers in a factory nearby who won the struggle to have their union recognized. For a year, the workers pushed for recognition from the government and a contract with the factory. They pressured their boss to listen to them through creative actions such as boycotting the cafeteria and taping blue solidarity ribbons on all their machines. After lunch, they marched back into the factory together. They held 5-minute work stoppages.

The workers were harassed. Some were fired illegally and the factory threatened to close, but the union stayed strong and won a contract. The owners agreed to pay higher wages, increase benefits, and meet with a workers' health and safety committee every month. It was a big win. Then the union began supporting workers in another Yoo Yang-owned factory who formed a union. They too were working to gain recognition, win a contract, and to stop the intimidation of union supporters. When workers from the 2 factories got together to share their experiences, it helped a lot.

The right to organise and form a union

The **ILO Core Labor Standards** (see page 454) are considered to establish fundamental labor rights internationally. They include the Elimination of Forced Labor, the Abolition of Child Labor, the Elimination of Discrimination in the Workplace, and the Right to Organise and Form Unions. These conventions specifically address the right to organise unions:

The **ILO Freedom of Association and Protection of the Right to Organise Convention (No. 87)** says:

- Workers and employers have a right to organize and join organizations.
- Workers' and employers' organizations have a right to draft their own constitutions and rules, elect representatives in full freedom, and organize activities and programs.
- The government should not prevent workers from exercising their right to organize.
- Workers' and employers' organizations have a right to join federations and confederations, as well as to affiliate with international organizations.
- Workers' and employers' organizations should be protected from suspension or dissolution.

The **ILO Right to Organise and Collective Bargaining Convention (No. 98)** protects against acts of anti-union discrimination in employment. Workers are protected from:

- employment conditions that force workers to give up union membership or that prohibit them from joining a union.
- dismissal due to union membership or participation in union activities.

The roles of the UN, ILO, and other international organizations that promote workers' rights are explained in Appendix A.

A union struggles to raise health issues

From its very beginnings, the electronics industry has tried to stop workers from organizing. The industry saw demands for fair wages, good working conditions, and safe workplaces as a challenge to their control and to their profits. They claim, "Remaining non-union is essential to the survival of our companies."

But inside the Special Economic Zone in Southern Luzon, the Philippines, the NXP Worker's Union has been organizing workers for more than 20 years. Management has fired union leaders and clamped down on workers who fought for better wages and hours. By promoting union democracy and continuing their union-building efforts, NXP has remained strong in the face of these attacks and won many campaigns.

> If you have no union, you are not allowed to have one. If you have a union, it is not allowed to be effective.

While wages and conditions have improved, occupational safety and health has not. Many workers still believe electronic companies are safe places to work. Although NXP has carried out research to understand which workers are getting sick and why, safer and healthier work at NXP is still a challenge. The company still uses banned and dangerous chemicals, such as tetrachloroethylene (PERC) and trichloroethylene (TCE). Many workers suffer from hearing loss, but the NXP cannot get the company to reduce noise levels by installing quieter machines. Although the union tries to motivate workers to become active around occupational health, not enough workers respond.

> When life is so hard, it's difficult to convince workers that their health is the most important thing. More important than money.

But the NXP union is nothing if not stubborn. The union leadership was arrested and fired for protesting factory conditions. With strong support from the union members, after 5 months most got their jobs back, and their demands were accepted by the company. Now the leadership is trying to convince the workers to struggle just as hard for health and safety.

Plan campaigns around the most important problems

Gathering information about problems at work gets people talking and feeling connected. For many workers, those discussions will be the first time they feel their concerns about work are being heard. It can be a powerful experience to learn that others share similar problems.

When workers know and trust their co-workers, it becomes possible to begin talking about what they want to change. First they identify the problems and then they plan the solutions. Even when different groups of workers share similar problems, each group may support a different solution that they think best fits their situation.

Make your voices heard!

Step 1: Choose a problem

Although many changes are probably needed, your group may be more effective if it works on one at a time. First, pick a problem the group has a good chance of solving quickly. As the group learns to work together, you can take on more difficult problems. If you choose several problems at once, it usually requires a stronger group and a more complex campaign.

To help a group decide what problems to tackle first, it may be helpful to discuss questions such as:

- Which dangers affect the most workers?
- Which danger causes the most serious harm or is the most dangerous?
- Which dangers can be solved quickly?
- What will get strong support from co-workers?
- Which community groups, politicians, or community leaders can give support?
- Which local media — radio, newspapers, or TV stations — might give support?
- Is the company violating any laws?
- Are there international groups that can help?

You may need more information before deciding on a problem and going on to Step 2. See pages 31 to 32.

Step 2: Decide how to solve the problem

List all the ways the problem could be solved. Use the illustration from "Solve health and safety problems" on pages 8 to 9 to talk about the changes that could be made. But do not limit the group to those answers. Be open to any ideas about how to solve problems – ideas that come directly from the workers are more likely to be appropriate for their factory. Think about changes and solutions as steps in a ladder. The first step is the easiest change, and keep moving up towards more permanent, long-term solutions. Pick ways that best use your group's strengths and resources.

Step 3: Look at your strengths, obstacles, and allies

In addition to the strength of working together, what other strengths do workers have that they can use to solve these problems? Talk about and write down:

- What are our strengths? What opportunities for change do we see? What strategies would be most useful to pressure the employer to make changes?
- What are the obstacles we will have to overcome? What concerns do workers have about organizing? What allies does the employer have to resist workers' demands?
- What allies could we enlist to help pressure the employer?

It is important to know our weaknesses, but we also have friends and allies who can help us. Let's name some.

STRENGTHS:
common problems
people are angry
skilled organizers

OBSTACLES:
afraid
tired
can't talk at work
new workers
no money
discrimination

ALLIES:
union
families
teachers
radio

Church leaders.

Labor rights professors.

Maybe students from the university.

Step 4: Plan for action

Organizing workers to take action may take some time, especially if workers fear being attacked or losing their jobs. Make a plan and decide who will carry out each part. Talk about how to do each task. Share ideas and skills for successful organizing. Your first task might be to recruit more people to this organizing committee. Set a date when each task in the plan should be finished, then set a time to meet again to see how things are going.

Step 5: How is the plan going?

Have each person report on progress they are making with their tasks. Celebrate what you have accomplished, such as how many workers support the demands or are willing to take action. Then decide if you are seeing the results you expected or if you need to change the plan.

Step 6: Adjust the plan if you need to

If the work is not going according to plan, analyze why. What needs to be changed to make the plan work? Adjust the plan and decide which tasks each member of the group will do. As before, set dates when each task should be finished and when you will meet again to evaluate and adjust the plan.

If people need help to complete their tasks, talk over what is needed and who can help. A worker joining the group can take responsibility for tasks she has never done if she gets advice, training, and support from more experienced organizers. Be supportive rather than critical. Don't lose possible organizers because they make one or two mistakes.

Could an international campaign help?

Local and international organizations may be able to help workers in the factory. They can bring information and experience that may be useful. For example, they can help get information about the company that buys garments produced in a specific factory. They can find out about the labor conditions in other factories used by that company. Knowing who owns or contracts to a specific factory can be useful for organizing an international campaign to put pressure on a company to treat the factory workers better.

Is this your factory, dear?

**When corporations are global,
your campaign can be, too!**

International campaigns can get the word of local worker efforts out to the world. The large companies that buy the products made in export factories do not like the public to see them as "sweatshop" companies. Telling the personal story of the challenges of a factory worker is an excellent way to win the support of people around the world.

An international campaign can only support the factory workers' local campaign and goals if the workers tell the campaigners what support is needed, and if the international supporters listen. Communicating with campaigners is easier when workers are unified in a strong group. Workers can also have a strong relationship with an outside union or community group that serves as a liaison between non-unionized workers and an international campaign.

Take action to win change

There is no one way of organizing that works all the time. Many kinds of actions are possible, and many different actions may be needed to build power among workers and fix problems at work. You may win quickly or it may take months or years to win the changes you want.

Educate and reach out about workers' needs to other workers, the community, the employer and employer associations, and government officials and agencies.

Build relationships with allies and leaders in the community who can help persuade the employer and others to join in, or at least not oppose, the actions you organize. Try to build relationships with factory owners and government officials too. One of the biggest challenges you have as an organizer is to help bring out the best in all the people you work with. Focus on getting the support you need to win.

Organize many workers to take action together to demand solutions from the boss. This is a very powerful way to get employers to pay attention. It can also be risky for the workers who participate. But when more workers act together, the more powerful their message and the less risk there is to each worker. Remember, it is not your job to make deals with management. Take proposals back to the workers and let them decide. That is how collective power is strengthened.

Learn from other workers about what works

Here are different types of actions workers have used successfully in export factories around the world. Adapt them to the situation in your workplace or community to make them work for you. As a part of doing any of these or other activities, discuss what you will do to protect yourself and others from retaliation should it come.

Coordinate workers to take individual actions to make their work area better (such as bringing a pillow to sit on or making a foot rest). Or organize a boycott of an area (such as a loud machine shop) or service (such as a cafeteria). If you all do it at the same time, your boss will notice. See "Workers demand better food and win a new union," page 407.

Learn more about health and safety issues. The more you know, the more tools you will have to get the boss and the government to listen and act. See "Women workers organize through health promotion," page 374.

Set up a communication network among the workers, including workers from every part of the factory. Workers can pass information among themselves about chemical use in the factory, what management is planning, experiences of workers in different areas, and how workers could respond as a group. See "We now use a safer chemical," pages 188 to 189.

Stop work for a few minutes, an hour, or longer and tell the supervisors and bosses why you are doing it. Or have different parts of the factory stop at different times. These actions work best when many workers participate. If too few people stop working, it will not succeed. See "Stand together, fan together," page 234.

Take a delegation to the boss to discuss specific demands. Never go alone. Explain how resolving the problems will benefit the employer too. Take notes about everything that is said during the meeting, including the date and time, who was present, and what agreements were made. Take photos or record what happened with your phone.

File complaints with government agencies to get them to enforce labor, workplace safety, and anti-discrimination laws. See "How we won against forced overtime," pages 293 to 294.

Get advice and support from lawyers and take the government or the company to court. Legal cases often take a long time, but the rulings may improve conditions for many workers. See "Cleaning wafers gave Yu-mi the cancer that killed her," page 68.

Invite the media to your events and learn how to write news releases. Use social media to communicate among workers and with other interested people. Take and distribute photos. See "Our water turned bright blue!" on page 106.

Hold a public hearing where workers can testify to community leaders and their neighbors about problems in the factory and their demands for changes. See "We demand to know what chemicals are being used in the factory," page 184.

Hold rallies, conferences, and workshops to educate people about the problems workers face and also to push the government to listen and act. See "Workers should not die for fashion!" on page 103.

PART 2

Industries

4 Electronics factories

Millions of people work in electronics factories, making the phones and devices we use every day. Our world economies depend on them. So why should workers continue to be made sick by chemicals used in making electronics, repetitive stress injuries, low pay, and bad living and working conditions? Ensuring their health and well-being should be a priority for governments, corporations, and managers of electronics factories.

To improve the health of workers in electronics factories:

- **Governments and the ILO** must regularly assess dangers in electronics factories and push factories and brands to improve working conditions. Governments must provide medical and social support for workers made sick by their work and ensure compensation for them and their families.

- **Brands** must make sure factories follow local and international labor, occupational safety and health, and environmental standards. They should design products to be made without toxic materials, to last a long time, and to be safely recycled.

- **Factories** must comply with labor, occupational health and safety, and environmental laws. They should disclose all the chemicals they use, and where and how they are used (including byproducts and disposal) to workers, communities, and the government. They should share monitoring information about exposure and illness with workers, communities and the government.

- **Workers** must actively monitor their health and factory conditions. They should organize safety committees and unions in electronics factories.

Electronics factories may look safe but they are not

It is difficult for workers to know how they come in contact with chemicals in electronics factories because the factories look so safe. The rooms where many of the processes take place are very clean, with controlled temperature and humidity. Workers are covered from head to toe with special clothing which they are told protects them from dangers at work. Many processes are done by machines.

Electronics factories are set up to protect the delicate materials inside electronics, not necessarily the workers. For information about personal protective equipment (PPE), see chapter 18.

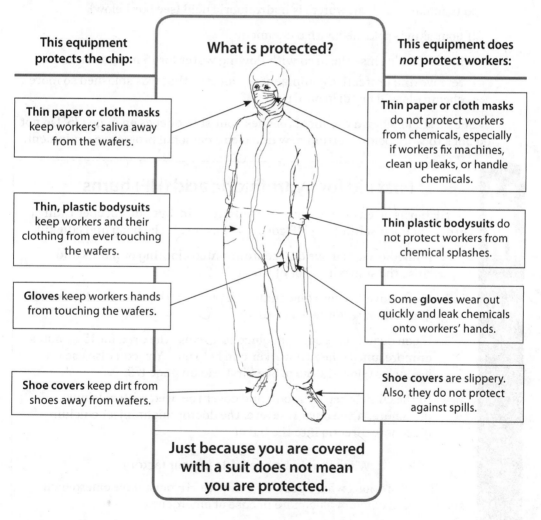

This equipment protects the chip:

Thin paper or cloth masks keep workers' saliva away from the wafers.

Thin, plastic bodysuits keep workers and their clothing from ever touching the wafers.

Gloves keep workers hands from touching the wafers.

Shoe covers keep dirt from shoes away from wafers.

What is protected?

This equipment does *not* protect workers:

Thin paper or cloth masks do not protect workers from chemicals, especially if workers fix machines, clean up leaks, or handle chemicals.

Thin plastic bodysuits do not protect workers from chemical splashes.

Some **gloves** wear out quickly and leak chemicals onto workers' hands.

Shoe covers are slippery. Also, they do not protect against spills.

Just because you are covered with a suit does not mean you are protected.

Making and cleaning the wafer

The chips that are the hearts and brains of electronics are made from slices of silicon called wafers.

Wafers are made by melting and spinning silicon into tubes called "ingots." Workers cut ingots into wafer-thin slices and then clean them with chemicals.

The chemicals used to clean wafers include solvents (pages 517 to 529) and acids (pages 474 to 476). These chemicals can irritate and burn your skin. Absorbed directly through the skin or from regular exposure by breathing, they can harm your internal organs. One of the most dangerous chemicals used to make and clean wafers is hydrofluoric acid (see box below).

If your skin is splashed with a chemical:

- immediately rinse the area with flowing water for 15 minutes or more.
- remove any protective equipment or clothing that was splashed so more chemicals will not drip onto you.

See First aid when a chemical touches your skin or eyes on page 175. Do not go back to work before getting new and clean personal protective equipment.

First Aid

First aid for hydrofluoric acid (HF) burns

HF burns often do not cause immediate pain, but burn deeper than other chemicals. Inhaling HF causes burns inside the body and can kill.

1. Immediately remove any contaminated clothing or gloves and rinse the skin with a lot of water for 5 minutes.

2. If you have calcium gluconate gel, put it on the skin. Do this even if you cannot see or feel a burn.

3. If you do not have calcium gluconate, rinse the area for 15 minutes or more, until a health worker can help you. You can also use an icepack to slow the burn. See First Aid on page 175.

4. In the clinic, they will soak and cover the area with calcium gluconate. If the burn is severe, the doctor might inject calcium gluconate directly into the burn.

What should be available in your factory

All workstations where people work with HF must have emergency showers and calcium gluconate in case of emergencies.

For more on treating burns, see page 217. For more on HF, see pages 475 to 476.

Prevent chemicals from getting in your nose and mouth

Electronics factories use so many chemicals they need to have well developed and well maintained ventilation systems to clean the air or bring fresh air into your work area. See more about Heating, Ventilation, and Air Conditioning (HVAC) systems on page 249.

Even when air is filtered and refreshed with clean air, you might still have health problems from chemicals in the air. Pay attention to signs you might be breathing chemicals:

- You see or smell a chemical. But many chemicals do not smell or you might be used to them.
- You have problems breathing, skin or eye irritation, feel dizzy, confused, or nauseous.
- You have health problems that might be caused by the chemicals you are working with.

If you breathe in chemicals, leave the workplace immediately and get fresh air. Seek medical attention. See First aid when you breathe in a chemical on page 174.

Your factory should also have an emergency plan for chemical releases, including where to find and how to use emergency PPE. If your factory does not have an emergency plan or has not trained you on what to do, leave an area where there has been a spill as fast as you can.

Breathing chemicals can cause health problems

Heath Info

Chemicals in the air can irritate your nose, throat, and lungs and cause breathing problems, making it harder for your body to get the air it needs. Your chest might feel tight, as if you cannot take in enough air or full breaths. Many people also get a cough that does not go away or one that only goes away when they are not working.

If you have any of these signs, especially if you have been breathing chemical vapors, see a health worker. She might do an X-ray or lung function test to check how well your lungs work, and test your blood to see how much oxygen is in it. Treatment varies for breathing problems: breathing oxygen from a tank or taking cortico-steroids or other medicines may reduce breathing problems. Staying away from chemicals and not smoking cigarettes always helps. Antibiotics do not.

Although widely used, sometimes cortico-steroids are used in harmful ways. See page 51 of *Where There Is No Doctor* and page 503 of *Where Women Have No Doctor* for more information.

Cleaning wafers gave Yu-mi the cancer that killed her

When workers get sick from exposure to chemicals at work, they often have to fight for their illnesses to be recognized as work-related.

That's what happened to my beautiful daughter. Yu-mi was only 21 when she got leukemia, cancer of the blood. She worked cleaning wafers at a Samsung semiconductor plant in Korea. Soon after Yu-mi was diagnosed, so was another woman in the same work area. Samsung offered to pay their medical expenses but said their illnesses had nothing to do with work. They said it was a personal problem. Yu-mi fought the leukemia for many months, but the disease was too advanced. She passed away in 2007.

Yu-mi got leukemia from working at Samsung. Her plant used chemicals that cause leukemia. Other families of Samsung workers also lost their children to cancer from working there. We decided to fight to make Samsung take responsibility, and stop poisoning workers and destroying families.

SHARPS (Supporters for the Health and Rights of People in the Semiconductor Industry) brought together Samsung workers, former workers and their families, unions, and human rights groups. We held rallies, protests, and campaigns. We met with groups from all over the world that fought the electronics companies poisoning the workers. Academics and scientists began studies to find out which chemicals were making workers sick. We went to court many times, asking the Korean government to recognize workers' cancers as work-related. But Samsung is very influential in Korea, and the courts kept ruling that workers' cancers did not come from work.

In 2011, a Korean court ruled in our favor. Since many of the chemicals and byproducts were known to cause cancer, they said it was likely that Yu-mi got cancer at Samsung. Samsung immediately hired a consulting firm called Environ to "prove" Samsung workers had no more cancer than any other group in Korea. They got the court to change its ruling. But we appealed again. Finally in 2014, it was decided that Yumi's leukemia was caused by her work at Samsung.

The ruling was a big win for us. It showed that people standing firm can challenge the most powerful electronics company in the world. We will continue to fight for the Samsung workers, and for the memory of my daughter Yu-mi.

Making the chip on the wafer

To make individual chips on the silicon wafer, workers put the wafers through several machines that cover them with chemicals and expose them to ultra-violet (UV) light. The chemicals and the light build the design for each individual chip on the wafer. The process of layering chemicals and exposing them to light is called "photomasking." The process of removing unwanted chemicals to complete the design is called "etching."

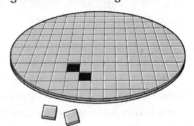

Even though photomasking and etching happen inside closed machines, workers can be exposed to chemicals when:

- **machines, pipes, and vents have leaks or are not working well.** Leaks can be found by regularly inspecting all equipment, and checking and replacing air quality monitors. Then leaks can be fixed as soon as they are noticed. A planned maintenance schedule keeps workers, production, and communities safer than just responding when there is a failure. Factories that run 24 hours a day in shifts might not respond to leaks as well or as quickly as factories that have time to repair a machine without affecting production.

- **workers open machines, pipes, and vents to clean and repair them.** Maintenance workers or engineers who open the machines and come into direct contact with chemicals face the most danger, but all workers are affected when chemicals get in the air.

To protect all workers, maintenance workers should:

- follow all shut down, lock out, and tag out procedures when they repair machines (see page 201).
- wear the highest level of protective equipment (see chapter 18: Personal Protective Equipment).
- make sure other workers leave the area if chemicals may be released.

Photomasking dangers: photoresist chemicals

Workers, activists, and health professionals believe photoresists are one of the most toxic chemical mixes used in making electronics. The companies that make photoresists usually refuse to disclose which chemicals and how much of each are in them, saying that is a "trade secret." However, the danger they pose to health is no secret.

Photoresists contain a mix of chemicals from 4 basic categories: sensitizers (chemicals that react to heat or light), solvents, polymers, and additives. When exposed to light, some of the chemicals in photoresist break down into other chemicals, called byproducts. These chemical byproducts can also be very harmful to workers' health.

Photoresist is quickly absorbed by the skin. Wear the right kind of chemical-resistant gloves, clothing, and respirators to protect against photoresist and its byproducts (see chapter 18: Personal protective equipment).

Some of the toxic chemicals in photoresist

There are so many different chemicals in and released by various photoresists that it is difficult to know which ones are causing health problems in your factory. Some of the chemicals of concern are:

- **phenol formaldehyde,** a polymer commonly known by its trade name, *Novolak* resin. When heated, phenol formaldehyde releases formaldehyde, which causes asthma and cancer. It also releases aromatic hydrocarbons such as benzene, toluene, and xylene when heated. These aromatic hydrocarbons damage the liver, kidneys, brain, and nervous system, and some cause cancer and reproductive health problems. (See: polymers, pages 511 to 513; formaldehyde, pages 496 to 497; and aromatic hydrocarbons, pages 522 to 523.)

- **glycol ethers,** solvents which have been banned in many countries because they are so harmful. Several glycol ethers cause reproductive health problems. Alternative chemicals for glycol ethers used in photoresists include xylene, butyl acetate, acetone, and methyl chloroform. These also harm people. (See: glycol ethers, pages 527 to 528; xylene, pages 522 to 523; butyl acetate, page 526; acetone, page 529; and methyl chloroform, pages 524 to 525.)

- **aliphatic hydrocarbons,** solvents used as sensitizers. They can affect the brain, causing headaches and dizziness. Some may damage the liver and kidneys. High doses of some aliphatic hydrocarbons can kill you. (See aliphatic hydrocarbon solvents, pages 520 to 521.)

Photomasking dangers: UV lights

The UV lights inside photomasking machines are supposed to turn off when the machine is open and workers are loading or unloading wafers. UV light can quickly damage your eyes, even in an enclosed machine. Workers in this area need UV-protected polycarbonate goggles, nitrile gloves, and face masks (see chapter 18). Clothing must cover the entire body, especially the wrists. Even a small gap between shirt cuff and glove can let UV light burn any exposed skin.

UV light bulbs break easily. As they contain mercury, a broken UV light not only poses a risk injury from cuts, it also exposes workers to mercury.

When a UV light breaks, small pieces of mercury scatter. (This is also true with compact flourescent lights (CFLs), but these contain much less mercury.) Turn off any machines, heaters, fans, and air conditioners. Leave the area and make sure all workers are out before closing the door. Inform the supervisor so maintenance can clean up the spill.

| How to | **Clean up a mercury spill** |

If you have to clean up a mercury spill, you will need gloves, an eyedropper, 2 pieces of stiff paper or cardboard, 2 plastic bags, sticky tape, a flashlight, and a glass container with a lid and with water in it.

1. Do not touch the mercury.

2. Remove watches and jewelry. Mercury sticks to other metals.

3. Shine a flashlight on the area to make the mercury easier to see, even during the day.

4. Wear chemical-resistant gloves if possible. If you have only latex gloves, wear 2 pairs.

5. Use small pieces of stiff paper or cardboard to gather the mercury and broken glass into a small pile.

6. Use an eyedropper to suction up the mercury beads, and put the mercury in the glass container with water.

7. Pick up any mercury that is left using sticky tape.

8. Place tape, eyedropper, gloves, and cardboard in a plastic bag.

9. Label the bag "mercury waste" and put the bag in the glass container with the water in it.

10. Seal and label the container. Put it inside another plastic bag.

11. Dispose of it as toxic waste.

Etching dangers: wet etching

Wafers are dipped into several baths containing nitric, acetic, and hydrofluoric (HF) acids to remove photoresist. This work area must be enclosed and have strong local exhaust ventilation (see pages 250 to 251).

Acids can quickly burn your skin, eyes, and insides, so you need acid-resistant protective equipment, including respirators if your ventilation is not good enough or if you move materials between workstations. There must be a shower and eye wash station nearby. See First Aid on page 175.

Etching dangers: dry etching

Wafers are sprayed with fluorinated hydrocarbons and heated with radio-frequency (RF) radiation. The heat from the radiation causes the gases to move, "attack," and remove the photoresist chemicals. RF radiation can harm your nervous system and cause reproductive problems. The best way to protect yourself from radiation is to limit how much time you work with it and use barriers and PPE to shield yourself from it. See Radiation, pages 514 to 516.

Fluorinated hydrocarbons are dangerous because they accumulate in our bodies. Over time, even small amounts can build up and make us sick. People who breathe or touch them might have problems breathing and skin irritation. Some cause heart problems, reproductive problems, and cancer.

Protect workers from etching chemicals:

- Regularly check that machines seal completely. Fix leaks immediately.
- Ventilation must be strong enough to remove all chemical fumes. There should be emergency ventilation in case of a spill.
- All workers should have PPE. Maintenance workers need special PPE. An OSH professional can help identify the PPE you need.
- Etched wafers should sit in a ventilated "waiting area" before they are removed, to reduce the amount of fumes in the air for everyone.
- Pregnant women should not work with fluorinated hydrocarbons. These chemicals can harm babies inside the womb.

I work for Ericsson in Batam, Indonesia. Of all the stations in the factory, the workers in dry etching get colds most often. When a worker gets sick, they are 'rolled' into a different job in the factory and a new worker comes into the etching room and stays until he starts to get sick. They don't tell us why we get sick, they just move us.

Adding more layers and special qualities to the wafer

Wafers pass through several processes to:

- add more layers onto the chips already designed on the wafer (oxidation).
- make some of the layers more conductive to electricity (ion implantation).

Dangers from dopant gases

Dopant gases such as arsine, phosphine, diborane, and boron are heated by RF radiation so they will form layers with different electrical properties on the surface of the wafer. Workers are exposed to dopant gases when loading and unloading wafers from the machines, when changing gas cylinders, and when repairing or cleaning machines.

Dopant gases might make you feel weak, tired, sleepy, or confused, and might give you a headache or muscle cramps. They can also make you have problems breathing, faint, or feel paralyzed. If you have any of these signs:

- Leave the area immediately.
- Remove your protective equipment and clothes, and wash your entire body with water and soap.

Don't wait until you feel sick to put on protective equipment or stop production to get a machine fixed.

See 'First aid when you breathe in a chemical' on page 174. See pages 482 to 484 for information on dopant gases.

We noticed a strange smell and complained. Tests showed high levels of arsine. It turned out the wafers were releasing the gas when they came out of the machine. They gave us fancy respirators after that. But what would have happened if arsine didn't smell?

Arsine smells like garlic. If you can smell it, you are exposed to levels that can cause harm. See arsine on pages 482 to 484.

Dangers from heat and fire

Dopant gases burn easily. Some explode when heated or when they accumulate, so vents and machines must be cleaned often, on a planned maintenance schedule. Some machine parts, such as pumps, must be cleaned frequently because the oil in the pumps absorbs gases and can harm workers. Also, the machines can get very hot. Workers in this area can get burned from accidentally touching the machines. See First Aid for burns on page 217.

Dangers from X-rays

The combination of RF radiation and dopant gases generates X-rays, a form of radiation that can cause cancer and severe damage to the reproductive system for both women and men. X-rays are also used during inspection of the wafers, to see if they have enough metal. See pages 514 to 516 for more information on the health effects of X-rays and other radiation.

Dangers from adding metals to the wafer

To make electrical connections between the different parts of the chip, metal is added to the wafer. Aluminum is most commonly used, but so are chromium, copper, tin, lead, nickel, gold, silver, titanium, and platinum. Some metals cause more harm than others, but all are easier to breathe or accidently ingest as gases or vapors. Find information about metals on pages 503 to 505.

Protect workers from:

- **Dopants:** Make sure all dopants are extracted before opening machines. Maintenance workers who clean or repair the machines should have air-supplying respirators and personal protective equipment for chemical exposure and heat (see chapter 18: Personal protective equipment).

- **X-rays:** Machines should have X-ray shields. All workers in areas where X-rays are present need badges that detect X-ray levels. Shielding and badges must be checked regularly. If badges show high levels of X-ray exposure, workers need to be transferred out of the area and given access to medical services.

Banning lead and toxic chemicals

The **European Union Restriction of Hazardous Substances Directive (RoHS)** bans the use of 6 of the most harmful materials used in electronics sold in Europe:

- lead
- mercury
- cadmium
- chromium hexavalent – Cr(VI)
- polybrominated biphenyls
- polybrominated diphenyl ethers

Removing these chemicals from production helps protect workers, the community, and the environment. Although the RoHS only covers countries of the European Union, knowing a chemical is banned in one country can help you fight to get it banned in yours. The RoHS has influenced laws in other countries, including China, Japan, Thailand, Australia, South Korea, and the United States.

Making the individual chips

The chips built up on the wafers are then cut into individual chips and glued onto ceramic or plastic frames. Very tiny electrical connections are soldered or bonded to the chip, and dozens of metal connectors are soldered onto the base frame. The chip is then covered with plastic or epoxy which is heated and melted to form a shell. The chip on a frame is called an integrated circuit (IC).

Chemicals and repetitive work are important dangers workers face in this area. ICs can also break and release chemicals into the air.

Soldering and wire bonding: Workers are exposed to chemicals in solder and flux, and to the degreasers and solvents used to clean the soldered connections (see Soldering on pages 80 to 82, and metals and fluxes in Appendix B).

Encapsulation: Brominated- or phosphorous-based flame retardant chemicals are added into the plastic shells to make them more resistant to heat (see Flame retardants on pages 488 to 492). Workers are exposed to chemicals in the epoxy as it is heated.

Trim and form: Cutting, forming, and tooling the wires to a specific shape can cause repetitive motion strain injuries (see chapter 7: Ergonomics). Workers are also exposed to solvents used to clean tools.

Marking, testing, packaging, and inspecting: The chip will be marked with ink or lasers, tested and packaged. Workers inspect wafer and ICs with magnifiers, computers screens, or X-ray machines. Inspection is hard on the body, especially the eyes. Keep your eye muscles strong and reduce strain by regularly looking away at something across the room. While this is no substitute for regular rest breaks, it is a good way to supplement them and protect your eyes.

First look at something close to you.

Then look away to something about 3 to 4 meters away for 20 seconds.

3 to 4 meters

Do this a few times each hour. Also, scan the room: hold your head still and move your eyes up one wall, around the ceiling, and down the other wall.

Making the printed circuit board

The chips, or integrated circuits (ICs), are attached to a larger panel called a printed circuit board (PrCB). The PrCB and many other components (parts including ICs, electrical connections, and transistors) together make the electronic product. Many of the processes to make a chip are used to make a PrCB, so many of the dangers, such as photomasking (page 70), etching (page 72), and adding more layers (page 73) are similar but on a larger scale.

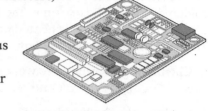

Any time larger quantities of chemicals, metals, or potentially dangerous processes are used, it is more likely workers will be harmed. It also creates more waste and pollution.

Making the board

The printed circuit boards are made of fiberglass epoxy (a thin plastic sheet that contains threads of glass to make it stronger) and a thin sheet of copper pressed on each side. Sometimes aluminum, nickel, and other metals are used.

Even with gloves, my skin gets irritated and raw from the fiberglass dust. The boss won't give us better gloves. He says these are safe enough.

Excess copper is stripped from the board to leave behind metal connections for the components. Different kinds of boards are used: 1-sided, 2-sided, and multi-layered (with electrical connections inside and components on the outer sides).

Health Info

Dangers of fiberglass

Fiberglass dust on PrCBs can get on your skin, nose, and throat. You can develop an itchy rash anywhere on your body. A doctor can see fiberglass on your skin with a microscope.

To prevent fiberglass injuries:

- Do not let the fiberglass touch your skin. Use long sleeves and pants.
- Vacuum newly cut boards and clean fiberglass dust from the edges.
- Use gloves made out of rubber or neoprene.
- Use a dust mask.

Dangers of Photomasking PrCBs

PrCBs go through a photomasking process that covers the areas of copper required for the design. This layer over the copper hardens when exposed to UV light, leaving the unwanted material soft and easy to remove.

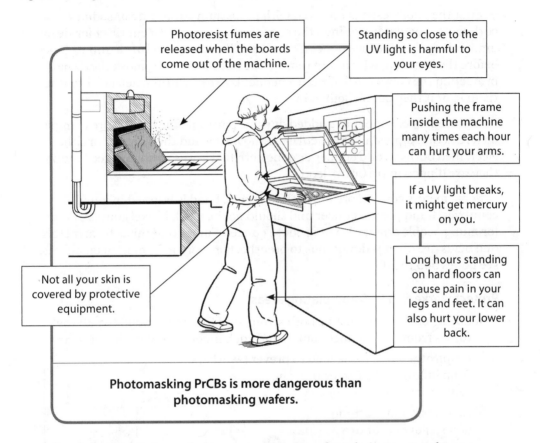

Photoresist fumes are released when the boards come out of the machine.

Standing so close to the UV light is harmful to your eyes.

Pushing the frame inside the machine many times each hour can hurt your arms.

If a UV light breaks, it might get mercury on you.

Not all your skin is covered by protective equipment.

Long hours standing on hard floors can cause pain in your legs and feet. It can also hurt your lower back.

Photomasking PrCBs is more dangerous than photomasking wafers.

- Good ventilation is needed to protect workers from being exposed to photomasking chemicals while working with this machine and when handling PrCBs after they come out of the machines (see pages 250 to 251).
- Workers need protective equipment including chemical-resistant clothing and UV glasses. See chapter 18: Personal protective equipment.
- Shock-absorbing mats to stand on and enough rest breaks will prevent muscle pain and strain and overuse injuries. See chapter 7: Ergonomics.

Dangers in the DES (Develop, Etch, Strip) Processes

A conveyer belt usually moves the printed circuit boards through multiple machines in the large DES work area. Many chemicals are put on and then removed from the boards, and can create problems for all workers in the area.

First the photoresist is removed with potassium carbonate or sodium carbonate monohydrate. Then the copper is removed with cupric chloride or ammonium chloride (see pages 479 to 481). There are several cleaning stages before the last step, which is to remove the hardened photomask that was protecting the copper. All of these chemicals are harmful when you breathe them in or if they get on your skin.

More layers of copper are added during "plating." The boards are clamped on a rack and dipped in chemical cleaning baths and then dipped in either electrified baths to add copper or nonelectrified baths to add nickel. Finally, they are dipped in tin or tin/lead.

Some metals cause more harm than others. Lead is banned in many countries. It may cause cancer and should not be used. Nickel causes allergies for many people and it also may cause cancer. Fumes and mists from metals and acids are always dangerous to breathe. For more information on metals, see pages 503 to 505.

Protect workers in DES and plating areas

- Local ventilation must be both strong and focused enough to pull the fumes from the chemical baths and each machine out of the work area.
- Respirators may be needed to prevent workers from inhaling the fumes that the ventilation does not remove.
- Acid-resistant clothing, boots, gloves that are changed every day, eye protection, and other gear will be needed to protect workers from the dangers of splashes, burns, slips, and other injuries related to working with acids, solvents, and other chemicals.

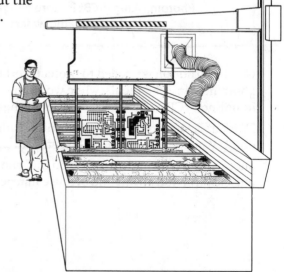

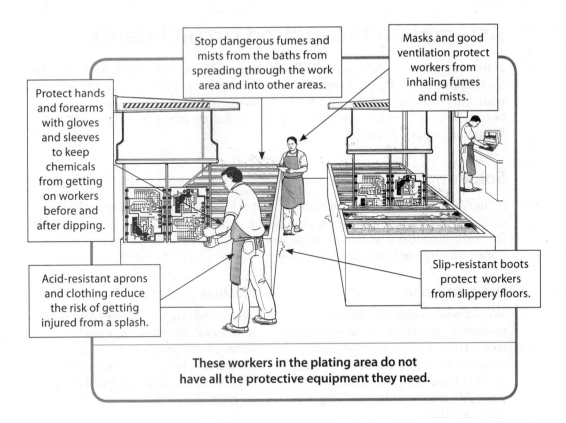

Stop dangerous fumes and mists from the baths from spreading through the work area and into other areas.

Masks and good ventilation protect workers from inhaling fumes and mists.

Protect hands and forearms with gloves and sleeves to keep chemicals from getting on workers before and after dipping.

Acid-resistant aprons and clothing reduce the risk of getting injured from a splash.

Slip-resistant boots protect workers from slippery floors.

These workers in the plating area do not have all the protective equipment they need.

Making a board ready for components

Before going to assembly factories, the boards may go through a number of processes from which employers must protect workers, taking similar precautions as in the DES area. These processes include:

- **Solder mask:** The boards are coated with a chemical to protect the non-metal areas from the soldering process.
- **Legend:** The boards are printed with ink or lasers to show where components will be placed during assembly and to help during repair.
- **Removing tin/lead:** The tin or tin/lead is stripped with a mixture of nitric acid and ferric ion to expose the copper.
- **Final surface finish:** Parts are polished so components can be glued on. Boards are dipped in nickel and gold so they better conduct electricity.

Assembling the printed circuit boards

The components are added to the PrCBs by hand or by machines. Both workers and machines use flux to prepare the metal surfaces of the parts and the board to better accept the solder which makes the electrical connection between them. Flux is a mix of chemicals, including solvents and acids. See Fluxes on pages 493 to 495.

Soldering

Soldering means melting a little bit of metal to make a bridge connecting 2 different components. Solder is usually tin, a mixture of tin and lead, or a lead-free mix of copper and other metals (see pages 503 to 505). Soldering can be done manually or by machines.

Hand soldering

Workers who solder by hand need mounted extractors on the soldering iron, strong local extractors, and respirators. If you notice signs that you are breathing in chemicals (see page 73), stop working and improve your ventilation or PPE.

Machine soldering

Wave soldering machines and other machines that solder should have strong local ventilation. PrCBs should rest in a well-ventilated area after they are soldered until they stop off-gassing.

These workers need extractors, respirators or both. Why don't they have them?

Soldering can hurt workers' health

Flux and solder contain chemicals which can irritate your skin or lungs immediately or later. They also contain chemicals that can cause chronic health problems. Rosin in flux and lead in solder are 2 of the chemicals that we know cause health problems in the soldering area.

Heating flux and solder releases fumes. Signs you are breathing the chemicals in flux and solder are:

- headaches
- nose bleeds
- problems breathing
- feeling tired and weak
- sore throat
- red and irritated eyes
- skin rashes

If you have any of these or other problems, tell your health and safety committee and boss. Talk to a health worker about where you work, what you do, and the chemicals you are exposed to. Smoking or just being around smoke will worsen these problems.

If your boss makes no changes to the workplace and you keep breathing the chemicals in flux and solder, you are likely to develop other health problems.

 Record all health problems and changes in solders and fluxes in your health notebook (see page 46).

Protect workers from the dangers of soldering

Soldering is safer when flux does not contain rosin and solder does not contain lead. We know these materials are too dangerous to use.

Soldering can be made safer when workstations have good local and general ventilation (see chapter 17: Ventilation) and workers have the correct personal protective equipment for the chemicals they use and well-fitting PPE (see chapter 18). When workers can tell the boss and the health and safety committee about safety issues, and get them resolved, everybody is safer.

Soldering can also be made safer by:

- turning the heat down on the soldering iron, so less fume is released into the air. See page 167.
- "following the air" (see the activity on page 253) to check your local ventilation, and organizing to improve ventilation for everyone.
- finding out the dangers of the chemicals in your flux and solder. Look them up on pages 493 to 495, get an SDS (see pages 180 to 182), try other resources (see page 464), and organize to get safer flux and solder.

Is lead-free solder really safer?

After the European Union banned the use of lead in solder and other materials used to make electronics for Europe (see page 74), some companies resisted the change. They claimed lead could be used safely, that it was "necessary" for production, and that lead-free products were not as good and were more expensive.

But they lost the argument: any electronics company that wanted to sell to Europe after 2006 had to prove they were not using lead.

Alternatives to lead solder began to appear and chemical companies produced them quickly. One uses copper, tin, and nickel instead of lead.

But as with any new process, the new solders brought new problems: lead-free solder uses more flux (see pages 493 to 495), which can contain harmful chemicals, is heated to higher temperatures, and may release more particles than lead-based solders. Few of these new solders were studied to show if they were safer for workers than lead.

Making the production of electronics safer and more sustainable should mean that dangerous chemicals are replaced by chemicals proven to be safe – not just different and hoped to be safe.

Testing the PrCBs

Workers check the boards and their components visually and electronically before they are assembled or packaged for shipping. Lifting, checking and removing the PrCBs can lead to muscle strain and overuse injuries. Often, to prevent static electricity from damaging the boards, workers are required to wear grounding wrist cords. The wrist cords contain nickel, a chemical that can irritate the skin.

- Adjust carts, work tables, and chairs to limit the amount of lifting and twisting you must do. See chapter 7: Ergonomics.

- Wear gloves to protect your hands from the hard edges of the fiberglass boards.

- If you already have or develop an allergy to nickel (see pages 504 to 505), ask for a nickel-free grounding cord.

Assembling electronics

On long assembly lines, workers glue, solder and screw together all the pieces that make the electronic product. Workers then clean, polish, and test them. Products that do not pass the tests are sent to a fixing area, where workers reopen the defective piece and repair it manually.

When people assemble electronics at home, it can lead to health dangers for workers, families, and neighbors. See chapter 20: Doing factory work at home.

Making other components

Non-electronic parts are made in other factories and become part of the final product in the assembly area. Making these components is also dangerous for workers and the environment.

Plastic shells and casings: Electronics use plastic outer shells because they are lightweight, durable, and cheap. Many dangerous chemicals are used to make the shells stronger and fire resistant. Companies can make less toxic shells by:

- **using alternative chemicals** and replacing brominated flame-retardants with phosphorus- or nitrogen flame-retardants. See pages 491 to 492.
- **changing materials so they do not need flame-retardants,** for example, making shells with aluminum instead of plastic.

Batteries: Whether electronics use disposable or rechargeable batteries, all batteries contain toxic materials. The workers who make the batteries (and their families) suffer the most, but the dangers begin even earlier for the workers who mine the metals used in them. And after the product is thrown away, the chemicals in batteries leak into and pollute our water. Safer batteries and designing products to use less power will reduce the spread of toxics from batteries.

Wires and cables: Cables and wires are made from copper covered with plastic. Polyethylene and PVC (polyvinyl chloride) are the most common plastics. Most plastics are safe to touch, but heating them releases toxic chemicals that can irritate your nose, throat, lungs, and skin and may cause cancer.

Monitors and screens: The CRT, LCD, plasma, and LED screens used in electronics are often welded and glued together with a chemical that hardens when exposed to UV light. They may be filled with liquid crystals or neon and xenon gas. While most of the processes are automated, workers in screen factories are exposed to harmful gases while producing and testing screens, and maintaining factory machinery. Larger TVs and monitors weigh more and cause more muscle strain for workers.

Battery workers fight the company that poisoned them

Workers making nickel-cadmium batteries for Gold Peak Batteries in China were poisoned with cadmium. Cadmium is a toxic metal that damages the lungs, kidneys, and bones, and causes cancer. When a Gold Peak worker told her doctor she was suffering from pain, the doctor did some blood and urine tests. They showed very high levels of cadmium in her body. Other workers had dizzy spells, headaches, nausea, and miscarriages. When they were tested, their levels were also high. As word got out, many more workers, their children, and families were tested and found they were poisoned.

Gold Peak workers believed the company should take responsibility for poisoning them. They demanded treatment and compensation for their lost health.

The company tried to quiet them down. They falsified tests to show lower cadmium levels, claimed they could remove the cadmium, subjected people to ineffective, painful treatments, and fired the most vocal workers. They also closed several factories and moved them to more remote towns.

Workers held protests, sued the company, appealed to the local and national government, gathered support from non-governmental organizations, and educated others about cadmium poisoning. The company was forced to start a fund to cover yearly testing and medical expenses for former and current workers. But every year more workers are found to be poisoned with cadmium and they struggle to get compensation.

In 2006, cadmium was banned by the European Union and now lithium-ion and nickel-metal hydrate batteries are more common. However, China still allows the production of cadmium batteries. Gold Peak produces them in remote parts of China where workers still lack proper protections and information about cadmium poisoning. In 2015 Gold Peak will stop paying for workers' yearly tests and will only offer compensation to workers who can prove they were poisoned.

Fast assembly lines

Work in assembly factories is very repetitive and very fast. The stress and strain this creates causes many injuries. Some ideas to change your workplace are in this section, and many more are proposed in chapter 7: Ergonomics.

To meet the quotas, workers have to place parts every few seconds.

The Foxconn suicides and death from overtime

Workers in a Foxconn factory in China make mobile phones and other products for many big electronics companies around the world. The factory has rules, like other factories in China: "No talking!" "No looking away from work!" People can take breaks only for meals. Supervisors and managers yell and insult workers to make them work even when they are in pain or sick. The factory forces them to work overtime, sometimes keeping workers on the job for 24 hours or more.

In 2010, a young technician, Yan Li, died from exhaustion after being forced to work 34 hours straight. That same year, 18 workers tried to kill themselves to escape their inhumane working conditions.

Foxconn made excuses about why workers were committing suicide and why Yan Li died. Instead of addressing the main problem — bad working conditions — they made small changes. They raised wages a little, put nets around buildings to prevent people jumping from the roof, and opened some recreation rooms. But when they build larger facilities in other cities, Foxconn continues the same working conditions that led to the suicides in the first place. And the suicides continue.

Changing the workplace to reduce muscle strain and overuse injuries

Having everything you need close at hand to do a job strains your body less, especially when you repeat movements hundreds of times during a shift. Supporting the part of your body that is moving, such as your wrists, fingers, and elbows, and having a chair and table that fit your body can also help reduce pain and injury from work.

Look at your workstation to see what is causing your aches and pains:

- How far do you have to reach to get the components and the tools you need?
- How far do you have to reach to get the product from and to the assembly line?
- How heavy is the product you are picking up and putting back on the line? Are the parts heavy? Your tools?
- How does your chair or stool fit you? Or do you work standing up?
- Do you rest your arms or wrists on a sharp edge or a padded surface?
- How comfortable is the workstation?

You can find suggestions about making changes to your workstation in chapter 7: Ergonomics.

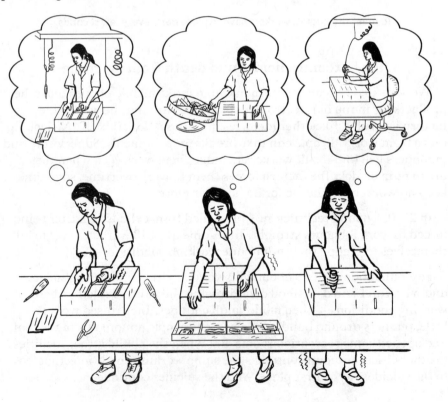

Changing jobs to reduce injury

Sometimes your work makes you repeat the same movements too many times and for too long, and no amount of change in equipment or stretching will prevent pain and injury. Workers can protect themselves by taking more control over the work process itself. Talk with your co-workers and bosses about:

* slowing down the speed of the line and adding more workers.
* changing jobs a few times a day so no set of muscles gets overused.

Better protective equipment

Some factories do not give workers protective equipment or clothing. Others give all workers the same equipment regardless of the dangers specific to their work or whether a worker's body is large or small. When necessary, employers should provide:

* **anti-static and dust-proof clothing**, including hats and wrist bands. They protect the product from static and dust, but must also protect you from metal dust.
* **gloves and finger covers.** Protecting your hands and skin can lessen irritation from dust, small cuts, and scrapes. Workers in the cleaning and polishing area need gloves that protect them from the cleaning chemicals they use. See pages 262 to 265.
* **masks and respirators.** Paper masks prevent breathing in large dust particles, but they will not protect you against fumes from plastics, glues, solder and flux, small dust particles, and the new, tiny nanoparticles (see page 94). More information about which respirator protects best for your work can be found on pages 271 to 272.
* **ear protection.** Most assembly factories are so loud they harm workers' hearing. If you have to shout to talk to a person 2 arm lengths away, the area is loud enough to cause hearing loss. See chapter 13: Noise.
* **face shields or eye protection** should be used by workers in areas where dust is created, such as grinding, packaging, and shipping.

Cleaning finished products

Workers clean electronics with different methods and chemicals, including pressurized air, polishing machines, isopropyl alcohol (IPA), and other solvents and degreasers that contain methanol or other harmful chemicals.

Cleaning chemicals can get on your skin, causing irritation and rashes. Some can be absorbed through the skin, harm your internal organs, and cause blindness. Breathing their fumes can make you dizzy, tired, or give you a headache or stomachache. Some are flammable and can cause fires. Polishing metal casings generates a lot of dust.

• Good ventilation will remove fumes and dust. See chapter 17: Ventilation.

• Wear gloves, eye protection and other protective gear to protect against chemicals used in cleaning and polishing. See pages 517 to 529 for more information on solvents and degreasers.

• Filter masks, not paper masks, may be needed to protect against dust (see pages 266 to 270).

Factory saves money by poisoning workers

I worked at the Wintek electronics factory in China, cleaning computer screens. We used to clean them with IPA alcohol, but one day the factory owner gave us a new chemical. A few weeks later, I started feeling dizzy and weak. I was not the only one. Many of us complained to the supervisors that the new chemical was making us sick, but they just told us to keep working with it or quit.

One day I woke up and couldn't move my body. My family took me to the clinic and we found many of my co-workers there too. The tests showed we had been exposed to hexane, a chemical that can cause paralysis and death. Four workers died.

We found out the boss had switched from IPA to hexane because it dried faster and he could make more money. But the factory did not have the right ventilation or provide the right protective equipment for us to use this chemical. Many organizations supported us in our fight to get the factory to provide health care and compensation to the sick workers. They told us we should go to the big companies that Wintek supplied because even though they were subcontracting their work, they were also responsible. The brand said they didn't know anything about hexane. They said they told Wintek not to use it.

This same problem also happened to us in our workplace in the USA.

Testing, packing and shipping

Workers test products before packing and shipping. Much of the testing is done by machines. However, workers in the testing area are exposed to:

- **noise:** Machines open, close, tap, thump, shake, and vibrate when testing electronic products. They beep and sound alarms when electronics pass or fail tests. Workers hear these sounds over and over without earplugs. Find out if your workplace is too loud (see page 225), how to use earplugs (see page 271), and how to reduce noise in your factory (see pages 226 to 228).

- **light:** Workers who test screens are exposed to bright light as they set screens and monitors to the right colors. See chapter 14: Light for more information about eye health and lights.

- **injury:** Larger electronic products become a danger when they are moved from place to place. You can get hurt if something falls or breaks open, exposing you to sharp edges or chemicals. Sometimes you can still smell chemicals being released from the product. Knowing what chemicals were used to make it and clean it can help you be better prepared in case anyone becomes ill from exposure.

Disposing of waste

Chemicals used in the factory are recycled or just thrown away as waste. This can harm workers as well as the surrounding communities.

- **Air pollution:** The fumes from acids, plastics and solvents go through the ventilation systems. In some factories, ventilation filters out the chemicals but usually the fumes are directly released into the air without filtering.

- **Water pollution:** The chemicals in the many baths used in electronics manufacturing go through different processes designed to separate, filter, and neutralize them. Some can be reused. Some are sent to a landfill. After the water has been "cleaned," it is released into the community water system. Sometimes the water still contains a lot of chemicals. And when it combines with water from other factories, the people in the community may get very poisonous water!

- **Solid waste:** Metals, glues, and other chemicals in solid form are usually not separated. Whatever cannot be recycled or neutralized is sent to a landfill.

Worker and community groups have joined together to get factories to take responsibility for the safe disposal of factory waste. Or even better, not to generate any waste at all! See chapter 33: Pollution from factories.

Make electronics easy to repair

Companies design electronics to break or go out-of-date after a short time, so people will have to buy new ones. They change models every year, make them impossible to fix, and keep repair instructions and programming secret. They do this to encourage consumers to buy new products because the more often people buy, the more profit the companies will make. This is wasteful and expensive.

Sustainable design is a movement to push companies to make electronics easier to repair, and to produce products that last instead of designing for the dump. Sustainable electronics have:

- cases that are easy to open, using standard screws instead of glue.
- parts that need regular replacement, like screens, are easy to access.
- standard-sized parts that are easily interchangeable.
- free and easy-to-find repair instructions.

Designing electronics so they are easy to repair reduces the need to mine for materials, produces less waste during production and recycling, and makes electronics more affordable.

Recycling electronics

After they are thrown away, many electronics are dumped in communities in Asia and Africa. People working by themselves or in small groups open the electronics, breaking screens and shells to get to the PrCBs. They melt plastic casings and wires to get inside to the gold, silver, and other metals that they remove and then sell to make a living.

If you work recycling electronics, you are exposed to many of the chemicals used in production as well as other, even more dangerous chemicals created by burning the material.

You can reduce the amount of chemicals that get into your body by:

- Wearing gloves and clothing that covers all your skin.
- Wearing eye covers or goggles.
- Wearing a mouth and nose cover. A bandana or cloth will not protect you from chemical fumes, but it will keep some of the dust out.

Making electronics safer

From computers to cell phones, electronics have become so central to our lives that it's hard to imagine living without them. But the dangers to the health of workers and communities are often too high to live with them! A number of groups internationally have formed to change the way we make, use, and dispose of electronics. They say:

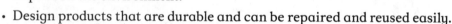

Involve workers and communities to create solutions!

You make them toxic so you should recycle them safely!

Make them safe

- Design less toxic electronics – find safer substitutes for dangerous chemicals.
- Don't use workers or customers to test whether materials are safe or dangerous.
- Design products that use less energy and have less of a bad impact on the environment.
- Design products that are durable and can be repaired and reused easily.
- Make products that can be recycled easily.
- Use as many recycled materials as possible.

Take it back

- Electronics manufacturers must create programs to take back and recycle their products for free.
- Electronics manufacturers must be responsible for their products. It is their job to ensure they are recycled safely.

Recycle responsibly

- Recycling laws should be passed to make recycling safer for people and the environment.
- Work towards zero waste – find ways of reducing and reusing materials.
- Do not dump toxic electronics waste (e-waste) in developing countries.
- Do not use prison labor to do recycling – it's toxic forced labor!

5 Garment factories

Cutting and sewing clothing is hard on the body. But low wages, fast production lines, unsafe conditions, lack of unions, and harassment hurt workers even more (see Part 4: Social Dangers and Solutions).

Garment work can be designed and organized to protect workers' health by ensuring high standards in all factories for:

- good ventilation (see chapter 17) and the right personal protective equipment (PPE, see chapter 18).
- fire exits, fire prevention measures that include sprinklers and fire extinguishers, and emergency evacuation plans (see chapter 11).
- freedom to organize unions and health and safety committees (see chapter 2).
- maintainance of equipment and worker and management trainings on health and safety.
- respectful treatment including a living wage and social benefits required by law (see chapter 19).

Achieving these basic human rights is still a struggle in most factories. The challenge is to connect and organize with other workers and consumers to win these changes from the factory owners, the international corporations that contract them (the "brands"), and the government.

Treating cloth with dyes and chemicals

Before it gets to garment workers, cloth is often treated with different chemicals that give the fabric color, fire resistance, permanent press, or other qualities. Bleach makes the fabric white and easier to dye. Dyes give the fabric specific colors. Mordants improve how color sticks to the fabric. Sealers and fixers prevent dyes from washing off with water or sweat.

The chemicals stay on the fabric. If you get rashes when working with cloth, it might be caused by the dyes or chemicals used to make it.

Dyes

Dyes and chemicals can irritate your skin and cause rashes, allergies, or breathing problems.

Cleaning your hands with solvents after working with dyes also can cause rashes, allergies, and breathing problems. Stay away from benzene or chemicals that smell sweet or pleasant. These chemicals, called aromatic hydrocarbons, are breathed in or absorbed through the skin. Some of them cause cancer.

Alcohols (such as isopropanol, IPA) are less dangerous but they still irritate your skin. Even though it may take longer to get the dye off, wash your hands with water and soap instead.

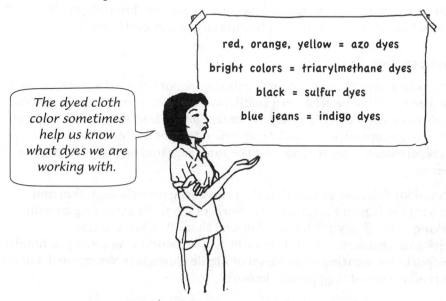

red, orange, yellow = azo dyes

bright colors = triarylmethane dyes

black = sulfur dyes

blue jeans = indigo dyes

The dyed cloth color sometimes help us know what dyes we are working with.

Some azo dyes are banned because they can cause cancer and are very harmful to your health. See Dyes on pages 485 to 487.

Permanent press and waterproofing

Formaldehyde is added to fabric to make it smooth and less likely to wrinkle or crease. Workers dip the fabric in formaldehyde baths, or put fabric in large chambers filled with formaldehyde gas. Workers in this part of the process are exposed to the most formaldehyde, although without good ventilation, all workers in the shop will be exposed to an unhealthy amount.

Formaldehyde irritates the skin, making it red and itchy. Breathing the fumes harms the nose, throat, and lungs. Formaldehyde causes asthma and cancer. See pages 496 to 497.

Fire resistant chemicals

Fire resistant chemicals, such as brominated flame retardants, make clothing less likely to burn. However, these chemicals can harm the reproductive system and cause cancer. See pages 488 to 492.

Antibacterial treatments

Garments are dipped in baths containing silver, triclosan, or trichlocarban. These keep bacteria from growing in the garments and make them less likely to smell. Workers add the chemicals in liquid, powder, or pellet form into baths which are then heated. Antibacterial chemicals gradually wash out when the clothing is washed at home.

Silver is particularly dangerous because it does not break down. It accumulates in and poisons people, animals, water, and land.

Nanoparticles

Some chemicals are used in a form called nanoparticles, which means they have been made to be very, very small. Nanoparticles can be spun into fibers or coated on them after the cloth is made. Cloth is treated with a variety of chemical nanoparticles to make it sturdier, to fight bacteria, to resist stains and repel water, to protect against the sun's rays and against fire, and for other uses.

Nanoparticles are so tiny that they can easily pass through skin and into our blood and internal organs. Workers should be extremely careful working with nanoparticles and demand that all safety systems – enclosures, ventilation, and others – be in good working order. If you handle nanoparticles, wearing a double set of nitrile gloves is recommended, but no one really knows if they protect enough.

Keep chemicals out of your body

Health Info

Reduce the amount of chemicals that get on and inside your body.

- **Wash your hands often**, especially before eating, drinking, or smoking. This can stop chemicals from going into your mouth.

- **Wash your hands only with water and soap.** Avoid using solvents to clean your hands.

- **Use skin lotion or hand cream on your hands** after washing to prevent skin from drying. Healthy skin keeps out chemicals better than cracked, red skin.

- **Wear long sleeves** to protect your arms.

- **Wear the right kind of protective gloves**, especially if you add chemicals to the fabric. See Gloves on pages 262 to 265.

- **Wear a mask.** If you can see, smell, or feel the effects of a chemical, the ventilation is probably not working or not strong enough to keep these chemicals away from your nose and mouth. See Masks and respirators on pages 266 to 270, and chapter 17: Ventilation.

- **Tell your employer** which fabrics cause rashes or breathing problems. Get him to change the fabric to one that does not cause rashes or other health problems.

Materials besides cloth can also cause allergies and rashes, such as nickel in rivets.

If you get a rash, see page 158 to learn how to reduce the discomforts of a rash and watch for signs of other health problems.

Organize to demand that your employer:

- Label chemicals in the language workers speak and share Safety Data Sheets (SDS) with workers (see pages 180 to 182 to learn how to read an SDS).

- Train all workers on safe chemical handling.

- Improve machines and ventilation before trying to solve the problem with personal protective equipment.

- Respect your country's laws on chemicals at work.

Keep information about your rashes or breathing problems in a health notebook (see page 47).

Cutting the fabric

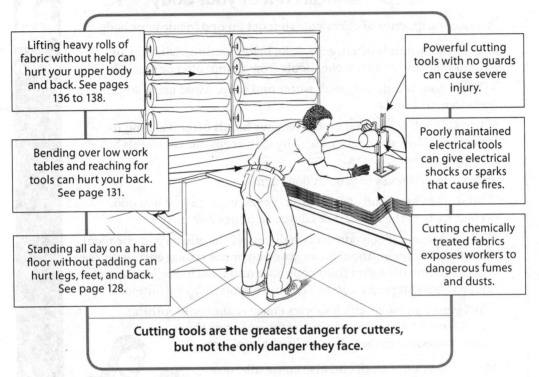

Lifting heavy rolls of fabric without help can hurt your upper body and back. See pages 136 to 138.

Bending over low work tables and reaching for tools can hurt your back. See page 131.

Standing all day on a hard floor without padding can hurt legs, feet, and back. See page 128.

Powerful cutting tools with no guards can cause severe injury.

Poorly maintained electrical tools can give electrical shocks or sparks that cause fires.

Cutting chemically treated fabrics exposes workers to dangerous fumes and dusts.

Cutting tools are the greatest danger for cutters, but not the only danger they face.

Cutting tools can be very dangerous. To protect workers from being cut or injured when cutting fabric:

- Machines should have guards that surround the blade. See pages 195 to 197.
- Workers should wear metal mesh gloves so they don't cut their hands. See page 265.
- Workers should receive training on how to use the machines safely – especially how to turn them off quickly!
- Factories should have a first aid plan and supplies for treating cuts and injuries. See First aid for machine injuries on pages 203 to 204.
- Factories should also have a health plan to care for and provide rehabilitation to injured workers. It should include compensation to injured workers and their families for temporary or permanent disability that stops them from working.

Dangers from dusty factories

Air thick with fabric dust is very common in garment factories and harmful to health. But dust is an easy problem to solve:

- Local exhaust ventilation prevents dust from getting in the air (see pages 250 to 251). Check local ventilation by doing the Following the Air activity on pages 253 to 254. For local ventilation to work it needs to be checked, maintained, and cleaned regularly.
- Enclose machines or processes that produce a lot of dust (see page 169).
- Clean your work area regularly with a vacuum, mop or wet rag (see page 221).

Breathing problems caused by cotton dust

Health Info

Inhaling dust from cotton and other fabrics can cause breathing problems such as:

- dry, itchy nose
- cough that does not go away
- mucus (phlegm) the same color as the fabric
- trouble breathing

Breathing cotton dust day after day can also cause a more serious lung disease called brown lung or byssinosis. Signs of byssinosis are:

- chest tightness
- wheezing
- bronchitis that keeps coming back
- cold or allergy signs

If you have these signs, see a health worker who can test you for byssinosis or another lung disease.

Stop smoking and try not to be around people who are smoking.

Home remedies including physical exercise, breathing exercises, and inhaling steam can help, but will not cure it.

Asthma medications might lessen the signs of byssinosis but do not cure it. A person with advanced byssinosis might need an oxygen machine to help her.

We fought for 15 years to get compensation

We formed the Council of Work and Environment Related Patients' Network of Thailand (WEPT) because our work in a garment factory in Thailand was making us sick. We had trouble breathing from cotton dust, hearing loss from noisy machines, and damaged eyesight from poor lighting.

A doctor diagnosed a number of us with byssinosis, an occupational disease. This diagnosis enabled us to make a case against our employer. He knew there was a lot of dust but didn't protect us. We told him we had trouble breathing but he didn't do anything. The result was we got sicker and sicker until we got byssinosis. So 200 of us joined together to fight for our lives. The court told our employer he needed to compensate us for making us sick. But the employer did not want to pay. He made us go through more than 100 different court cases and appeals.

After more than 10 years, we got a little compensation, but only a pittance. We couldn't live on that! So 37 of us decided to continue fighting.

After 15 years, in 2010, the Supreme Court on Labor Affairs said our employer had to pay an adequate amount of compensation. This money could never give us back our health or make up for all that we suffered fighting for justice while trying to earn a living. But it was a big win for us. Many workers have byssinosis but never get it diagnosed and often their employer refuses to take responsibility. This win, our win, proves it is possible to fight for justice and be successful.

WEPT fights for workers!
Workers can fight and win!

Sewing

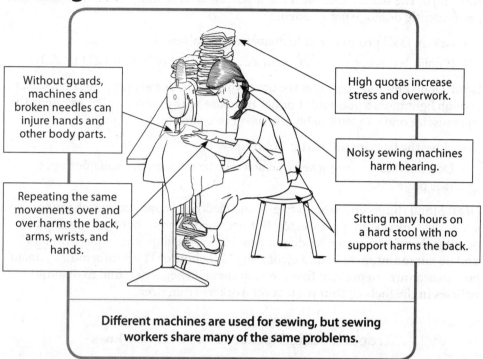

Without guards, machines and broken needles can injure hands and other body parts.

Repeating the same movements over and over harms the back, arms, wrists, and hands.

High quotas increase stress and overwork.

Noisy sewing machines harm hearing.

Sitting many hours on a hard stool with no support harms the back.

Different machines are used for sewing, but sewing workers share many of the same problems.

Machine injury: Needles in the machine can cut your fingers and hands and can break and fly into your eyes. Moving parts can catch hair and pull it out or pull a person into the machine.

- Machine guards and shields can protect workers from getting cut, stabbed or injured by needles. See pages 193 to 197.

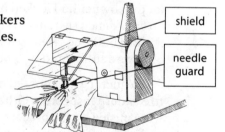

shield

needle guard

- Enclose drive shafts and moving belts (above and under the table!) to keep hair, clothing, or anything else away from moving parts. See page 193.

Strain and injury: Sewing machine operators do the same movements over and over. Reduce overuse injuries caused by repeating the same movements:

- Take breaks, rotate among jobs, and stretch and strengthen different muscles.

- Improve your workstation to support your body and reduce the reaching, strain, and strength needed to operate your machine. See chapter 7: Ergonomics.

Noise: Sewing machines and riveting machines are very loud. When many are running at the same time, the noise level can be very high. Too much noise can permanently damage your hearing.

- Ask an OSH professional to measure the noise level.
- If noise levels are too high, wear ear protection (see pages 271 to 272).

Light: Good lighting helps you see your work without straining your eyes. Not enough light makes you squint or get too close to the work, which weakens the eye muscles and can lead to blurry vision (see chapter 14: Light).

- Have the boss install better lighting.
- Do exercises to strengthen and stretch the muscles around your eyes (see page 75).

Fires: Many things can start a fire — bad electrical connections, chemical spills, dust, or smoking cigarettes. But fires in garment factories quickly turn deadly when factory owners do not provide fire extinguishers or sprinklers and do not maintain safe and clear exits. See chapter 11 for information about how to organize to prevent fires, to stop them if they start, and to demand policies in the factory that protect all workers from fires.

Trapped behind locked doors and windows

The Ali Enterprises factory fire in Karachi, Pakistan in September 2012 was one of the deadliest fires in history, killing 289 people.

A boiler exploded and the chemicals stored near it caught fire. The factory owner had locked all the exit doors "to stop theft" and there were no emergency systems to stop the fire. Workers on the top floors of the 5-story building tried to jump out of windows. Others found no escape and were suffocated by smoke or burned to death.

The factory had passed a safety audit just a few weeks before the fire. Safety inspectors either missed or ignored unsafe conditions, or were misled by the owners. But even without corruption, an occasional audit cannot compare to an active, joint worker-management safety committee, present in the factory all day, every day.

In response to this tragic fire, 70 Pakistani trade unions and community groups formed the Workers' Rights Movement. They are demanding compensation for injured workers and families, the arrest of the factory owners, and enforcement of safety laws in factories.

Finishing the garments

After the garment is sewn, it will be processed again to add certain qualities or colors. End-of-the-line workers correct mistakes and wash and spot-clean the garment. Then it will be dried, pressed, and pleated before the final counting, sorting, and packaging.

Dangers from acid-washing

One of the final steps of making some jeans is to put them in a large washing machine filled with pumice stones. The stones rub against the cotton of the jeans to make it softer and lighter. Some jeans are then acid-washed. Workers sponge or spray potassium permanganate bleach, chlorine bleach, or other bleaches on the garment to make it look worn. Or they soak pumice stones in the bleaches and put them in the washing machine where the jeans are washed. Sometimes jeans are tied or twisted to create different patterns. (The job of tying or twisting garments is often done by homeworkers. See chapter 20: Doing factory work at home.)

The bleaches used in acid-washing can burn your skin and irritate your eyes, nose and throat. Potassium permanganate bleach can also cause other health problems, including decreased fertility for men and women, and liver and kidney problems. See pages 477 to 478.

If you work in an area that uses bleaches to wash jeans:

- Make sure there is good ventilation.
- Wear acid-resistant gloves, clothing, and face shields.
- See that wash stations and first aid are nearby.
- Pressure your boss to stop using acid-washing.

Dangers from sandblasting

Another way to lighten and soften denim is for workers to use a high-pressure machine to spray the jeans with sand. Sandblasting is so dangerous to workers' lungs it has been banned in many countries. Sometimes brands prefer jeans sanded by hand. But sanding by hand creates many of the same health dangers and can be worse when workstations do not have strong ventilation to remove the sand.

Unsafe sanding and sandblasting expose workers to sand dust, also called silica dust. When silica dust gets in the lungs, it cannot be breathed out. Silica dust causes an illness called silicosis. Silicosis makes breathing difficult and can cause auto-immune diseases, lung cancer, and death. There is no cure for silicosis and a person who continues to be exposed to silica dust will continue to get worse. People exposed to silica or who have silicosis are also more likely to get TB (tuberculosis). Smoking tobacco makes silicosis damage worse.

For sanding and sandblasting workstations to be safer, workers need:

- Enclosed workstations to keep sand from spreading.
- Strong vacuum extractors to remove the sand. See page 250-251.
- Good ventilation to move sand away from workers. See pages 251 to 252.
- Respirators with supplied air are needed for sandblasting. Dust masks or respirators will not protect enough. See pages 266 to 270.
- Work areas designed to stop sand from spreading in the factory.

Safer alternatives are now used in many factories. Levi's and some other brands have stopped using sandblasting.

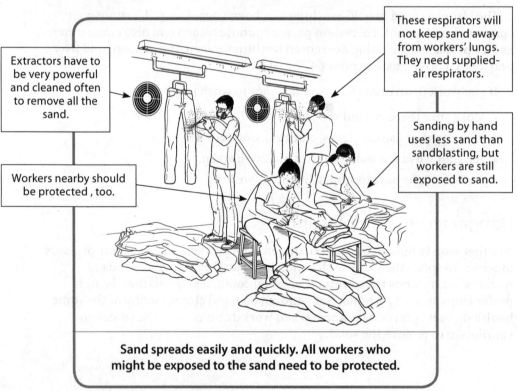

These respirators will not keep sand away from workers' lungs. They need supplied-air respirators.

Extractors have to be very powerful and cleaned often to remove all the sand.

Sanding by hand uses less sand than sandblasting, but workers are still exposed to sand.

Workers nearby should be protected , too.

Sand spreads easily and quickly. All workers who might be exposed to the sand need to be protected.

Workers should not die for fashion!

We came from other countries and got jobs sandblasting jeans in Turkey. We worked and lived in the workshop. We used machines to blast sand on the jeans to create a special look. The sandblasting was very strong.

Our boss gave us nothing to protect ourselves. We used bandanas or whatever cloth we could find to cover our mouths and noses. But our eyes and hands were not protected. After work we would go upstairs from the workshop and that's where we would sleep.

Soon, many of us starting having breathing problems. And as time went on, we got bad coughs that did not go away. It became harder to breathe. Many of us started losing weight. Some people became so sick they went back home to their families. We never heard from them again.

A few of us went to the occupational clinic and were diagnosed with silicosis. We discovered we would never be able to work again, or walk, or run because our lungs were so damaged. But we were the lucky ones. Dozens of workers died from silicosis. And those were just the ones we knew about.

The workers disabled from silicosis were very angry. Why did the bosses do this to us? Jobs should not kill people! We began organizing with other workers in Turkey. Soon we connected with organizations around the world, such as the Clean Clothes Campaign. They helped us put pressure not only on the factory owners but on the brands whose products we made. The factory owners had to take responsibility for making workers sick. But nothing was going to change if we didn't get the brands to stop demanding that factories sandblast jeans. We also needed to make sure no more people got that horrible disease. We organized rallies, conferences, and talks and, finally, the government of Turkey agreed to outlaw sandblasting in the country.

Then we turned our attention to the brands. With pressure from the people, labor unions, organizations, and even some governments, we got several brands to ban sandblasting! Some companies began using other methods, which are just as bad as sandblasting. But we were ready for them. The campaign and strong networks we built will continue fighting against sandblasting and any other process that harms workers. Workers should not die for fashion!

Dangers from screen printing

Sometimes workers screen print pictures or designs on garments, especially T-shirts. For many years, the inks used in printing, and the solvents used to clean up, were all petroleum-based and toxic for workers. Much of the industry now uses vegetable- or water-based inks and solvents, which are much safer for workers and the environment.

After the image is printed on the garment, it is put in an oven-type dryer. This machine gets very hot. To reduce risks:

- Vent machines out of the workplace.
- Install machine guards against burns and injuries (see pages 193 to 197).
- Train workers in the safe use of machines.
- Turn off and lock out all machines before cleaning (see pages 201 to 202).

Fire is a danger because of the chemicals used in screen printing.

- Make fire extinguishers available and train workers to use them.
- Store chemicals in closed metal containers and label them.
- Dispose of rags used for clean-up in tightly closed metal garbage cans.

Quality control

Workers inspect the garments and correct small mistakes by undoing and hand-sewing to fix the problem. They also cut and pull any remaining threads. They make sure the garment looks clean and neat.

They don't let us sit. Only the people sewing get to sit. They say sitting slows down quality control. But we need chairs!

If the garment is dirty, workers usually clean it with solvents. But many solvents used for cleaning are toxic (see the box on the next page). Ask your employer to use less toxic solvents, wear gloves, and make sure you have good ventilation at your workspace.

These cleaning chemicals cause serious health problems:

- **Methylene chloride** can cause lung, liver, and pancreas cancers.
- **Tetrachloroethylene (PERC)** hurts the liver and kidney and can cause cancer.
- **Trichloroethylene (TCE)** causes liver damage and may cause cancer.
- **Toluene** can cause birth defects, kidney and liver damage, and catches fire easily.
- **Trichloroethane (TCA, or methyl chloroform)** causes nerve damage.

These chemicals are less dangerous, but catch fire easily:

- **Acetone** irritates eyes and nose.
- **Ethanol** (or **ethyl alcohol**) irritates eyes and nose.
- **Isopropyl alcohol** (or **isopropanol**) irritates eyes and nose.

Protect workers by:

- Using less dangerous chemicals and processes.
- Labeling all chemicals, giving workers SDS in the language they speak, and training workers to use them safely.
- Replace toxic cleaning chemicals with water-based alternatives.

See Appendix B for more information.

Drying and Pressing

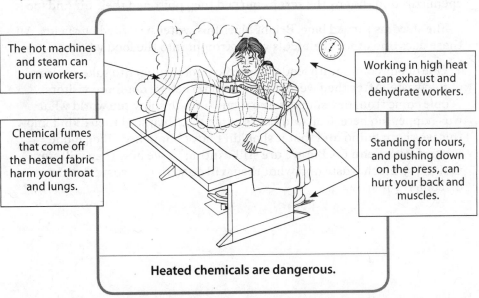

The hot machines and steam can burn workers.

Chemical fumes that come off the heated fabric harm your throat and lungs.

Working in high heat can exhaust and dehydrate workers.

Standing for hours, and pushing down on the press, can hurt your back and muscles.

Heated chemicals are dangerous.

Pollution from garment factories

Garment factories are often built in areas where there are few industrial services available. So garbage from the factory is burned or dumped on the land, and chemicals are released into the air and water. For more information, see chapter 33: Pollution from factories.

Our water turned bright blue!

Our government in Lesotho, Africa invited big brand names to set up factories here. Gap and Levi's opened factories and many people were happy to have jobs.

Making jeans produced a lot of waste. Many materials could not be recycled. Water used to treat, rinse, and wash the fabric was polluted. And there was a lot of waste from machine maintenance and all the paper and plastic from the office.

The companies said they had systems to collect and take care of the waste. But the factories in Lesotho didn't have a system. They just dumped solid waste onto the land and polluted water into our streams.

The dumps filled with fabric, needles, chemical containers, and many other things the factories threw away. People from the community went to the dump to collect what they could use or sell. Children would carry chemical containers back to their homes for storing water. They would pick up needles and tools. Some women began burning fabric scraps in their cooking fires. They didn't know the fabric was treated with chemicals and that as the scraps burned they poisoned their air and food.

The streams turned blue. Bright blue! This water irrigated our fields. All those dyes and other chemicals went straight into the food we ate.

One of our community leaders asked a photographer to take pictures of the waste. After they were put on the Internet we got more visitors. People came from newspapers and magazines to show the world what was happening here. Gap and Levi's came too. They said they didn't know this was happening and that it shouldn't have happened. They made the factories clean up. But we are still waiting to see how they will stop making so much waste and what they will do with the waste they have already thrown away.

Shoe factories 6

Making the materials for shoes, and gluing and stitching them together, are the jobs in shoe factories where workers are most likely to be harmed. Using glues and heating plastics release chemicals in the air that can make you sick.

To make work in shoe factories safer for workers, employers should:

* Use safer chemicals in all stages of production. Water-based glues are safer than glues made with solvents, but only if workers have good ventilation and protective equipment.
* Design safer work processes.
* Make sure all machines have guards (see pages 193 to 197), especially sewing machines and machines that get hot.
* Have good ventilation (see chapter 17), especially in areas where rubber is mixed or glues are used.
* Give workers personal protective equipment (see chapter 18), especially when working directly with chemicals or with hot materials.

Even the shoe factories that have taken steps to improve health and safety conditions for workers rarely pay their employees a living wage. Workers' right to organize for a decent standard of living must be recognized in the global shoe industry.

Preparing leather for shoes is dangerous work

Processing animal skins into leather pollutes large amounts of water with salts and chemicals such as chromium hexavalent (see pages 503 to 505). Tanning chemicals can cause bronchitis, asthma, and other breathing problems and they are also extremely irritating to the skin. If a person is exposed to them day after day, some of these chemicals can cause birth defects and cancers. Cancer of the nose has long been a problem for shoe workers.

The chemicals and dyes may remain on the leather, even after it is cleaned at the tannery. These chemicals can harm the health of workers when the leather arrives as a material to make shoes in factories.

The waste from tanning is often dumped into rivers and other waterways, contaminating the water of communities near the tanneries.

New ways of tanning leather are less harmful to workers and the environment. See Cleaner Production in Tanneries in *A Community Guide to Environmental Health,* pages 460 to 461.

Making the upper parts of shoes

Workers cut, sort, and prepare the material of the upper and lining. The leather, cloth, and synthetic materials are cut to pattern on presses with sharp molds. Then the leather is thinned at the seams to make it easier to sew or glue. The lining is hot-pressed onto the pieces of material to be sewn. Then the different pieces of the upper are sewn or glued together.

Many different sewing machines are used to sew the upper parts of shoes. They are very powerful machines. All sewing machines should have guards around the needle and on the machine to protect workers from injuries. See pages 193 to 197.

Machine injuries

Eyelets, rivets, and ventilation openings in shoes are made on a loud, puncturing machine. The sewn uppers are then put on a mold, and the insole is nailed onto the mold.

The upper will then go through several shaping machines which heat the material and make it smooth. Stiffeners might be added to the heel and toe so they hold their shapes better. For leather shoes, hot cork is spread on the bottom of the insole.

Presses, stampers, rollers, riveters, sewing machines, die cutters and other cutting tools can cause serious injury to workers' hands. Sewing machines used to make shoes are powerful and use large needles that can cause severe harm to machine operators. The belts can catch workers' hair or clothing and cause serious injury.

Workers who sew leather shoes by hand also get injured with needles.

The hole-making machine and the nail machine are not sharp. But to make the holes in the upper and the insole, these machines use a lot of pressure. They also vibrate when they come down fast and hard on the material. Fingers can easily be caught in these machines, crushing them. Over time, the vibration damages nerves and can reduce the amount of blood that goes to the fingers, causing Vibration-induced White Finger (VWF) where the fingers tingle, hurt, or lose feeling. In the worst case, you can no longer hold objects or use your hands.

Hand injuries caused by vibrating tools

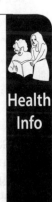

Health
Info

Nailing machines and other equipment that vibrates can lead to a problem called "dead hand," vibration-induced white finger (VWF), hand-arm vibration (HAV), or Raynaud's phenomenon. The vibration limits blood from flowing freely to the fingers, causing them to tingle and lose feeling, turn white, then blue, and even develop ulcers. This injury is not curable. The best way to reduce the damage from it is to ensure that any person who develops signs is immediately changed to a job with no vibration. It can be prevented by making sure workers do not work too many hours with vibrating tools, regularly rotate out of jobs with vibrating tools, and inspect and maintain tools on a schedule.

Cold and stress can also trigger these problems. Ensure workers stay warm and dress to keep the whole body warm, not just wear gloves for the hands. Smoking reduces circulation and makes the injury worse.

Injuries from cutting, crushing, and catching can be prevented. Machines need:

- guards on the needle areas and on the v-belts above and below the table. See page 193.

- 2-handed controls on cutting, puncturing, nailing, and stamping machines. See page 198.

- electric or other sensors to shut off power to a machine if the worker's body is in the wrong place. See page 198.

> In 2006, my hand was crushed by a punching machine. They took the machine apart to try to save my hand, but my hand was already badly damaged. The factory refused to pay for my medical treatment. Without rehabilitation, I am injured for life and can't work any more.

To prevent injuries to workers who are cleaning, fixing or adjusting machines, it is important to follow lock out and tag out procedures for repair and maintenance work. See pages 201 to 202.

Strain and overuse injuries

Workers often sit or stand in the same position all day. If you can sit, chairs might not support your back and legs. In badly equipped factories, you might have only short stools instead of chairs, causing neck, back, leg, and knee pain. See chapter 7: Ergonomics to find ways to prevent injuries, such as:

- Rotate jobs during the day so no one does any job too long.
- Demand that the factory provide you with chairs and equipment that fit your body and your job.
- Set up your work area so you have what you need close at hand, and you do not have to reach, bend, or twist too much.
- Exercise to stretch and strengthen your muscles.

Some workers sew and glue shoes at home or in other people's homes. Homework may give workers some flexibility with their time, but it also increases problems from strain and overuse injuries and exposure to chemicals. See chapter 20: Doing factory work at home for ideas on setting up a comfortable and safe area in your house where you can work while reducing the health dangers of homework.

Dangers from dust

Cutting, buffing, and skiving (thinning seam edges) generate a lot of dust and small bits of material. Breathing these can cause irritation and other breathing problems. Breathing leather dust, which may contain heavy metals such as chromium, nickel, cadmium, and other chemicals used to tan leather, can cause problems for very young, pregnant, or older workers, and over time can cause skin irritation and allergies, sinus and nasal cancers, and other problems.

- An extractor can remove most of the dust from the workstation and area around it. See pages 250 to 251.
- A cloth over your nose and mouth may keep a little of the dust out, but it does not protect you very well. Use a dust mask that fits tightly over your nose and mouth. See pages 266 to 270.
- Use a vacuum cleaner or at least a damp cloth to clean the dust from surfaces around your work area at least 2 times during your shift.
- Use leather that was tanned without heavy metals and toxic chemicals.
- Wash chemicals and dust off your hands regularly, especially before eating or drinking.

Dangers from noise

Shoe factory workers operate many large and noisy machines. When possible, noise should be controlled at the source by enclosing and insulating the machine. Well-maintained machines make less noise. See chapter 13: Noise.

- Ask the boss to measure noise at different places around the factory.
- Where it is too loud, workers should wear earplugs or earmuffs. See pages 271 to 272.

Making the soles

Plastics and synthetic rubber are the most common kinds of soles made today. Natural and synthetic rubber is mixed with various chemicals to make it more flexible, stronger, and give it color and other qualities. The rubber is then kneaded and rolled over and over again to complete mixing and get the right texture. The rubber or plastic is shaped into soles on revolving or sole-molding presses. Workers then trim, scour, and clean the soles.

Chemicals mixed into the material for soles

With so many chemicals mixed together to make soles, it can be difficult to know which are causing a problem for your health:

- **Binders** make the material for soles flexible. Binders are often sulfur or peroxides but sometimes nitrosamine.
- **Pigments** give soles color, such as iron oxide, carbon black, azo dyes, and other synthetic dyes.
- **Fillers** make plastic and rubber stronger, such as silica, magnesium carbonate, calcium silicate, and sawdust.
- **Plasticizers** make it easier to mix and make soles more flexible. Phthalates are the most common plasticizers.
- **Accelerators** cure soles faster, such as mercaptobenzthiazole (MBT). These chemicals create allergic reactions very quickly and are quite dangerous to use. Most health problems in making soles come from the accelerators.
- **Fire retardants** make soles fire resistant, such as antimony trioxide, phosphorus, and halogen.
- **Dusting agents** keep soles from sticking, such as zinc stearate.

Not all of these kinds of chemicals are always present. For more information about these chemicals, see Appendix B: Common Chemicals and Materials.

Dangers from mixing materials and chemicals to make soles

Most soles are made from ethylene vinyl acetate (EVA), polyurethane, or rubber, both synthetic and natural. These are heated and mixed with many other chemicals while getting rolled into sheets. Putting all the chemicals together creates dust, vapor, and fumes that are all dangerous to breathe.

Workers who measure and mix chemicals may be exposed to chemicals through spills, splashes, dusts, and fumes. One way of reducing the risk of exposure for workers is to use pre-mixed chemicals. Nike, for example, uses a pre-mix process in which the chemicals are measured, mixed, formed into pellets, and packaged, all before they arrive at the shoe factory. The shoe workers then add a packet of pre-mixed pellets into the machine that mixes the rubber or plastic to make the soles. This not only limits exposure for workers but also reduces waste. If the process of manufacturing the pellets at the supplier factory is also safe, it is an improvement for everyone.

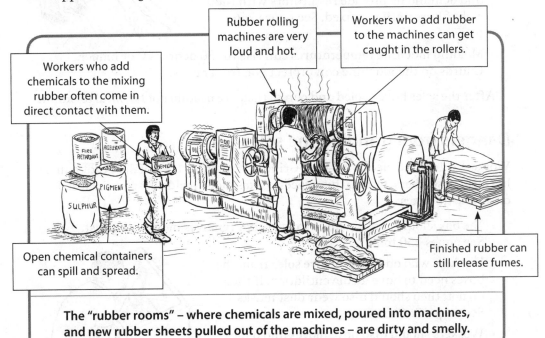

Rubber rolling machines are very loud and hot.

Workers who add rubber to the machines can get caught in the rollers.

Workers who add chemicals to the mixing rubber often come in direct contact with them.

Open chemical containers can spill and spread.

Finished rubber can still release fumes.

The "rubber rooms" – where chemicals are mixed, poured into machines, and new rubber sheets pulled out of the machines – are dirty and smelly.

Workers in this area need:

- safe, well-ventilated places to store and mix chemicals
- good maintenance for both the work area and the machines
- good ventilation to take heat and fumes out of the work area and factory
- access to respirators, gloves, and other protective equipment when needed

Dangers from molding the soles

Soles can be made by putting a sheet of rubber in a mold that is heated and cuts to the right shape. Or the rubber can be injected directly into a mold in an enclosed machine.

No matter which method is used, when workers remove the soles from the molds, the soles are hot and release fumes from the chemicals used to make them and release them from the molds. The soles continue to release these fumes as they cool in the waiting area.

- Molding machines should have good local ventilation to remove dust and fumes. See pages 250 to 251.

- If workers are exposed to fumes, they should tell the boss to repair the ventilation system and demand he provide respirators with the right filters until it is fixed. See pages 266 to 270.

- Molding machine temperatures can rise to 150 degrees C or higher. Guards on the machine can protect you from burns.

After the soles have cooled and cured, they are usually not harmful to handle.

Dangers from grinding the soles

Workers grind and clean the soles. Grinding produces a lot of dust that can be harmful to workers. Often, this process takes place inside of semi-enclosed, clear plastic boxes.

- The box should contain an extractor that removes most of the dust. See pages 250 to 251.

- Workers who add and remove soles from the boxes need to have local ventilation. If they do not, they should also wear dust masks. See pages 266 to 270.

- Workers should also have gloves and a face shield with goggles, since rubber dust can irritate skin. See chapter 18.

Sometimes grinders are used to rough the surface of soles so glue will hold better. Because this creates harmful dust, newer methods use a water-based detergent to achieve the same thing.

Assembling the shoes

The soles are glued to the uppers with glue or hot cement. Leather soles are sewn. Then the shoe is heated to cure the glue before the shoes are inspected, cleaned, and packed.

Many chemicals are used to join the sole and the upper together, including primers and glues (see Most glues and primers are harmful to workers, on page 116). Solvent-based glues and primers contain different kinds of solvents (see Solvents on pages 517 to 529). Water-based glues are made with different chemicals and are considered safer than solvent-based glues. Some of them, especially isocyanates, can still harm workers.

Pay attention to any signs that people are getting sick from primers and glues. Breathing problems, headaches, and fainting are signs that you are breathing in these chemicals.

To prevent harm while using glues, your factory should:

- replace toxics with less toxic alternatives.
- use closed, mechanical systems to apply glue. If glue must be put on by hand, use containers with smaller openings and smaller tools to apply only as much as is needed. See page 166.
- store glues and solvents safely, and mix them in a work area with the right tools, work surfaces, and ventilation.
- label all glues in the languages workers speak.
- provide workers with Safety Data Sheets (SDS) including information about the glue, such as ingredients, danger signs for exposures, safety procedures, and so forth, in your language. (See How to get and read an SDS on pages 180 to 182.)
- make sure there is good ventilation (see chapter 17).
- give gloves, respirators, safety glasses or goggles, and personal protective equipment to workers who need them (see chapter 18).
- install body and eye wash stations in areas where glues and primers are used, and give first aid trainings on how to handle chemical spills and splashes (see page 175).

Most glues and primers are harmful to workers

The most dangerous chemicals in glues are the solvents added to make them stickier, stronger, or quicker to dry.

Benzene is very harmful to people's health. Benzene causes cancer and reproductive damage, and is so bad that many countries and companies have banned its use. But it is cheap, it dries quickly, and it smells nicer than other solvents. So though it is banned, it is still widely used, sometimes on purpose and sometimes unknowingly as an ingredient in a mix of chemicals. For more information on benzene, see Aromatic hydrocarbons on pages 522 to 523.

Toluene and xylene are often used instead of benzene. But they are also in the same chemical family as benzene, called "Aromatic hydrocarbons." They might cause birth defects and cancer, as well as many health problems. See pages 522 to 523.

MEK (methyl ethyl ketone) is another benzene replacement. If MEK touches your skin or eyes, they will get irritated and red. If you inhale it, you might feel dizzy, drowsy, and have headaches and blurry vision. MEK smells like mint. Getting exposed to MEK repeatedly can cause problems with your nervous system, and it may affect the brain or cause birth defects. See Ketone solvents, page 529.

Other chemicals used in glues and primers include **acetone, ammonia, cyclohexane, di-chloromethane** or **methylene chloride, di-methyl formaldehyde (DMF), ethyl acetate** (can cause cancer), **tetrachloroethylene** (may cause cancer), **polychloroprene, polyurethane, propane,** and **trichloroethylene** (TCE – a known irritant).

Water-based glues are thought to be safer, but are still considered dangerous chemicals.

The company gave us new water-based glues, called isocyanates, and told us they were totally safe. When many workers began to develop asthma and other breathing problems, it was clear that isocyanates were not safe.

Safer chemicals for the whole factory

The owner of Elegant Top Shoes factory decided to stop using toluene-based glues because toluene is toxic to people and the brand he sold shoes to was pressuring him to change. To replace the glues made with toluene, he found a new glue that was supposed to be safer.

But in one section of the factory, the team leaders still wanted to use the old glue. They said, "The new glue does not work as well," and "The new glue makes the shoe harder to clean."

If the shoes are not clean when they come off the production line, the quality standard of that production line goes down. The line is penalized if it takes too long to clean and finish production of the shoes. Because the pressure to meet production quotas never lets up, the team leaders continued to force the workers on their line to use the toxic toluene glue.

The factory administration knew about this but did nothing to stop it, because the toluene glue was less expensive. Finally, when the problem was pointed out during a factory visit by a representative of the brand that purchased the shoes, they stopped using the harmful glue.

A few months later, workers started to feel sick. They wondered if it was from the new glue. The new glue was water-based and only bonded well when they used a primer that included a chemical called MEK. Although the boss said it was safer than toluene, it made them feel worse more quickly. When the workers asked for and got a safety data sheet (SDS), they found out MEK was dangerous too.

The workers were mad at their supervisors, and the supervisors were mad at the boss. The boss was angry at the chemical salesperson who told him that the glue and primer were safe, and at the brands for demanding he change. He felt he had tried to do the right thing and everyone got mad at him anyway.

The only way to make the situation safer was to install new, more powerful extractors and use better protective equipment. But that cost more money, and most of the workers were hired through a temporary worker agency and would soon be gone anyway.

Dangers of finishing

Final finishing of shoes includes shaping and leveling, waxing, coloring, spraying, cleaning, threading, polishing and packaging.

- **Dust** from finishing machines must be ventilated away from the workstation. See chapter 12: Dust.

- **Polishes, stains, and color dyes** may irritate your skin. Solvents used to clean the shoes can quickly harm your health. Work areas must have good ventilation, and workers should have gloves, aprons, safety glasses, masks, and good washing and sanitary facilities.

- **Unguarded and unsafe machines** that can cut and crush must be repaired. See chapter 9: Machine injuries.

It is frightening how the hands of a person change after gluing soles for a long time.

Fire dangers in shoe factories

The solvents and sprays used as glues and finishing materials are usually petroleum-based, causing them to catch fire easily. Being heavier than air, when solvents are not ventilated away they tend to drift toward the floor where they can concentrate. They then create an increasingly dangerous possibility for an explosion, which could be set off by a spark or bad electrical connection. See chapter 11: Fire.

- Use solvents that will not catch fire at low or normal temperatures. Water-based solvents are safer.

- Install good ventilation and local exhaust in spraying booths and drying racks to remove the dangerous fumes from the work area.

- Remove wastes from workstations, as well as other material that can burn, such as rags and cardboard.

- Use fireproof metal containers for solvents and oily wastes.

- Keep aisles and exits open and unblocked.

- Make sure fire extinguishers are full, charged, and of the right type for the materials in your workplace.

- Regularly check electrical equipment to be sure it is in good condition and grounded (see pages 205 to 206).

Pollution from shoe factories

Most factories haul their waste materials off to be disposed of in dumps. When their waste contains chemicals, this can result in the contamination of the ground and groundwater. Where it is prohibited to dump chemicals in ordinary landfills, unethical companies try to save money by pouring wastes such as dyes, glue, and other chemicals directly into the sewer. While this practice may be against the law, it can be difficult to find a government official willing to challenge the company to stop this practice.

But there is another environmental problem with shoe wastes that is harder to stop. What happens to shoes when they are worn out? Some leather shoes are made to last a long time. But most of the shoes we buy break easily (such as plastic sandals) or go out of style quickly (such as sport shoes).

In some countries, shoes get repaired or reused. In others, shoes go straight into the dump. From there they go to the landfill or incinerator. As the soles degrade, the chemicals used in processing the rubber or plastic while making them become a pollution problem as they are released into the environment. If they are burned, chemicals get into the air even more quickly.

Phthalates are one of the most common chemicals released. They are harmful to the reproductive system. Other harmful substances include heavy metals such as lead, cadmium, and mercury as well as aromatic hydrocarbons. See Appendix B: Common chemicals and materials.

Old shoes make new things

A few shoe companies have programs to reuse and recycle old shoes.

Nike uses waste materials and old Nike shoes to make flooring for playgrounds. The material is ground up and divided into rubber, foam, and fibers, and then mixed with other chemicals to make flooring. Many people who buy and use Nike shoes like the idea that their old shoes can become new things. However, the flooring made from Nike contains the same harmful chemicals used to make the shoes and can poison the land and water. To make shoe production truly sustainable, the company should eliminate all toxic chemicals from production and ensure that reused materials do not contain toxic chemicals.

Some plastic shoes, such as sandals and Crocs, are easier to recycle because they can be ground up and melted to make new ones.

PART 3

Work Dangers and Solutions

7 Ergonomics

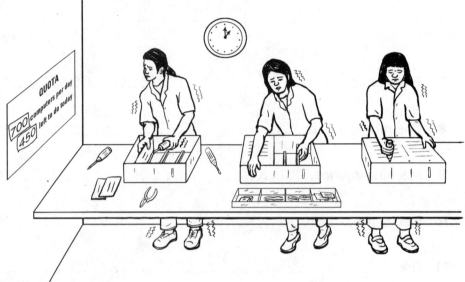

We are not machines. When workers do the same work over and over without enough rest, our bodies become tired and hurt. Our mental health can suffer, too (see chapter 27: Stress and mental health).

Ergonomics helps us understand how work can hurt our bodies and what we can do to reduce and prevent injuries from repetitive work and overuse of our muscles, joints, and tendons.

Tired eyes and muscles that have a sensation of discomfort are the first signs that work is pushing you past your body's limits. Eye and body strain, aches, tingling sensations, numbness, weakness, or pain in any part of your body are signs that your work is injuring you.

Ergonomic injuries can be prevented by making changes to the way work is done, improving our postures and how we move our bodies, and by ensuring tools, equipment, and workstations fit workers and the jobs they do. Anything that reduces the stress and strain on your body can help protect you.

If you already have pain, see a health worker and also read pages 143 to 149 for movements and treatment that can help you feel better.

Small changes make a big difference

Working as a sewing machine operator in a garment factory in Oakland, USA was hard work. We would get there early and leave late, and every day our bodies hurt. But it was a good, steady paycheck.

We heard about an organization called the Asian Immigrant Women Advocates (AIWA) which was helping people in other factories in Oakland. When we first met them, they listened to us talk about our work and our jobs. For so long we felt that nobody cared about our problems, but AIWA did. We could not stop ourselves from crying during that meeting.

Then we met women from other factories. We talked about our aching shoulders, backs and arms, and the constant pain in our elbows, wrists, and hands. We talked about going home and being too tired to care for ourselves and our families. We learned we were not alone in our pain.

AIWA connected us with the Ergonomics Program at the University of California. They taught us about our bodies and how the workplace could be changed so we didn't have to live with pain.

We discussed changes needed at our factory. We focused on reducing knee pain because everybody had it, and decided to try padding the knee switches on our machines. It worked! The very next day we had a little less pain. Such a small change made a real difference.

Slowly we began to push for other changes. We put footrests under the machines and got new, tilted tables so we could see our work better without bending forward. We even got padded and adjustable chairs!

Before AIWA, we never knew the power we had to improve our workplace. We thought pain from working was just the way work was. This lesson we learned from the project was something we took with us even after we left the factory and it has changed our lives.

Reduce your risk of injury

Changing tools, machines, workstations, and work processes can reduce pain and injury. Some solutions can be done by workers themselves. Some will require organizing and unity among workers to convince the boss.

* Change positions during the day and move your eyes and body as often as you can in the opposite direction from how you move them while working.

* Listen to your body and find out what processes are causing you pain. Talk with other workers to find out if they also have signs of strain or overuse. Carry out the survey Strain and overuse injuries in your factory, on page 126, or do the activity Draw a map of the body, on page 42.

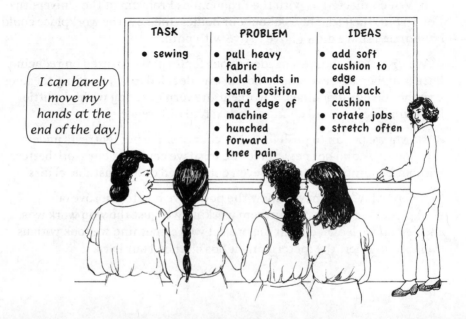

Convincing the boss that better ergonomics is good business was the hardest part. He didn't agree to many changes at first, but now he understands that if our bodies stay healthy and strong, we will work well—even better than before!

* Massage yourself, stretch, and strengthen your body to treat strain early and avoid further injury. See Stretches and massage reduce pain, on pages 143 to 149.

* Find ways to modify your workplace to fit you and organize to make them happen in your factory. See Workplace changes to reduce injury, on page 127.

* Find ways to change how work is done so it does not exceed your physical limits, and organize to make these changes happen for others in your factory as well. See Protect workers from injury, on page 141.

I can barely move my hands at the end of the day.

TASK	PROBLEM	IDEAS
• sewing	• pull heavy fabric • hold hands in same position • hard edge of machine • hunched forward • knee pain	• add soft cushion to edge • add back cushion • rotate jobs • stretch often

| Activity | Ergonomic dangers in your factory |

These numbered survey questions are followed by information suggesting what changes might be made to respond to people's answers. When you make your own survey, thinking ahead about how you would improve working conditions can help you better form your questions.

1. Do you have **tingling**, **weakness**, or **pain**? Where?

2. Do you **repeat** the same movement over and over again?

   Tools and materials that fit your hands comfortably will make repetitve movements less harmful to your body. But the best way to reduce the harm from repetitive work is to have less of it.

3. Do you work **long hours** without breaks?

   Your body needs time to recover from the stress and strain of work. Take breaks during the day and take time to relax after work.

4. Do you work in **uncomfortable** positions?

   Tables, chair, and workstations that fit your body reduce twisting, bending or stretching too much.

5. Do your body and eyes **stay** in the same position for a long time?

   Your body and eyes need to move around to stay healthy and strong.

6. Do you **lift** heavy loads?

   See Lifting, carrying, and moving supplies safely, on pages 136 to 140, for ideas on how to lift safely and which lifting and pushing tools can help prevent and reduce injuries.

7. Do you retrieve **heavy items** from high or low places?

   Store heavy things or items you use often at waist height to prevent strain.

8. Do you use too much **force**?

   Using your fingers, hands, and arms to pinch, pull, or hold too hard can injure you.

9. Do you use furniture or equipment with **hard or sharp edges**?

   Reduce or eliminate hard edges on tables and tools by covering them with soft material.

10. Do you work with tools that **vibrate**?

    Stand on padded mats to reduce the impact of vibration on the body. The best solution is to rotate jobs and not use vibrating tools more than a few hours a day.

11. Do you work in very **cold** or very **hot** temperatures?

    Both can increase your risk of getting injured by repetitive work.

Activity   **Using a survey to improve ergonomics**

You can use the questions on the previous page to help you organize a survey in your factory. A survey gives you a reason to talk to every worker (see page 39). You can find out what problems your co-workers think are most important, who is eager to help change conditions, and who will work on making or expanding a network for sharing information among workers. A survey can also create a shared understanding among workers and build hope that change is possible.

Review and change the questions to fit your situation. Add questions that are specific to each production line and work process. Do not forget the cleaning and maintenance workers who move around the factory.

Gather a group of workers to review the questions and create new ones. The group might decide to ask about pain and injuries or the number of hours worked over the past month. Workers in different departments will have different questions. You might need to ask questions in several languages so all workers can participate. Ask workers with the most interest to help gather and evaluate information and then to plan a campaign.

Recruit workers from each work area to survey 5 to 10 co-workers. With a committee of volunteers, it should be possible to talk with every worker in the factory, even a large factory. Volunteers could speak with workers individually or in small groups at lunch or after work.

Record what workers say and discuss their answers as a group. Note when workers agree or disagree on problems and solutions. Depending on their jobs, gender, or general health, workers often have different opinions. Note who seems most interested. Maybe they will lead the push for changes in their area.

Summarize the responses to the survey and share them with all workers.

People were very eager to talk with other workers about their jobs and about what hurt. A few were surprised... nobody had ever asked them before. We found that almost everybody in the factory had strain and overuse pain. Some had severe problems. When we informed everyone about the survey results, people got angry at the boss and wanted to do something. We arranged a training in ergonomics from an NGO and created a health and safety committee. Changes come slowly, but knowing others care about their pain keeps people motivated.

Workplace changes to reduce injury

There are ways to change the workplace to prevent and reduce pain and injury from strain and overuse. Here are some examples.

Tables that fit you

A table should be the right size and shape for the task you are doing and the right height for you:

- If you are sitting, your arms should rest comfortably on the table with your wrist mostly straight. If the table is too low, you will have to hunch forward straining your neck, back, and shoulders. If it is too high, you will have to raise your arms, straining your shoulders, neck, and upper back.
- A table should be big enough to hold all the materials you need to do your job. It should be high enough to allow your legs to fit underneath.
- A table tilted towards you makes it easier to see your work without bending forward. If you sew heavy fabric, a tilted table might help pull the fabric through the machine.
- Edges should be padded to put less pressure on your arms.

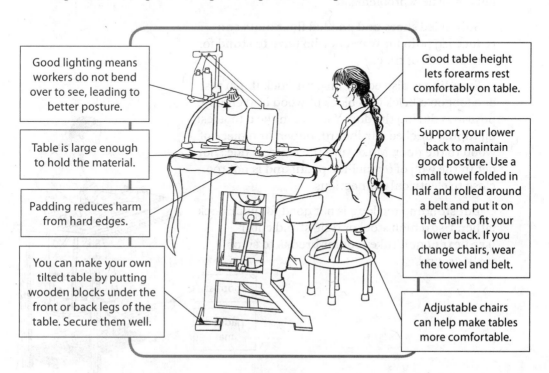

Good lighting means workers do not bend over to see, leading to better posture.

Table is large enough to hold the material.

Padding reduces harm from hard edges.

You can make your own tilted table by putting wooden blocks under the front or back legs of the table. Secure them well.

Good table height lets forearms rest comfortably on table.

Support your lower back to maintain good posture. Use a small towel folded in half and rolled around a belt and put it on the chair to fit your lower back. If you change chairs, wear the towel and belt.

Adjustable chairs can help make tables more comfortable.

Tables for when you stand

If you work standing, use your elbow to determine the safest height of your table. If you are doing very precise work, your table should be a bit higher so you can rest your elbow on the table. If you are doing assembly work that requires you to use some force, it is better for the table to be a bit lower than your elbow.

The best tables for people who work standing are ones that can be adjusted up or down to fit each person who uses them. Adjustable tables can also make it easier to switch between sitting and standing.

If you can not get an adjustable table, change your table to fit you better. If the table is too short for you, add blocks under it or raise the work closer to you. If the table is too high, you can stand on a platform. Make sure any changes you make to the table are safe, secure, and will not cause new problems.

Soft-soled shoes and padded floor mats can reduce leg pain for workers who have to stand for long periods of time.

Standing is also easier on your back if you rest one foot on a brick or a block of wood and change positions during the day. You can make a footrest by taping stacked cardboard, paper, or a piece of wood to the floor. Make sure the footrest does not get in the way of a machine pedal and is not too close to electrical connections.

But standing too long is not good for your back either. Use a high stool or a sit-stand chair (see next page). Take regular breaks to sit or walk around.

A padded floor mat might reduce the pain and health problems caused by vibrating tools.

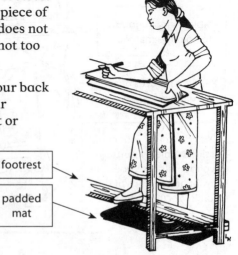

footrest

padded mat

Chairs

A chair should support your legs, hips, back, and body while you work. To be comfortable, a chair needs to fit the size and shape of the worker who sits on it, and have a padded seat and backrest.

Bad: hard chair
or stool

Better: chair with
cushion and backrest

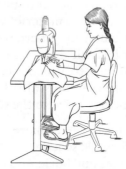

Best: adjustable, padded
chair with backrest

Adjustable chairs can fit many different people. The chair should be adjustable for height, tilt of the seat and backrest, and height of the backrest. Small changes can make your chair or table fit you better (see pages 127 and 130).

A "sit-stand" chair
lets you alternate
between sitting
and standing with
support.

Now we have chairs!

We didn't have chairs at our factory in the United States. When our backs and knees hurt from standing, we sat on empty buckets. We told our union representatives, and they raised the problem with a joint worker-management committee in charge of preventing injuries. Under our union contract, the committee can demand that the boss make changes to protect workers' health. Now we have chairs with backrests and foot rails. I change between sitting and standing every hour. And I feel the difference!

If all you have is a stool or a non-adjustable chair, you can still make it fit you better:

Make the chair taller so your arms can be at a comfortable length from the table: Use items from your workplace to make chairs taller. Garment workers use thread cones and spools. You can use wooden blocks or other materials. Check the cones or other materials for cracks and make sure the chair is stable and does not wobble. You might have to attach them to the legs or make the chair taller by adding a cushion to the seat.

Make the chair more comfortable so it does not hurt your legs and back: Add a cushion to the seat or backrest. To give good support, a backrest should fit against your lower back and help you sit upright, with a slight forward curve in your lower back.

make a
backrest
with cushion

make a seat
cushion

empty cones
raise the chair

Attaching fabric or other padded material to the hard edges of tables and chairs will also protect you from pressure while sitting or leaning.

If your feet do not touch the floor, add a platform underneath them.

How to	**Make a seat cushion**

1. Use rough material to keep the cushion from slipping. Attach the cushion to the chair with string, tape, or strips of fabric.

2. Use a firm cushion. Material that is too soft will quickly lose shape and support.

3. Adjust the thickness of the stuffing so you can work at a comfortable height. Too high will make you bend your neck forward. Too low will make you raise your arms or shoulders.

4. Make the cushion wedge-shaped to allow your knees to be a little lower than your hips.

Workstations

Rearrange your workstation and tools to reduce the amount of reaching and bending you do. Put tools or materials in constant use (such as scissors, drills, and glues) in front or beside each worker in a way that limits reaching to about 40 centimeters (16 inches) or less. That is about the distance between the tip of your middle finger and your elbow.

Parts and tools should be easy to reach.

Workers who sit down can place bins and carts as close as possible to their chairs, or far enough away that they must stand up and move to use the bins. Alternating between sitting and standing reduces body strain during the workday.

Bending to reach the bin puts strain on the back and shoulders.

Bins are easier to reach if they are beside you at waist height or close to your elbow.

Add good lighting to your workstation

Workers need proper light to see clearly. Bending, squinting, and straining to see your work can injure your back, shoulders, neck, and eyes. An adjustable task light at each workstation can put more light where it is needed most. For more ideas about improving lighting in the factory, see chapter 14: Light.

Switches and pedals

Foot pedals, knee switches, and other controls
are safest when you can operate them without
using much force.

Machine switches, levers, and handles should
be easy to reach without stretching, bending,
or raising your arms above the shoulders. You
should be able to operate a switch with only a
small movement of your arm, leg, or foot.

Foot pedals are best for seated jobs.
Raising your foot off the floor every time you
press the pedal strains the legs and lower back,
especially if you are standing. A pedal wide
enough for both feet allows you to use either
foot or alternate between feet.

A pedal should be positioned so you can sit
or stand at a comfortable distance from the
machine. A moveable electronic treadle may be
the best choice for machines shared by workers on
different shifts.

A platform can also make it easier for shorter people to reach switches, controls, and handles comfortably.

Pedal-operated machines should have safety
systems to protect you from injury if you accidentally hit the pedal.

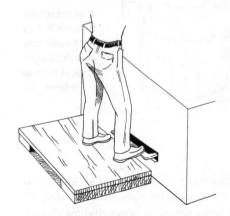

**The platform helps reduce strain
from pressing the pedal, but
operating a pedal while standing
can hurt your back.**

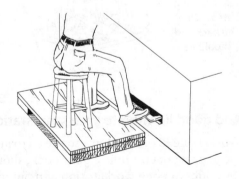

Using a chair or stool can help.

Tools

Having the right tool that fits you for each task means you can work more accurately, safely, and quickly.

How can these tools be changed to reduce injury?

Fit each worker's unique hands

Most hand tools come in different shapes and sizes, just as workers' hands also come in different sizes. To help prevent strain to fingers, hands, arms, and shoulders, each worker should use tools that fit the size and shape of her hands.

Tools you hold with your fingers for control and accuracy should be small enough to hold between your fingers and thumb.

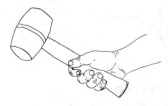

Tools you hold with your whole hand for power, such as a hammer, should be large enough so your fingers wrap comfortably around the handle.

Tools with 2 handles should close easily and open on their own. Often they have a spring that pushes the handles back open.

Designed to make work easier

A tool should be only as large and heavy as needed to do the job. The shape and features of a tool, such as a bent handle or a ratchet, can make repetitive or forceful tasks easier.

Tools with straight handles keep your wrist straight when you point the tool in a direction other than the way your arm points.

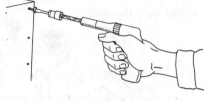

Tools with bent handles keep your wrist straight when you point the tool in the same direction as your arm.

Have comfortable handles

A comfortable handle fits in your hand. It is not too large or too small to grip, and does not have sharp edges that press into your fingers or palm. It does not put your hand or fingers in unnatural positions.

With this tool, the thumb has to stretch and work alone to press the trigger.

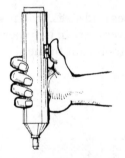

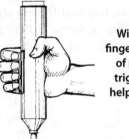

With this tool, the fingers share the work of pressing a wide trigger. The thumb helps grip and guide the tool.

Rubber sleeves over handles can reduce injury from vibration. But they have to fit the tool well. A rubber sleeve can make the tool less stable and increase the danger of injury. A sleeve can make the tool wider. Do not use a rubber sleeve if it makes it harder for you to grip the tool comfortably.

Clamps and handles help you grip tools and parts more securely. Handles also help protect your hands from sharp points and edges.

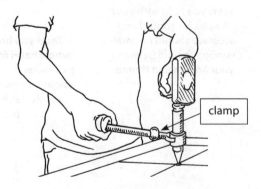

clamp

A clamp can be used as a handle to hold a tool.

Balanced weight

A balanced tool is evenly weighted so you do not have to strain to hold the tool in position. Tools should be balanced for the way they are used.

This drill is unbalanced because the handle is behind the heavy motor. To use the drill you must support the front end with your other hand.

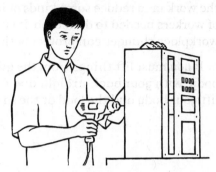

This drill is balanced because the handle is below the heavy motor. This drill can be used easily with one hand.

Supporting heavier tools with a spring-loaded arm positions them in the right direction for work, so you do not have to pick up, set down, and support the tool each time you use it.

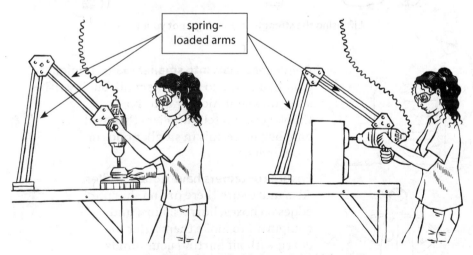

spring-loaded arms

Spring-loaded arms hold the weight of the drill while the worker is using it.

Lifting, carrying, and moving supplies safely

Moving supplies, materials, products, and waste around a factory can be hard work and causes many injuries. Using more machines instead of people to do the work may reduce some kinds of injuries, but may also reduce the number of workers needed to do the job. It is important for workers to discuss how any workplace changes can protect both their health and their jobs.

If you must lift things from the ground, try to lift with the load close to your body, with your back straight and feet stable on the ground. Use your legs to lift your body and the load at the same time.

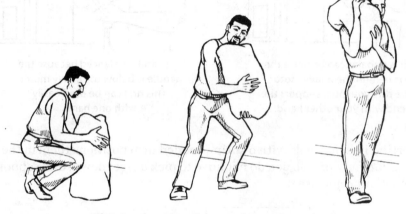

Lift using the strength in your legs, not your back.

Divide materials into smaller loads. It might take a bit more time to move them all, but it will be safer and healthier for your body. Employers can tell suppliers they will only buy materials in smaller bags or containers.

Ensure containers have good handles. Also make sure there are no sharp edges on boxes, barrels, bins, and equipment to make them safer to carry without hurting your hands and arms.

Carry balanced loads. They are easier to carry than a load carried on one side. Pack the loads to prevent the contents from shifting.

Make factory surfaces the same height. This reduces lifting from the ground and above the waist. Carts with shelves at the same height as work tables make loading and unloading easier.

Have or make raised, tilted bins and spring-loaded bins. Bin bottoms that rise as the bin empties reduce the need to bend over to reach parts at the bottom of the bin.

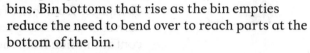

How to	# Make a spring-loaded cart

Adding a spring-loaded bottom to a deep cart can make it easier to reach items at the bottom of the cart. The spring-loaded bottom moves up as you unload the contents of the cart.

Materials needed: canvas fabric, grommet-holer or button-holer, 4 strong elastic cords (bungee cords).

1. Make a rectangle out of the canvas to be the false bottom for the cart. You may need two or more layers of fabric.

2. Make a hole in each corner of the canvas rectangle. A reinforced button hole or metal grommet will last longer than a punched or torn hole.

3. Place an elastic cord through each hole in the canvas and secure it. Place the canvas in the cart and secure the other end of the elastic cords to the cart's top corners.

4. Adjust the length of the elastic cords to allow the false bottom to rise to just below the top of the cart when it is empty. The cords should stretch to the bottom when full. If your cords don't do this, use a different kind or different length cord.

Use mechanical or power tools

A **hand truck** can help you move heavy materials, but do not overload it.

Use powered machines, such as **fork lifts, conveyor systems, and rail systems,** to do the work of lifting and moving materials. This eliminates those dangers for the worker. However, these machines add new dangers to the workplace, such as injuries from fork lift collisions or moving conveyor parts. They can also cause air contamination from fuel and engine exhaust.

A **passive conveyor** allows you to push parts and boxes over rollers between workstations instead of carrying them by hand or cart.

A **rail system** allows you to push or pull parts or tools around the work area from a rolling holder. This is especially useful when things need to hang, such as finished clothing or material ready for dipping or spray coating.

In an ergonomics training we learned that pushing carts was better than pulling them. Pushing hurts our backs less. We also put a little less weight in each load so it is less effort. We make a few more trips but the lighter loads hurt us less.

Make sure moving equipment has good wheels

Wheels make moving easier. Wheels that are kept in good repair and changed when they are broken will make hand trucks, trolleys, carts, and bins more useful.

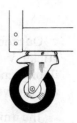

Wheels **covered with rubber** or a similar plastic last longer and are easier to move than uncovered metal wheels.

Carts are easier to move when the **back wheels swivel**.

Use carts with good, sturdy wheels.

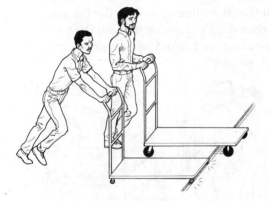

Larger wheels are easier to push and maneuver, especially on rough floors and over gaps in the floor.

A workstation **bin on wheels** can be used to bring supplies and remove waste in the same container, reducing the need to move things from one bin to another.

Wheel brakes help workers control movable equipment and keep it from moving unexpectedly. Moveable bins, carts, and tables should have brakes on the wheels. You should be able to easily lock or unlock wheel brakes with your foot. You should not have to use much pressure or bend over to do this.

Wheels need to be cleaned often to keep turning smoothly. You can remove dirt and debris from a wheel with a stiff brush, but replacement wheels are needed when a wheel can no longer be cleaned or repaired.

A parade of broken, squeaky carts

Our factory creates a lot of waste that makes the factory floor wet and sticky. When workers move products around the plant, the waste on the floor gums up the wheels so the carts do not roll smoothly and get banged up. The wheels also rust because they are rarely cleaned or repaired.

The union had asked for new carts several times, but the boss didn't respond. One morning, we lined up all the carts in front of the door to the office. Everyone who passed through that door had to look at the broken carts. When the managers arrived, they didn't understand why the carts were in front of the door. The director came and asked what was going on. He ordered us to remove the carts, so we did.

The carts made a terrible noise as they lurched forward, bumping into each other because the wheels would not turn smoothly or straight. The director glared at the managers and slammed the door as he returned to his office. New carts arrived 3 weeks later!

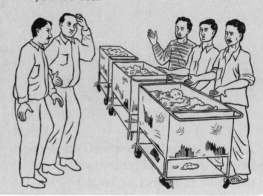

Maintenance and repair

Workers do their jobs best when their workstations, tools, and equipment are clean and in good repair. Dull cutting tools, machines clogged with dust, and unstable furniture can cause strain and other injuries. Poorly maintained machines are noisier, less efficient, and break down more often. Good maintenance is good for safety and good for business.

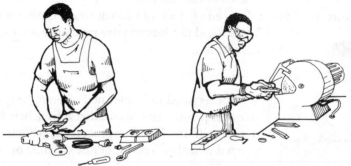

Regular maintenance makes equipment last longer and prevents injuries.

Protect workers from injury

Working too much and too fast causes ergonomic injuries, even when workstations fit workers. To prevent strain and injury, workers also need better working conditions.

Less overtime

Letting our bodies rest and recover between work shifts helps prevent strain injuries. But for many workers, overtime is either forced or they need it to make enough money. Any campaign or organizing to limit overtime should go along with a campaign to improve wages. See chapter 19: Working too much, too fast, for too little money.

Piecework and incentive pay force workers to work as fast as possible, often past their physical limits. Campaign to switch from a piecework pay rate to an hourly wage system.

Varied tasks

Do different jobs and tasks during the day. Changing from jobs that are sitting to ones that are standing gives workers an opportunity to move different parts of their bodies. Being able to rotate among jobs or workstations makes work more interesting and gives workers the opportunity to learn new skills. This also benefits the company.

Training

Demand training for all workers on how to do jobs safely, taking into account each worker's size and strength. If you know how to do a job in a way that causes less strain, show your co-workers.

Shared workloads

For jobs that are very hard on the body, such as lifting, having two or more workers do the job together can reduce the risk of injury.

Regular breaks

Having several regular breaks during the day to move the body, rest, and drink water helps workers stay healthy. During breaks, move your body! If you work sitting, stand up and stretch your back.

Some employers might fight against more breaks. But pain and illness reduce productivity more than breaks do. Everybody works better when they are healthier and happier.

Use your body more carefully

As you make workstations more ergonomic and change working conditions to reduce strain on the body, you can reduce some of the strain of work by improving your posture.

Change your posture several times during the day. Stretch your body in ways that are the opposite of your work movements. Use any moment you can during the day, such as breaks, shift changes, process changes, or other regular occurrences as a reminder to change your posture:

- Straighten your back, keeping it relaxed.
- Push your chest out.
- Relax your shoulders and pull them down.
- Bring your head up above your neck. Keep your neck straight and relaxed.

A rounded back and neck pull at back and chest muscles and cause muscle strain.

Move differently at work

How you work becomes a habit very quickly. Even when you want to change, it can be hard to remember to do things differently. But don't give up! Make small changes where and when you can to improve your posture and how you move as you work. The more you repeat the new ways, the more natural they will feel. It takes time and practice to change old habits.

Change the way you move at home

Chores at home can also add to pain from strain and overuse at work. When women do housework after working in the factory, they further injure their already tired and stressed muscles. If you have pain from work, ask your family to help more in the home. Men and boys can do housework, too! See the activity What do you do in a day?, on page 313.

Stretches and massage reduce pain

Aches, pains, swelling, tingling, burning, or numbness in the parts of your body you use on the job may be signs of injury from repetitive work.

Resting can help your body heal. But movements, such as stretches, massage, and exercise, may also help reduce and prevent injury. Do the movements in this section or other things known in your community to help lessen muscle and joint pain.

Pain is common but it is not the only way

Every person I know, even the new hires at my factory, feels pain from working. I don't think there is a single factory worker that is pain-free. But after a recent "ergonomics" training where we learened that work could be modified to not hurt us, we were very excited: maybe work didn't have to be so painful. We made small changes in our workstations that made work easier. Some of us went to the boss to ask for better tools.

The boss listened to us, but nothing changed. And the improvements we made helped a little, but we still had pain. Many workers became discouraged. They said, "What is the point of organizing for ergonomic changes if we will hurt anyway?" We knew we had to help people feel less pain as well as organize to prevent pain from happening. We can't talk about prevention with someone who is already sick.

So we began asking around: What did people do to feel less pain after work? Some took herbs, others took medicine. We learned about stretches, exercises, and massage. The techniques didn't work for everybody, and some people just refused to do anything. But more workers began trying different things to deal with their pain. It is still true that pain is the cross we have to bear, but now we have some tools to manage pain instead of letting it rule our lives. And with less pain, we have more energy and hope that we can change our lives.

Stretch

Most movements that allow your muscles to stretch will give you some relief. Move and stretch as often as you can at work and at home. Some stretches are better if you can hold the position for a few seconds or minutes, but do not push your body beyond its limits.

Stretching with other people at work or at home helps you stay motivated. And you might learn new stretches!

Hands

1. Make a fist.

2. Open your hands, stretching your fingers out.

3. Curl your fingers into a claw. Then open your hands again.

4. Gently roll your hands in a circle at the wrist

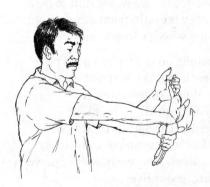

With your arm stretched out in front of you, lift your palm up so it is facing away and your fingers are pointing up. Use your other hand to pull your fingers back toward you.

Then fold your hand down at the wrist, so the palm is facing your body and the fingers are pointing down. Use your other hand to pull the back of the hand down and toward you. Grip the main part of the hand when you pull, not the fingers.

Neck and shoulders

  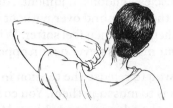

Roll your head slowly in a full circle.

Move shoulders up and down, roll them forward and backward, pull your shoulder blades together and apart.

Put your thumb or fingers on the muscle between your neck and shoulder. The closer it is to your neck the better. Keeping the pressure, move your head to the side opposite to where you are pressing. Hold for a few seconds.

Back

Pull your knees towards your chest. Relax, still holding your knees.

Lie on your back with your knees bent. Push your lower back into the floor by slowly tightening your stomach and buttock muscles. Relax, and your back will curve up the way it usually does.

Stretch your arms to the sides with your knees bent. Slowly let your knees drop to one side. When they touch the floor, turn your head to the opposite side, trying to keep your shoulders on the ground. After a few moments, bring them back to the center and slowly bring them over to the other side, turning your head the other way.

Massage and press the muscles

Your muscles, tendons, ligaments, and other soft tissues become tense when you use them over and over without rest. When they are tense, they feel hard. When they relax they feel softer. When you do the same movements over and over, your muscles never get an opportunity to relax.

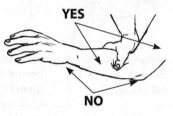

One way to release the tension in your muscles is to massage them. You can do this with your hands or a hard object. Massaging and pressing on the muscles will work better if you do it regularly, not just when you have pain. It helps to do it several times during the day. The massage may feel a little painful at first, when you are working on muscles that have been tense for too long.

Use any kind of massage common in your community. Only press the muscles, and not the joints.

Forearm

With your wrist relaxed and palm pointed towards the floor, close your hand in a fist.

Place your thumb right on the muscles of the forearm, close to the elbow (but not on top of it).

If you move your thumb from side to side while pressing, you may feel the muscle jump a little bit.

You can press and just stay there, or you can roll it. You can also move your wrist up and down.

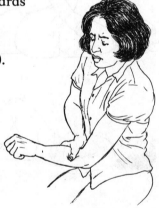

If you feel any tingling or numbness, change the position of the pressure.

Wrist

Place your thumb on your wrist and hold it there for a few seconds as you move your wrist up and down.

Press on the flesh, not the bone.

Elbow

Apply pressure to the muscles around the elbow, not directly to the elbow.

Put your thumb on the upper, underside of your elbow, the part that faces toward the back of you, and try to find the muscle that hurts.

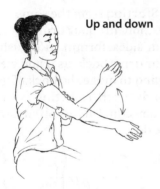

Up and down

Stretch and curl your arm several times as you press on the muscle.

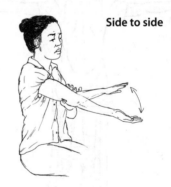

Side to side

Then move your hand from palm down to palm up several times as you press.

Shoulder

Put your fingers on the area of your arm that connects with your shoulder. Find the place that feels sore and push it as you move your arm slowly up and down.

Strengthen and improve your posture

Most people get tired of keeping their back and neck straight. Exercises that make your upper back strong will make it easier for you to hold a good posture, even if your chair does not have a good back rest.

Sit or stand. Keeping your shoulders down and relaxed, squeeze your shoulder blades as if you were trying to make them touch. Hold this as long as you can. Do this often during the day. You can also do this laying belly-down on a bed.

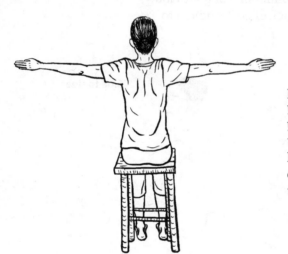

Starting from the same position, lift your arms out to your sides, forming a T. Push your arms back, as if you were trying to make the back of your hands touch. Hold this as long as you can. Do this often during the day.

Starting from the same position, raise your arms straight up. Keep them straight and push your arms back without arching your back. Hold this as long as you can. Do this often during the day.

Strain and pain

The best thing to do when you feel strain and pain is to stop using the muscle at work and home or use it less and massage, stretch, and strengthen it.

Put ice or a cold cloth on the muscle for 20 to 30 minutes a few times a day. The cold helps reduce inflammation so your muscle can heal. Apply cold several times a day and any time you have pain. You can apply heat after a few days.

Take aspirin or ibuprofen. They help with pain and also reduce muscle inflammation. But these medicines can cause other health problems and are not a long-term solution. Ask a health worker or others in your community about plants and traditional medicines that might help you with pain and swelling.

Different kinds of injuries need different times to heal. But see a health worker if:

- you feel tingling or numbness.
- the pain from a strain does not go away after 1 or 2 weeks.
- you fell, twisted, or pulled a muscle and the injury does not improve in 2 to 4 weeks.

A health worker might recommend you stop working for awhile and give you exercises and stretches that will help your body heal. She might give you more or different medicines.

When you visit a health worker, explain why you think your pain is due to your work. She has probably never done the work you do, so you must show her. Act out the physical moves required by your work so she can see clearly what you do all day. For more information about getting health care, see chapter 25: Access to health care.

HEALTH CLINIC

Show the health worker how your back hurts from reaching deep into carts.

8 Chemical dangers

Chemicals surround us. They are in our homes, our schools, our work, and in our water and air. We get so used to them that sometimes we forget about them and ignore them. Other times, we fear them.

What we really need to know is: If a chemical can harm our health, what can we do to make ourselves safer? The answer depends on:

- What chemical is it?
- What form do you use it in?
- How does it get onto or into your body?
- To how much and for how long are you exposed?

No chemical is more important than a human being. We have the right, as workers and consumers, to live free from the illnesses caused by the use of dangerous chemicals.

Why would anybody use chemicals that can harm, disable, or kill people? Chemical companies and factory owners say chemicals can be "easily" controlled and used safely. But when the controls fail, do not protect enough, or are not used in the first place because the bosses think they cut into profits, it is the workers or people in surrounding communities who pay with their health.

To protect workers, the environment, and the community, we have to reduce the use of chemicals that harm our health, replace them with safer chemicals used in safer ways, and eliminate and ban toxic chemicals.

For information on specific chemicals, see Appendix B: Common Chemicals and Materials. For our sources for chemical information, see pages 463 to 464.

WITHOUT CHEMICALS LIFE WOULD BE IMPOSSIBLE

WITH~~OUT~~ CHEMICALS LIFE ~~WOULD~~ HAS BEcome IMPOSSIBLE

Safe chemicals: Who's responsible?

Thousands of chemicals are created and used each year. But as important as they are to our economies, the laws and practices about chemicals do not protect people enough from their harmful effects. Chemical companies, governments, factory owners, and others who oversee their development, sale, and use are part of a system that has harmed people all over the world.

- **Chemical companies should prove a chemical is safe before it can be sold and used.** Only a few thousand chemicals have been studied for their effects on people and the environment. Almost none have been studied for how they interact with other chemicals in the body. If testing is carried out, it often does not include all health effects.

- **Companies and governments must take responsibility for chemicals in use.** The company that sells or uses the chemical should be responsible for making it safe for workers and consumers. If people get sick from a chemical, governments must move quickly to regulate or ban it.

- **Chemicals should be safe for people inside and outside the factory.** "Safe" exposures for workers are set higher than what is considered safe outside the workplace. We all deserve to be safe from toxic chemicals. Employers should use the same, most protective standards in and out of the factory.

- **Use fewer chemicals in the workplace.** Many products release some of the toxic chemicals used to make them after they leave the factory, as they are used, discarded, or recycled. Products should be designed to use fewer chemicals in their manufacture so they will cause fewer problems "from cradle to grave."

- **A chemical should only be replaced by a safer chemical, not by another toxic one.** Many companies want to stop using toxic chemicals. However, they often replace one toxic chemical with another one that has not been well studied for health and environmental effects. The new chemical is often just as dangerous, but because its problems have yet to be discovered, it is considered "safer" or "greener."

Safe chemicals in the workplace

If a chemical is to be used in a workplace, it is the employer's responsibility to choose one that:

- is essential to the product, which could not be made without it.
- is safer than other possible alternatives.
- is used in smaller amounts than other alternative chemicals.
- can be used and disposed of without harming the workers or the community.

It is the boss's responsibility to give you chemical information in a language you understand. Workers who do not read well can learn about chemicals from pictures, videos, demonstrations, explanations, and hands-on practice. When you start a new job or are assigned new work, your supervisor should train you on the safe use of the chemicals you work with, their health effects, and what to do if there is an accident.

To work as machine operators, we are trained in how to work with and use chemicals. We learn how to mix them, how to store them, and how to clean the machines. But when we saw our co-workers getting sick, we realized the trainings didn't teach us about the chemicals' health effects.

Exposure to chemicals

The chemicals used in a factory can affect your health when they get onto or into your body. Chemicals in some forms are more dangerous than others. For instance, solids and heavy liquids stay in one place and are less likely to get in the air unless grinding, heating, and sawing generates dust and fumes.

Powders, sprays, or gases, as well as the dust, smoke, fumes, and mists created when using some chemicals, are more dangerous because they can quickly get in the air. They are also small enough to get in the nose and lungs. As chemicals spread and settle on floors, windows, work surfaces, and inside machines, vacuums, and ventilation ducts, it is more likely that you will come in contact with them.

Caution! Do not sniff, taste, or touch chemicals to find out what they are.

Signs of exposure

You can know you have been exposed to chemicals when:

- You have irritation of the nose, throat or lungs, or trouble breathing.
- You feel a chemical on your skin, especially if it burns or itches. You might also get a rash or other skin problem where the chemical touched you.
- You have a chemical taste in your mouth, either from breathing, ingesting, or absorbing it through the skin.
- You feel the effects of the chemical, such as feeling dizzy, confused, irritable, or ill.

If you have any of these signs, get away from the chemical and tell your co-workers and supervisor there is a problem.

Since signs of many health problems take a long time to develop, especially for reproductive problems and cancers, if you are worried there is exposure, tell your co-workers and supervisor, and act to prevent the problem from getting worse (see pages 164 to 172).

Occupational safety and health (OSH) professionals are often asked to investigate and limit chemical exposures. When asking about chemical exposures, they should hold private interviews with several people from each factory area so no one can guess who gave what particular information.

Who knows best?

How chemicals get on or in your body

Through breathing through your nose and mouth. When you smell a chemical, you are breathing it. But some chemicals do not have any smell, or you get used to the smell and no longer notice it.

Through your skin and eyes when the chemical gets on you, or through cuts on the skin. Sometimes you can see mists, droplets, fumes, and gases. If they are not removed by extractors or another type of ventilation, they can be absorbed through the skin and watery area of your eyes, as well as through the nose and mouth.

Through your mouth. This does not happen because you intend to eat it, but it can happen when the chemical is on your hands or clothes and you touch food or a cigarette that goes into your mouth. Chemical dust or a splash can get on your lips or inside your mouth. You also swallow chemicals that are already in cigarettes, food, or water. This happens more often than you would think.

Most workers use more than one chemical at their workstation. Those chemicals might react with others already in the materials they are working on. When leading trainings about chemicals and health effects, keep in mind that sometimes workers' health problems are related to the combination of many chemicals at a time — not just one!

Measuring exposure

If you get a little chemical on you and wash it off very quickly, this may not be much exposure. If you are splashed with a chemical and breathe it, this may be a lot of exposure. Different chemicals are dangerous in different amounts.

When there are accidents in factories, usually workers and employers all know there was exposure. But often the exposures that harm workers most are those that happen every day and are so routine that no one pays attention to them. And although you might be exposed to only a very small amount, if that exposure happens every day for a long time, it can cause serious problems.

OSH professionals are taught that most chemicals can be used safely. They learn you will not be harmed by a chemical if you are not exposed to too much of it. But as researchers prove that some chemicals are dangerous even at very low levels — levels that used to be considered safe — it becomes clear that some "safe use" standards were not safe at all. For example, BPA (bisphenol-A), phthalates, and lead cause harm at very low levels. As we learn more, levels considered safe will be lowered again and again. But who wants to be "safely" exposed the day before the levels change?

Industry cannot decide what level is a safe level.

Your employer and your government are responsible for monitoring chemicals in the workplace and for taking action to reduce exposures that can harm people's health. Unfortunately, many companies do not measure exposures and do not do enough to prevent them. And government agencies are often understaffed, unequipped, or too corrupt to enforce safety standards.

The boss says it's all safe and it won't make us sick. But we don't see him measuring it and we can't do it ourselves!

For many chemicals, levels considered to be safe still hurt workers' health. If you are worried or believe you are getting exposed to something that makes you sick, ask an OSH professional, other workers, a union or environmental group, or a health worker to help you find out as much as you can about the chemicals you work with. Many OSH professionals can tell you if they think the standard, while legal, does not protect enough, and help you track your symptoms and those of your co-workers in a health notebook (see page 47). Workers who did not give up have fought employers, chemical companies, and even governments to stop the use of chemicals that harm people's health.

Testing for chemicals

There are 2 ways to measure how much of a chemical you are exposed to. The best way is to measure the amount of chemical in the air around you and compare it to levels of exposure considered safe. The second way of measuring chemicals is to measure the amount of chemical in your body and compare it to levels that are considered safe. Most of these tests are expensive and companies only do them when a government agency forces them to.

Measuring chemicals inside your body

Some companies test all worker's blood and urine when they are hired (baseline testing) and then again later so they can tell if the workplace is creating problems. Obviously, it is much better to use safer chemicals and better processes in the first place. Even so, these tests can prove useful if health problems develop years later.

Safety Data Sheets (SDS) usually include information about what amounts of chemicals are considered safe, and sometimes include information about how to test for a chemical.

Measuring chemicals in the air

Small, specialized pumps are used to trap samples of air from the workplace at different times of day. The filters inside the pumps are then sent to a laboratory to test the amount of chemical inside. The laboratories *can* test for many chemicals, but they *will* only test for the chemicals they have been told to look for. There are also ways to test workplace air on site for a specific chemical or chemical families.

If you work with radiation, your boss should also make sure that your work area is tested for radiation. The factory should install meters in the work area or make sure all workers wear badges or personal meters to monitor their radiation exposure.

Health problems caused by chemicals

Chemicals affect people in different ways. Some people might have headaches, dizziness, skin rashes, and other short-term problems right away. Others develop problems that do not show up right away, or happen inside the body where you cannot see or feel them. Some chemicals may cause only one type of health problem, while others may cause several types of problems.

Acute health effects

When a chemical touches your skin or enters your nose, mouth, or belly, it can cause health problems right away. This is called an acute effect.

Burns, trouble breathing or seeing, coughing, feeling dizzy or fainting are examples of acute effects. Acute health effects should be treated quickly to prevent long-term damage.

Acute effects happen *right away*.

Chronic health effects

When chemicals get on or inside your body for many months or years, they can cause *chronic* health problems. Getting exposed to a lot of a chemical all at once can also cause chronic health problems.

Cancer, liver and kidney damage, and nervous system illness and brain damage are examples of chronic problems. They can take months or years to develop. Some chronic problems are treatable (some cancers) or manageable (kidney damage). Some chronic problems can be permanent (nerve and brain damage).

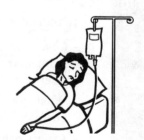

Chronic effects take a *long time* to show.

Tell your health workers about the chemicals you use

If you go to a health worker for a problem caused by chemicals, try to bring the label from the chemical container, or write down the name of the chemical or the product. Describe what the chemical looks like, how it smells, and what it is used for. Explain why you think the chemical is causing your illness or injury. Even though most doctors do not know much about chemicals, they do have access to resources to learn about their health effects.

Chemicals irritate skin, eyes, nose, and throat

When you work with chemicals, your eyes might get red and itchy. You might get a skin rash, sneeze or cough, or have a sore throat, runny nose, or difficulty breathing at or after work. The irritation usually improves when you are away from the chemical. Irritation can be the first sign you are being harmed by a chemical. To find out more about the chemicals in your workplace, see Appendix B: Common chemicals and materials.

Record rashes, sore throat, and other problems in your health notebook, noting when they started, when they got better or worse, and anything that might help you find out what chemical caused them.

Health Info

What to do if you have a rash

Skin rashes are uncomfortable and can be a sign of health problems caused by chemicals. Tell your employer if chemicals at work are causing problems, and see a health worker. If you continue to be exposed, you will continue to suffer.

To reduce some of the problems caused by a rash:

- Cover the irritated skin to keep the chemical liquid or mist away from your skin. Gloves might help, but make sure you are not allergic to latex gloves (see page 265).

- Wash your hands with mild soap and water. Strong soaps and chemical cleaners can irritate or damage your skin.

- After washing hands, put on a protective cream or lotion before and after work, and during your lunch break. Try a lotion containing antihistamine or cortisol to reduce itching and redness. Unfortunately, after a while these creams stop working.

- Make a compress using oatmeal water. Boil oatmeal or another starch in water and let it cool. Dip a clean cloth in the water and apply where it is itchy. Ask people in your community if they know of other remedies.

- Wear loose clothing that will not rub against the rash but will keep dust, chemicals, and germs off it, unless you work around machines with moving parts that could catch the cloth. The rash will heal better with fresh air, so uncover it when you get home.

Rub olive or another safe oil or lotion into skin after you wash to prevent dry or cracked skin.

Chemical burns

Mild chemical burns make the skin red but heal quickly. Serious burns cause blisters. Severe burns can go through the skin, such as burns from concentrated bleach or ammonia. Burns from hydrofluoric acid do not show or hurt right away, but burn deeply. Some burns make the skin feel cold and numb, for example, burns from dopant gases (see pages 482 to 484).

If you get splashed with even a small amount of a chemical, wash it off immediately, rinse with clean water for 15 minutes, and remove and replace your protective equipment and clothing.

Chemicals cause allergies

An allergy is when your body reacts to a chemical by developing skin rashes, eye or nose irritation, itching, eyes that water, or coughing or breathing problems. An allergic reaction to a chemical starts after you begin working with it and often improves when you stop using it. Other workers in your work area might not have a reaction, while you do. Allergies can develop at any time.

Once you are allergic to a chemical, you will always be allergic to it. A chemical allergy gets worse if you continue using the chemical and it can kill if you do not get immediate medical help. A worker who develops an allergy should be given a different job that will not harm him. He should not be fired.

If you develop an allergy

Health Info

At the first sign of an allergic reaction, talk to your supervisor.

Ask to switch to a different job where you are not exposed to the chemical you are allergic to. If you cannot change jobs, ask your employer for protective equipment, see chapter 18: Personal protective equipment.

Diphenhydramine (*Benadryl*) or another antihistamine can help calm an allergic reaction quickly.

Seek medical attention. The health worker might give you emergency medicine, for example, a salbutamol inhaler, in case you have an asthma attack or another allergic reaction.

See *Where There is No Doctor*, page 167, for information about what to do in case of an asthma attack and how to treat asthma.

Chemicals cause asthma and other breathing problems

Asthma happens when the breathing tubes of the lungs are inflamed, making it difficult to get enough air. Shortness of breath, tightness in the chest, and wheezing are all signs of asthma. Asthma can be a short-term health problem that stops when you are away from the substance that causes it. But most asthma is chronic, meaning it will last a long time, perhaps your whole life.

Some people are born with asthma, others develop it from allergies, and some get it on the job. Breathing small particles of materials used in factories, such as cotton, sand, epoxy resins, isocyanates, and some dyes and chemicals can cause asthma. If you have asthma, breathing these materials worsens it.

Chemicals harm internal organs

Some chemicals slowly poison and destroy specific parts of the body, such as the brain, nerves, liver, kidneys, or lungs. Swallowing or breathing some chemicals can cause immediate poisoning or burns inside the body. They can kill you if you do not get medical help right away. Other chemicals can cause slow poisoning over time that can make you very ill and kill you. Chemicals can also weaken your body's ability to resist infections and other illnesses.

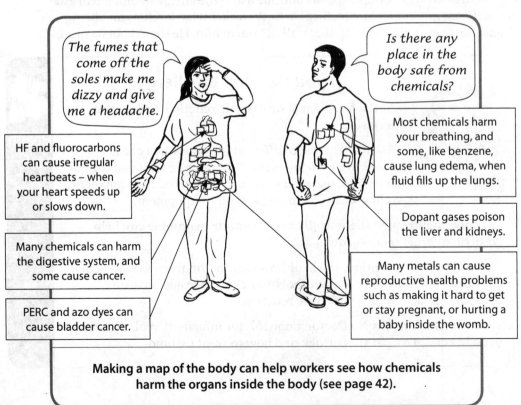

Making a map of the body can help workers see how chemicals harm the organs inside the body (see page 42).

Chemicals cause sexual and reproductive health problems

Most women can get pregnant, have healthy pregnancies, and deliver healthy babies. But chemicals used in the workplace can cause different kinds of reproductive health problems for both men and women. Some chemicals cause only one kind of problem, others can cause several.

Problems with menstruation: One of the first signs that chemicals may be harming her reproductive system is when a woman's menstruation changes. Irregular periods (no period, too few, or too many), when she was regular before, is a sign of problems. Too much stress and other social dangers can also lead to changes in menstruation.

Problems with sex: Some chemicals lessen the desire in both men and women to have sex. They can also lead to problems for men in getting an erection.

Fertility problems: Some chemicals reduce or affect men's sperm or testicles, and a woman's eggs or reproductive organs. They can lead to difficulty getting pregnant, carrying a pregnancy to term, or can cause infertility.

Miscarriage: Most miscarriages are normal and are not caused by chemicals. However, if you or your partner have had several miscarriages while or after working with chemicals, there might be a connection to the chemicals in your factory. For more information about miscarriages, see *Where Women Have No Doctor*, pages 234 to 235, and speak with a health worker.

Problems with the baby inside the womb: Some chemicals affect the baby inside the womb by stopping the baby from growing well. These babies are born small or with low birth weight. Some chemicals cause birth defects, including physical or mental disabilities that might be visible at birth or might take time to show. Chemicals that cause birth defects are called "teratogenic" chemicals. SDS sheets might include how likely a chemical is to cause birth defects. Some chemicals affect the baby's brain and will cause difficulty learning. Many chemicals can pass to a child in her mother's breast milk.

Sex and sexual health are hard to talk about. In many communities, women with fertility problems are discriminated against, so they might be unwilling to talk about these issues. But writing down your own sexual and reproductive health problems, or those of workers in your factory, can help identify and fight chemical exposures. Talking in small, informal, same-sex groups might be better than a large meeting. You can also invite people to send you notes, texts, or emails anonymously, and agree to keep them confidential.

Chemicals cause cancer

Cancer is a serious illness that attacks cells in the body and changes the way they grow. Cancer cells grow into lumps that can appear anywhere in the body: on the skin, lungs, liver, blood, bone marrow, brain, and other parts. Some cancers you can feel when you touch that body part, such as breast cancer. Some are inside the body and are harder to discover.

If cancer is found early, it often can be cured. But some cancers can be hard to cure and will kill a person.

There are many reasons people get cancer. One of them is exposure to chemicals. Because we are exposed to so many chemicals at work, at home, and in the community, it is often very hard to know and prove that a cancer was caused by a chemical at work.

Most cancers develop slowly, and signs of illness do not appear for years after exposure to the substance that caused the cancer. For many workers, this means that they get cancer many years after working with the chemical that caused it.

In a car accident, people are often injured in different ways. One person is only bruised, another is killed. Even though their injuries are different, nobody would say the car crash didn't cause them. But when one worker in an electronics factory gets cancer from chemicals while another worker is fine, the company says the chemicals didn't cause the disease. But we know, and science and the law agree, that the cancer was caused by chemicals regardless of which worker gets sick and which doesn't.

Cancers caused by some chemicals

- **Bladder cancer:** arsine (page 483), azo dyes (page 486), tetrachloroethylene (PERC) (page 524), X-rays (page 515).
- **Blood cancer (leukemia):** benzene (page 522), formaldehyde (page 497), tetrachloroethylene (PERC) (page 524), X-rays (page 515).
- **Brain cancers:** lead (page 504).
- **Kidney cancer:** arsine (page 483), lead (page 504), cadmium (page 504), trichloroethylene (TCE) (page 524).
- **Liver cancer:** arsine (page 483), azo dyes (page 486), dichloropropane (page 524), polychlorinated biphenyls (PCBs) (page 489), tetrachloroethylene (PERC) (page 524), trichloroethylene (TCE) (page 524), vinyl chloride (page 512), X-rays (page 515).
- **Lung cancer:** arsine (page 483), cadmium (page 504), chromium hexavalent (page 504), lead (page 504), nickel (page 504), trichloroethylene (TCE) (page 524), and X-rays (page 515).
- **Nose and throat cancers:** formaldehyde (page 497), nickel (page 504), tetrachloroethylene (PERC) (page 524), X-rays (page 515).
- **Prostate cancer:** cadmium (page 504).
- **Skin cancer:** arsine (page 483), UV light(page 515).
- **Stomach cancer:** lead (page 504).
- **Testicular cancer:** phthalates (page 509), polychlorinated biphenyls (PCBs) (page 489).

These cancers caused by chemicals are only the ones we are certain that are caused by the chemicals mentioned in this book. Other chemicals in this book may cause cancer, and certainly there are many other chemicals we have not included that can cause cancer too.

For chemicals that cause reproductive health problems see page 382. For information on how to detect reproductive system cancers see page 384.

For more information about chemicals that harm reproductive health, see Appendix B: Common chemicals and materials.

Protect workers from chemicals

Using fewer and less dangerous chemicals is the best way to make sure workers, the community, and the environment are not harmed. While working to achieve these long-term changes, we can organize our work in other ways to reduce chemical dangers.

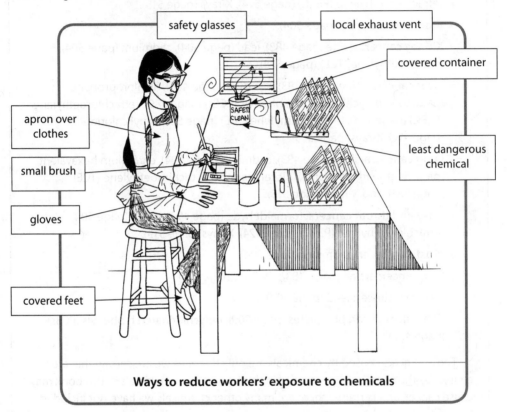

Ways to reduce workers' exposure to chemicals

Keep chemicals off your skin and eyes

When machines and equipment are not properly set up or in good working order, they leak and cause spills and accidents. The boss is responsible for providing the right equipment and hiring and training enough workers to protect you from chemical leaks, splashes, and accidents. But even if conditions in your factory are not ideal, workers can often arrange their work areas and job tasks to prevent chemicals from splashing, dripping, or leaking.

Use tools to handle chemicals

Avoid touching chemicals with your hands. Use brushes, ladles, and long-handled tools to mix, measure, or apply chemicals. The boss should supply these tools, but workers can sometimes adapt an existing tool or make a new one for a specific job. Also, use tools that fit your body. If a tool is too large or too heavy, it is bound to lead to more spills and waste.

Use protective clothes and equipment

Cloth, leather, and rubber gloves and aprons, long sleeves, and covered legs and feet can keep dust, paste, powder, and other solid chemicals off your skin. These can also protect you from very small splashes of liquid chemicals. See chapter 18: Personal protective equipment. If protective equipment is used, the boss should provide you without charge the correct protective clothing for the dangers you face, and he should replace it at no cost when it is worn or damaged.

splash guard

long-handled tool

gloves

face shield and safety glasses

protective clothes

Several controls protect workers better.

Protective equipment does not eliminate the dangers you face – it only limits the harm these dangers can cause you. Protective clothes can be hot and uncomfortable, and gloves, aprons, masks, or goggles can be dangerous if they do not fit properly. If they are too large or too loose, they may not protect you at all. Gloves that are too big make it difficult to handle tools and do precise work. Long, loose clothing can get caught in machinery or cause you to trip and fall.

If chemicals get into your clothes, remove the clothes and wash your skin right away.

Reduce the amount of chemicals in the air

When there are chemicals in the air, we can easily breathe them into our lungs. Mists and dusts can get onto skin, be absorbed through eyes, and get into mouths. Even if we can't completely get rid of chemicals in the air, there are ways to limit how much gets into our bodies.

Reduce fumes and vapors from open containers

Keep vapors out of the air by covering containers when they are not being used. Make openings smaller to fit the tools you are using. Try using a smaller tool that applies just the amount of chemical you need. The less chemical you use, the less vapor goes into the air you breathe.

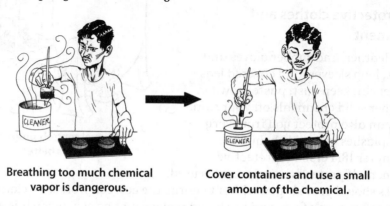

Breathing too much chemical vapor is dangerous.

Cover containers and use a small amount of the chemical.

Reduce fumes from chemical baths

Chemical baths release mists and vapors which can get inside your nose, eyes, mouth, and skin. When baths do not have rim ventilation, some factories add anti-foam agents to the baths to reduce misting. Others cover the surface of the baths with plastic chips or balls to lessen the amount of mist that escapes. Fewer vapors escape when heated baths are kept from getting too warm and are cooled when not in use.

Covering a chemical bath you are not using keeps vapors out of the air.

Reduce fumes from soldering and plastic molding

Solder and flux make fumes and smoke when soldering irons or wave soldering machines are too hot. If there is lead in the solder, the fumes are very dangerous. Local exhaust ventilation can remove fumes at the source. Workers can control the temperature on newer soldering irons and soldering machines to prevent overheating the solder. Fumes are less dangerous when soldering and welding are done at lower temperatures.

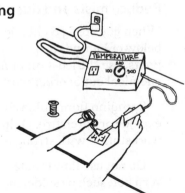

A maximum soldering heat of 200° to 250°C prevents lead fumes.

To keep plastic from creating dangerous fumes, workers need time to adjust and maintain their machines.

Plastic processing machines melt plastic and push or blow it into a mold. To reduce fumes, plastic should be heated only enough to melt and mold it. Machines should be set up for each new batch of plastic and maintained carefully to control the heat and processing times.

Clean work areas regularly

Chemicals in the form of dust, soot, and mist get on work tables, walls, and floors all over the factory. If they are not cleaned up right away, the chemicals can get on the skin or clothes of any worker who touches them. Regular cleaning reduces the amount of chemicals in the whole factory. Cleaning is especially important where toxic substances are used.

Reduce mists and dusts

When you spray a chemical, a lot of it is wasted in the air or on other surfaces below or behind the part you spray. If you must use spray to paint or coat parts, use the least amount to cover the part. A spray booth will help keep the chemical out of other work areas.

Spraying flammable chemicals can create explosive vapors which can explode or catch fire. Only spray flammable chemicals in a spray booth or workstation with strong exhaust ventilation.

Do not use flammable chemicals around processes that can spark or are very hot, such as soldering, hot baths, ovens, or plastic molding machines.

Spraying puts a lot of chemical into the air.

Use a brush or sponge to put the chemical only where it is needed.

Ventilation reduces chemicals in the air you breathe

You may not be able to prevent chemicals from getting into the air in the factory. But ventilation can help reduce the amount of chemicals you breathe. Local exhaust vents or extractors remove chemical vapors before they spread inside the factory. Roof vents and exhaust fans help move air with dust and chemicals out of the factory building. While this ventilation helps protect workers in the factory, if it is not filtered and cleaned it just dilutes and moves the chemical danger to the surrounding community. For more information, see chapter 17: Ventilation.

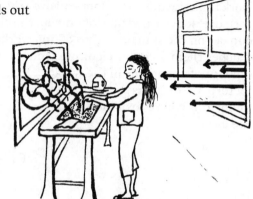

Enclose machines

Large machines that produce a lot of chemical vapor, mist, or fumes, are safest when they are enclosed in a large, ventilated box. The box stays closed when the machine is working, and is opened to load, adjust, clean, and repair the machine. Exhaust ventilation removes vapors and fumes from the machine and the factory. Some boxes collect the vapors instead of venting them, and filter the air before releasing it.

Many machines in electronics, shoe, and garment factories are enclosed, such as automated soldering machines, plastic processing and molding

machines, and ovens. These machines collect fumes, mists, and solids. They should be cleaned by workers trained in how to clean and dispose of the waste. Maintenance workers need to use the highest level of protective equipment available for these chemicals in order to protect them from exposure.

Use respirators if you must

Respirators may sometimes be necessary, but they are not the best way to protect against inhaling chemicals. The best ways are to use only chemicals that are not dangerous to breathe, to enclose machines so they do not give off fumes, and to have good ventilation. If you must use a respirator, the ones that protect most completely are respirators with filters or separate air supply. They are hot, uncomfortable, and make breathing difficult. Their filters and other parts need to be cleaned and replaced often.

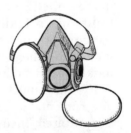

Respirators have to be tested on you to see if they fit you well. See Check that your respirator fits and works, pages 269 to 270.

Respirators are the last resort. Only use them if you think you might be exposed to chemicals in the air. Maintenance workers and workers who handle the more dangerous chemicals need respirators with the correct filters or with air supply. See the various types of respirators and their uses on pages 266 to 270.

Prevent chemicals from getting in your mouth and belly

No worker tries to get toxic chemicals in her mouth. But it is easy for chemicals to get on your hands or clothes, and from there into your mouth. Even if you wear gloves, you can get chemicals on your hands when you take the gloves off or if they leak. When chemicals get on your hands, they can also get on anything you touch.

To keep chemicals out of your mouth, wash your hands before you touch food, dishes, or cigarettes. This is especially important for workers exposed to lead, asbestos, pigments, solder, and toxic dust from grinding, foundries, and metal casting.

Wash off chemicals with plain soap and water.

Our water is poison

Tap water is supposed to be safe to drink in the United States. But in Silicon Valley, California, drinking water was polluted by the sloppy practices of the electronics industry. When electronics companies began making semiconductors here in the 1980s, we didn't know much about them. Neither did the government. So the companies did whatever they wanted. They dumped toxic waste into the water, and storage containers leaked thousands of liters of chemicals into our soil.

First they claimed it wasn't happening. Then they said it was not a problem — the chemicals didn't spread and weren't toxic. But we discovered the chemicals poisoned the water. We fought hard for the companies to take responsibility. Government and independent agencies tested the water and found many problems. Silicon Valley had more toxic areas than anywhere in the USA. After 30 years, it has some of the most toxic water in the country, solvents in the water are leaching upward, and cleaning up will take decades.

People drink bottled water because they don't trust that tap water is safe. But bottled water is not a solution; the plastic pollutes and is not sustainable.

Keep chemicals out of drinking water

Good health depends on drinking enough water. But when chemicals get in the water or on the cups you use, drinking water can become a source of illness.

- Make sure the factory provides you with enough clean water to drink.
- Keep water containers covered so chemicals and dust cannot get in.
- Put water bottles in a safe place. Wash your hands before opening them.

Never put a chemical in a container that is used for food or drinks, or that looks like a food or drink container. People expect a soft drink bottle to contain soft drink, not a dangerous chemical. Someone may drink from the bottle by mistake.

Never put food or drink in a container used for chemicals. Even if the container has been washed, it may still have small amounts of chemicals inside that can get into the food or drink – and you!

When you smoke, chemicals get in your mouth

Smoking cigarettes in the workplace adds dangerous chemicals to the air all workers breathe, whether they smoke or not.

Chemicals from work get on cigarettes

If you have chemicals on your hands and you pick up a cigarette, the chemicals get on the cigarette. When you put the cigarette with chemicals on it in your mouth, you ingest some of the chemicals. When you smoke a cigarette with chemicals on it, the chemicals burn and you breathe it in.

Cigarette smoke is dangerous

Cigarette and cigar smoke contain dangerous chemicals from the burning tobacco, paper, and the chemicals with which they are treated. The smoke carries small particles that irritate the eyes and throat. When breathed in, the chemicals go deep into the lungs and cause lung cancer, emphysema, asthma, and other serious diseases, and worsen health problems from other causes. Millions of workers die from smoking every year and the big tobacco companies make millions of dollars causing their deaths.

> *Cigarettes are a blight on the whole human race.*
> *A man is a monkey with one in his face.*
> *Take warning, dear friend.*
> *Take warning, dear brother:*
> *There's a fire on one end and a fool on the other.*

Prevent spills and leaks

It is easier and safer to prevent chemical spills than to clean them up.

- Design chemical storage and mixing rooms to be fireproof, well ventilated, temperature controlled, and easy to clean.
- Transport chemicals in closed containers that cannot break or shatter. If you move containers of liquids or powders on carts, use carts with sides and spill trays to catch leaks.
- Use small containers of chemicals in work areas. Preventing and stopping leaks is easier when bulk chemicals and large containers are kept in a separate storage area.
- Store chemical containers so openings or valves are at the top.
- Transfer chemicals from one container to another by using drip-preventing spouts for liquids, and scoops or other tools for solids, such as pastes, powders, and pellets. Use a tray under the containers to catch leaks and spills.

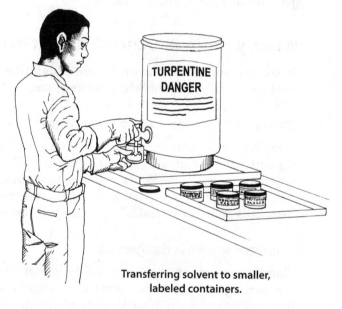

Transferring solvent to smaller, labeled containers.

- Put static control mats throughout the area where flammable solvents are stored to prevent static electricity from causing them to explode. When transferring solvents, you can also prevent explosions by connecting a ground wire to each container. Or only ground one container and attach a wire from it to other containers as a common ground.
- Control heat during plastic processing. When melted plastic gets too hot, it can leak or overflow.
- Inspect and maintain containers, pipes, pumps, valves and machines that could leak chemicals, especially their manual and automatic shutoffs. When damage and worn parts are noticed early, they can be repaired or replaced before causing a leak.

How to	**Clean up a small chemical spill**

The most important thing after a chemical spill is to protect yourself and your co-workers. If you cannot safely clean up the spill, help everyone leave the area.

- If someone is more prepared than you to clean up a spill — if there is a person trained to do this work — call that person first.
- Always wear protective clothing, including rubber boots, safety glasses, and gloves, to clean up a chemical spill.

1. Control the spill

Find the cause of the spill and stop it. Shut down leaking equipment. Turn a tipped-over container upright. Put a leaking container inside another.

2. Contain the spill

Absorb the chemical by putting soil, sand, sawdust, clay, or similar material on the spill. If the material may blow away, cover it with a plastic sheet.

3. Clean up the spill

Scoop the material into metal drums or thick plastic containers. Label clearly with the chemical's name and "Waste!" Do not wash the chemical away with water. This will spread the chemical and make the problem worse. The boss is responsible for disposing of chemical waste properly. If he does not, report him (anonymously) to local environmental authorities.

What should be available in your factory:

- Training to clean up spills.
- Evacuation practice.
- A place where tools, protective equipment, clean-up materials and containers can be kept close to where chemicals are stored or used.
- Telephone numbers of the agency to report a spill or accident, and emergency services to call for help.

First aid for chemicals

Despite our best attempts to prevent them, accidents happen in every factory. When they do, serious injuries may still be prevented if employers make sure workers receive regular trainings in first aid and have the materials they need. One or more workers in every area (and for every shift) should be trained to take charge in an accident, to get people out safely, to give first aid, and to get more help if needed. Make someone responsible to check regularly that first aid supplies are fresh and fully stocked, and that equipment, such as showers and eye wash stations, are clean and functional.

First Aid

First aid when you breathe in a chemical

If a person has difficulty breathing, feels dizzy, confused, or nauseous, or if you see, smell, or feel a chemical release:

1. Remove the person from the work area or factory so they can get fresh air. Make sure your workplace has a plan about what to do if a worker cannot move or loses consciousness.

2. Help the person stay calm and comfortable.

3. Give oxygen from an oxygen tank if the person has inhaled chemicals that:

   - cause a severe asthma attack, such as isocyanates and some dyes.
   - cause liquid to build up in the lungs (pulmonary edema), such as ammonia and chlorine.
   - reduce oxygen in the air, such as methane and nitrogen.
   - reduce oxygen in the blood, such as carbon monoxide and methylene chloride.
   - make it hard for the body to use oxygen, such as cyanide and hydrogen sulfide.

4. Take the person to a health worker, even if they feel better.

5. If the person has stopped breathing, begin rescue breathing (mouth-to-mouth breathing). Make sure your factory holds regular trainings on how to do rescue breathing.

First aid when a chemical touches your skin or eyes

First Aid

Every work area where chemicals are used should have an emergency body shower and an emergency eye wash station with enough water to flow for at least 15 minutes. Most important, workers should be trained in first aid for the chemicals they work with.

For chemicals on the skin:

1. Wash chemicals off immediately using lots of water for at least 15 minutes. The faster you begin pouring water over the area and the longer you do it, the more you will limit harm.

2. Chemicals that catch fire or absorb quickly through the skin must be washed for a longer time, 30 minutes to 1 hour.

3. After washing the chemicals off the skin, take the person to a hospital or clinic even if there are no signs of harm. Bring information about the chemical.

4. Burns from HF (hydrofluoric acid) must be treated with calcium gluconate. See page 66.

For chemicals in the eyes:

1. Stay calm.

2. Rinse the eye or both eyes immediately. Use lots of water and continue rinsing for at least 15 minutes.

3. If you have an emergency eye wash, turn it on and use your fingers to open your lids as you flush them.

4. If you have to splash water on your eyes with your hands, hold your eyes open as you splash them. Ask for help keeping them open.

5. If you are unable to stand, a person can pour water on your eyes. If only one eye is affected, tilt your head so the water runs from the bridge of the nose, over the eye, and towards the ear. Don't let the water run from one eye to the other. If both eyes were splashed, lie down and tilt your head back, while the person pours water over the bridge of your nose so it runs down both eyes.

6. See a health worker as soon as you can.

First Aid

First aid when chemicals get in the mouth

1. Help the person stay calm.

2. Find the chemical label or any information about the chemical. Usually the label will include a first aid section, with instructions about "ingestion." There you will find whether the person should vomit up the chemical or not. It is very important to follow that advice.

3. The label may list an antidote if the chemical is ingested. If you have that antidote, give it.

4. Activated charcoal is a common and inexpensive treatment to help someone who has been poisoned. Unless the chemical label or SDS says not to, you can give the person activated charcoal.

5. Unless the label says not to, you can give a glass of water or milk. But do not give more.

6. After following the instructions on the label as best you can, quickly take the person to a clinic or hospital. Bring the name, the label, and any information about the chemical with you.

7. If the person is unconscious, lay her on her side so she does not choke on her vomit. Check her breathing. Quickly get help so she can be taken to a clinic.

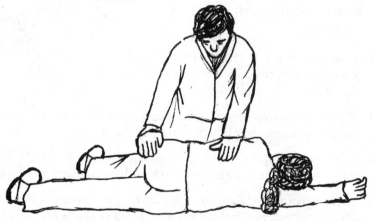

Lying on the side keeps the person's airways open.

What should be available in your factory

- A first aid committee and trainings so workers know how to respond to chemical emergencies, including how to give rescue breathing, how to operate emergency showers and eye washes, and how to get workers immediate medical attention.

- First aid supplies for the chemicals used in your factory, such as oxygen tanks, activated charcoal, and calcium gluconate or other treatments needed for chemical burns.

- Telephone numbers to quickly bring an ambulance and notify a clinic or hospital and the safety and health authorities in case of an accident.

- Emergency showers and eye wash stations in all work areas where there are chemicals.

- Air monitors with alarms to alert when chemical levels are high.

- Clean water to drink.

- Personal protective equipment for everyday use as well as in case of accident and for clean-up. There should also be extra clothing and shoes in a variety of sizes in case someone has to completely change their clothing.

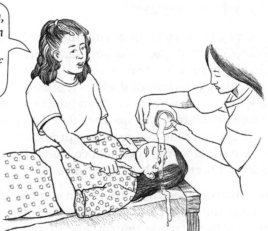

If there is no eye wash, pour clean water from the inside of the eye toward the outside of the eye near the ear.

Learn about chemicals used in your factory

Many workers do not know what chemicals they work with. You might receive chemical containers without labels or know a chemical by what it does ("glass cleaner") or by a name given to it ("yellow stinky"), not its real name.

You have a right to know what chemicals you work with. By learning more about the chemicals, you can seek medical or professional help, you can organize for safe chemicals with your co-workers, and together you can work with your employer to reduce exposures and eliminate toxic chemicals from production.

We won't use chemicals without knowing how they can harm our health.

You need to make sure we are protected, and give us training and tools to use them more safely.

Talk to other workers

Ask workers what they know or can find out about the chemicals in the workplace. Collect all the chemical names: brand names, generic names, and even nicknames. Write down any characteristics that can help identify the chemical, such as how and where it is used, its color, smell, and any instructions the employer gave about how to handle the chemical ("Always put the chemical into water, not the other way around!"). Talk with the workers in the shipping and receiving areas, and the people who inventory, store, mix, and dispose of the chemicals and their containers. They often know the names of the chemicals, or can find out.

Write down any health problems you or others feel while working with or transporting the chemicals. Ask: Do you feel ill at work or after work? Are some work areas better or worse than others? Do you feel better when you are away from work for a few days?

Show others how to keep a health notebook and how to look for patterns: Do you get sick more often when you work in certain areas? When you work with certain chemicals? Immediately, or after you leave work?

What chemical is it?

If you know the name of the chemical, you can usually find out about its health effects by looking up information about it. But if you don't know its name, you may be able to find out what it is by its color, smell, what it is used for, and other qualities. For help in doing this and to understand the dangers of specific chemicals, see the Appendix B: Common chemicals and materials.

But the truth is that nobody knows how dangerous many chemicals are because not many chemicals have been studied fully for their effects on people. It takes a long time to do scientific research and even more to make laws to protect people. And to make it even more complicated, it is even more unusual for scientists to study how a mix of chemicals affects peoples' health. And how often do you use only one chemical? That is why it is important for companies to use only chemicals that are already proven to be safe.

Just as we begin to understand how to use a chemical safely, the employer changes it to something we don't know anything about!

Read the label

Every chemical container should have a label on it, written in a language people in your factory can understand. If the containers you are working with do not have labels, ask the supervisor to provide you with this information, ask the shipping department workers if they could share the information on the label of the larger container with you, or try to find out more information yourself. In some countries, these labels are required by law to provide information in many languages.

ISOPROPANOL (IPA)
Contains: Isopropyl alcohol 70%
Inert: Water 30%

DANGER!

Highlighly flammable liquid and vapor. Splashes will cause serious eye irritation. May cause drowsiness or dizziness if inhaled.

Precautions during use: Keep away from heat, sparks, and open flames. No smoking. Keep container tightly closed. Avoid breathing in vapors. Use in a well-ventilated area. Wear eye protection.

First aid: If inhaled: Remove person to fresh air and keep comfortable for breathing. Call a doctor if you feel unwell. Eyes: Rinse cautiously with water for several minutes. Remove contact lenses if it is possible. Continue rinsing. If eye irritation continues, see a doctor.

Emergency: In case of fire, use water spray, alcohol-resistant foam, dry chemical or carbon dioxide to put it out.

Manufactured by: Greedist Chemicals Co. 111 Only Drive, Onlyville, Iowa, 11111 USA.

CAS #67-63-0

Get the Safety Data Sheet (SDS)

Companies that make chemical products publish an information sheet for each product they make. These used to be called Material Safety Data Sheets (MSDS) but are now called Safety Data Sheets (SDS).

We form groups and each group reads one section. We ask each other when we don't understand a term or a number. Then we go through the whole thing together.

An SDS is often long and difficult to understand. Though each sheet must use the same categories, the content in the SDS for different companies' sheets may be very different, even for the same chemical. To get more information, read several SDS of the same chemical.

How to	Get and read an SDS

The factory administration should have an SDS for every chemical used in the factory. Your boss should make copies of these SDS available to you and other workers in your language (see The right to know about chemicals, on page 183).

While you organize to make your boss provide you up-to-date SDS, you can try to get them in other ways:

- Ask the workers who receive, sign for, and store the chemical containers if they have the SDS and could get you a copy.
- Find the name and contact information for the company that produces the chemical from the label on the container and request they send you an SDS in your language.
- Ask staff in unions, worker centers, environmental organizations or universities for help in finding the SDS or chemical information.
- Research the chemical on the Internet. Search by the name and the CAS number. Look on websites of the companies that produce the chemicals as well as sites that provide SDS from all over. Compare the different SDS, they might have different information!

On page 464 you will find links to websites where you can find more information about chemicals, though many of the websites with SDS sheets are as hard to read as SDS themselves!

SAFETY DATA SHEET (SDS)
for ISOPROPYL ALCOHOL

1. Product name and company that makes it:

Isopropyl Alcohol   Poy Son Yu, Inc
Other names: 2-propanol,   P.O Box 555
   Isopropanol, IPA   Colinas Sucias, CA, USA
                       (900) 800-0008

Even secret trade mixes need to list the chemical ingredients (components) that are toxic.

2. Composition or information on ingredients

Isopropyl Alcohol   100%   CAS # 67-63-0
Component information:
This product is considered to be hazardous according to CFR 1910.1200.

Chemicals may have many different names but have only one CAS number. The CAS number is the best way to identify a chemical.

3. Hazard identification

This product is a clear, volatile, flammable liquid. Highly flammable.
Acute effects: Irritation of the skin and/or upper respiratory tract. Drowsiness, headache.
Chronic effects: Slightly hazardous in case of skin contact (sensitizer).Carcinogenic
        effects: A4 (Nor classifiable for human or animal.) by ACGIH, 3
        (Not classifiable for human) by IARC.
Inhalation: Mild irritation of eyes, nose, and throat.
Ingestion: Drowsiness, headache.
Dermal Contact: Dry, cracking skin.

This is a summary of the chemical's health and fire dangers. More information will be in Sections 4, 5, and 11. If health effects are not mentioned, it does not mean the chemical is safe.

4. First aid measures

Eyes: Flush with water, for at least 15 minutes. Obtain medical attention.
Skin: Wash with soap and water. Take off contaminated clothing and shoes. Obtain
    medical attention.
Inhalation: Remove victim to fresh air. Give oxygen if breathing is difficult.
        Seek medical attention.
Ingestion: Do not vomit. Seek medical attention.

For skin, see if flushing with water is enough or if another treatment is recommended. For ingestion, see if vomiting is recommended or not.

5. Fire fighting measures

Flammability of the product: **Flammable.**
Flash point: 12 °C (53.6 °F)
Auto ignition temperature: 339 °C (750 °F)
Fire Hazard: Highly flammable when there is a **spark** or **heat.**
      CAUTION: MAY BURN WITH NEAR INVISIBLE FLAME.
Explosion hazards: **Explosive** when there is a **spark** or **heat.**
Fire Fighting Instructions: Water may be ineffective. Do not use a solid water stream
    because it may spread the fire. Cool containers exposed to fire or heat with water.
SMALL FIRE: Use DRY chemical powder.
LARGE FIRE: Use alcohol-resistant foam, carbon dioxide, water spray, or fog.

See if the chemical is flammable and what can make it burn or explode. Following these instructions can prevent factory fires.

6. Accidental release measures

Small spill: Dilute with water and mop up. Put in disposal container.
Large spill: Keep away from heat and sparks. Use dry earth or sand to absorb it.

What to do and use to contain and clean-up a spill. See section 8 for information about protective and clean-up equipment.

See what material or chemicals will put out a fire. If you do not have the right supplies, you will not be able to stop the fire.

7. Handling and storage

Precautions: Keep away from heat. Keep away from oxidizing agents and acids.
      Ensure all equipment is electrically grounded.
Storage Recommendations: Keep in a cool area with good ventilation. Keep in a
      segregated area. Store in tightly closed containers.

Prevent factory fires and accidents with safe handling and storage of chemicals. Find more information in section 10.

See what ventilation is needed: local, general, enclosed.

These levels, measured in parts per million with expensive equipment, may not be safe enough to protect you, but they are a starting point to fight for at least those levels.

Chemicals and conditions to avoid to prevent dangerous reactions.

Look for information on what organs the chemical affects.

How and how long the chemical harms the environment.

How to dispose of the chemical safely.

Get an updated SDS.

See what kind of gloves, eye protection, clothing, and masks you should use every day and for accidents.

This section might help you identify a chemical by describing what it looks, tastes or smells like.

LD50 means Lethal Dose – how much will kill half of those exposed. The lower the number, the more dangerous it is.

Can it cause cancer?

Reproductive toxicity: affects ability to have healthy children. Teratogenic: causes birth defects. Fetoxicity: can damage baby in the womb. Development toxicity: can affect the baby's development.

8. Exposure controls and personal protection

Engineering Controls: Use explosion-proof ventilation equipment. Provide local and general exhaust ventilation to remove vapors and mists. Ground containers to prevent static sparks. Ensure eyewash stations and safety showers are proximal to work-stations.

Personal protective equipment:

Skin: Wear impervious gloves and flame retardant antistatic protective clothing.
Eye: Wear safety glasses with side-shields. For leak, spill, or other emergency, use chemical goggles and face-shield.
Respiratory: NIOSH approved respiratory protection when levels are high.

Personal protective equipment for cleaning large spills: Splash goggles. Full suit. Vapor respirator. Boots. Gloves.

Exposure limits: OSHA PEL= 400 ppm OSHA STEL = 500 ppm IDLH- 2,000 ppm TWA: 983 STEL: 1230 (mg/m3) [Australia] TWA: 200 STEL: 400 (ppm from ACGIH (TLV) [United States] [1999]

9. Physical and chemical properties

Physical state and appearance: Liquid.
Odor: Pleasant. Odor resembling that of a mixture of ethanol and acetone.
Taste: Bitter (slightly). Color. Colorless.
Boiling Point:
Odor Threshold: 22 ppm (Sittig, 1991) 700 ppm for unadapted panelists (Versch, 1983)

10. Stability and reactivity

Stability: The product is stable.
Conditions to avoids: Heat, ignition sources, incompatible materials
Incompatibilities: Reacts violently with hydrogen + palladium combination, nitroform, oleum, COCl2, aluminum triisopropoxide, oxidant

11. Toxicology information

LD50 – Route: Inhalation; Dose: 72.6 mg/L/4H
LD50 – Route: Oral; Dose: 4396 mg/kg
LD50 –Route: Dose: 12,800 mg/kg
Acute effects: Causes irritation of eyes, skin, and mucous membranes. Harmful by inhalation, if swallowed. Causes headaches and other effect to nervous system.
Chronic effects: Repeated exposure may cause damage to the bladder, kidneys and liver.
CARCINOGENIC EFFECTS: A4 (Not classifiable for human or animal) by ACGIH, 3 (not classifiable for human) by IARC.
REPRODUCTIVE TOXICTY: May cause adverse reproductive/teratogenic effects (fertility, fetoxicity, developmental abnormalities based on animal studies. Detected in maternal milk in human.)
DEVELOPMENT TOXICITY: Classified Reproductive system/toxic/female.

12. Ecological information

Ecotoxicity: Ecotoxicity in water (LC50): 100000 mg/l 96 hours [Fathead Minnow]. 64000 mg/l 96 hours [Fathead Minnow].

13. Disposal consideration

Dispose of as special waste in compliance with local and national regulations. Consider fuels blending as an alternative to incineration.

14. Transportation information

Information about what labels should be included while transporting.

15. Regulatory Information

Date of revision. January 13, 2014. Any other important information.

The right to know about chemicals

The **ILO Chemicals Convention (No. 170)** supports the protection of workers and the environment from harmful chemicals. It says employers must provide:

Information: The factory owner must provide information and the chemical data sheets for all the chemicals used in the factory to anybody that requests them. Workers have the right to request that information from the boss.

Protection: The factory owner is responsible for the safety of workers in the factory and must monitor chemical levels to make sure they are within the law. The owner should also provide workers with safety clothing and equipment at no charge and replace any that is no longer safe.

Safe disposal: The factory owner is responsible for safely disposing of all dangerous chemicals and containers.

Training: Factory workers must be trained in how to handle and dispose of chemicals and what to do in emergencies.

First aid and emergency care: Any factory that uses chemicals needs to have emergency showers and rinses in the areas where the chemicals are used. All workers and supervisors should know what to do in case of emergency.

If you fear you or others are at immediate and serious risk to your safety or health, you have the right to leave the area. You should inform your supervisor. This convention protects workers who do this from being punished.

The **ILO Occupational Cancer Convention (No. 139)** states governments must:

- Replace cancer-causing chemicals with non-carcinogenic chemicals.
- Prevent workers from being exposed to chemicals known to cause cancer.
- Inform workers of the dangers of cancer-causing chemicals and how to protect against them.

The roles of the UN, ILO, and other international organizations that promote workers' rights are explained in Appendix A.

Community resources

Labor unions, women's groups, and environmental organizations may be able to help you get information. If you know the name of a chemical, you can find information in libraries and on the Internet. But even if you do not know the name, you can sometimes find out the name with other information, such as use, color, smell, and so forth. Any information can be helpful.

We demand to know what chemicals are being used in the factory

In the early 1980s, a group of workers, environmental activists, and community members in New Jersey, USA got together to demand that the government pass the "Right to Know" law. This law would give workers the right to know what chemicals were used in their workplaces.

Workers and their unions had long demanded that employers tell them exactly what chemicals they worked with. But employers fought back, with the law on their side. Even after workers got rashes or had trouble breathing, employers didn't have to tell workers what was in the mixes. They said, "If we tell workers or health inspectors, our 'trade secrets' will be known and we won't be able to compete." They would rather let workers die than disclose those chemicals.

Although workers were at the front line of chemical exposures, they were not the only ones getting sick from chemicals they knew nothing about. Pollution of air and water, burial of toxic waste in the community, and accidental toxic releases and fires were exposing people in New Jersey to all kinds of chemicals. And they were getting angry, too!

Connecting workers inside the factory with people outside was a very successful strategy. It brought together activists from different sectors: mothers, politicians, environmentalists, and union members, all under one single banner: We have the Right to Know!

Environmental crises pushed even more people to support and organize for a new law. In 1983, the Right to Know bill was passed.

We didn't think we could do much to change anything in the workplace. It was like, you take a job and you know there are some really toxic chemicals, but you have no power to change that. Take it or leave it. It never occurred to us that people outside the factory could cause a dramatic change in policy inside the workplace.

The Right to Know law was a big advance, but it has not protected workers and the community enough from chemical exposures. While industry attacks the law, people continue to organize for public disclosure and safe handling of chemicals used at work, for safe disposal of chemicals, and for policies to stop accidents from happening and training to handle them when they do.

Protect our families and communities

Using safer chemicals is the best way to protect workers and their families. But if dangerous chemicals are used in your factory, you do not have to bring them home. Protect your family by changing clothes and washing your skin and hair before going home. If you work around chemicals and dusts, the factory should provide you with a place to wash yourself and your clothes.

What should be available in your factory:

- a clean place to store clothes and change clothes after your shift
- a place to shower with soap and warm water
- a service that safely cleans your work clothes and protective equipment every day

If you use a chemical to clean stains from your clothes, follow the same precautions for using chemicals at work. Take off the stained clothes, wear gloves, work in a well-ventilated area or outdoors, use a very small amount of the chemical, and wash the clothes well with soap and water before you wear them again.

At home, wash work clothes separately to prevent getting chemicals on other family clothes.

Handling chemical waste

Many factories dump chemical containers and other waste directly into sewers, water sources, and local garbage dumps. This is very dangerous for the community and sometimes for the region that uses the water downstream from the factory. For more information about the dangers of pollution from factories and ways to organize for safer waste disposal, see chapter 33: Pollution from factories.

If you handle chemical waste, use protective clothing and a respirator to prevent breathing in chemical dust or vapors, or getting chemicals on your skin and clothes.

Empty chemical containers are dangerous. Empty chemical containers should not be reused, taken home, dumped in open areas, or piled outside.

Washing empty chemical containers does not make them safe to use. A container that looks clean can still have enough chemical in it to cause harm. Chemical containers should never be used to hold food, drinks, or water.

Clean containers for community water

In our community, at least one person in every family works in a nearby export factory. There is plenty of water in all the factories, but we do not have running water or electricity in our homes. We have to carry water from a common tap and store it at home in big barrels.

A lot of people in the community used to have skin rashes and stomach problems. Some of us thought these problems were caused by something in the water. In our mothers' group, we decided to survey families to learn more about health in the community. We found out that everyone used water from the same source, but we used different kinds of barrels to store the water.

We asked more questions and learned that most of the families with the same health problems stored their water in empty barrels taken from a pile outside a factory. We did not know what the barrels had contained, because the labels were written in a language we cannot read. We asked some workers in that factory to find out what was in the barrels before they were thrown out. They told us that the barrels had contained dangerous chemicals.

The mothers' group decided to find safer water containers for all the families. We went to a local food factory and asked the boss to give us empty barrels that had contained cooking oil. He was glad we could use his empty barrels, and he makes sure they are washed clean for us. We are now delivering clean barrels with lids to each home, and people do not have to use old chemical barrels anymore.

Reduce and remove toxic chemicals

The best way to prevent harm from a toxic chemical is to stop using it and replace it with something safe. But if you cannot immediately remove a toxic chemical from your workplace, you can try to use less of it (as well as protect yourself from it). Workers may be able to convince their bosses that using less and fewer chemicals is better for everyone, is less wasteful, more efficient, and less costly. For example:

- Steam and detergent may work as well as chemical cleaners or solvents.

- Cleaner, more efficient processes and techniques can reduce the need to use chemicals for cleaning and degreasing.

- Low solvent/high pigment paints and low solvent coatings can coat the same number of parts with less solvent. These coatings also dry faster.

- A brush, roller, syringe, sponge, ladle, or other tool can help a worker to apply the smallest amount of chemical to the smallest area. When the worker uses less chemical, there is less waste and less mess to clean up.

We used to use solvents. Now we use soap and water in this ultrasonic degreasing machine.

- Cleaning up excess chemical right away protects other workers from exposure. For example, wiping excess oil from machined parts keeps it from spreading to other surfaces that will later have to be cleaned.

- Spot cleaning uses less cleaner or solvent than cleaning the whole piece.

Find a safer chemical

Your factory should use the mildest, safest chemical products needed to get the job done. For example:

- Use non-chlorinated hydrocarbon solvents instead of chlorinated solvents like methylene chloride or TCE (trichloroethylene).

- Use water-based cleaners, glues, paints, dyes, and coatings instead of products that contain a solvent.

- Use weaker-strength acid and alkaline baths and washes. They often work just as well as stronger ones. Use small plastic or metal pellets instead of sand as a blasting material to eliminate silica dust.

- Use vehicles with electric motors indoors instead of those that produce toxic fumes because they burn diesel, gasoline, or compressed gas.

We now use a safer chemical

Our factory in Mexico makes plastic drinking straws shaped to spell people's names. They are kind of a silly product, but there was nothing silly about what they did to our health.

We all had the same health problems. We suspected these problems were caused by the chemical we used to fuse the straws together. The containers we used did not have labels, so we asked the storeroom workers for a label from one of the large containers.

I talked to my neighbor Miriam, who always knows what to do. She brought us and the label to the office of the Comité Fronterizo de Obreras (CFO), an organization that works with workers in our area. The CFO had a whole box of chemical information sheets. We found the sheet for methylene chloride. It was very hard to understand. The CFO organizer explained what all the scientific terms meant and we learned methylene chloride does more than just give us sore throats and headaches. It can harm the liver and cause cancer!

When the boss refused to do anything about it, we took the information about methylene chloride to the local office of the national environmental protection agency, PROFEPA. We asked them to inspect the factory.

We had to pressure them several times. The inspectors finally came, but they told the boss ahead of time. Just before the inspection, the boss replaced the methylene chloride with another chemical.

The boss claimed he didn't want to pollute the air outside, but he did not care if we breathed dangerous chemicals all day inside the factory!

PROFEPA never required the boss to install the local exhaust fans. But after the inspection, the boss kept buying the less dangerous solvent, even though it was more expensive.

Ban the most dangerous chemicals

Some chemicals are too dangerous to use in factories or anywhere else. Thanks to years of protest by workers, OSH professionals, doctors, and health advocates, many countries prohibit the use of:

- lead and other toxic metals in pigments, dye, paint, and other coatings
- rosin or colophony flux for soldering
- solvents such as glycol ethers, methylene chloride, benzene, and carbon tetrachloride
- diesel and gasoline burned in engines used indoors, such as in forklifts
- sand for sand blasting

Manufacturers have developed safer products and processes that do not depend on these most dangerous chemicals. And workers, environmentalists, and responsible businesses are lobbying to ban:

- lead, chromium hexavalent, and cadmium in electronics, including solder
- chlorinated and fluorinated (halogenated) hydrocarbon solvents
- plastic made from vinyl chloride (PVC)
- brominated flame retardants

Banning very harmful chemicals not only protects production workers, it also protects recycling workers and consumers, and keeps pollution out of our air and water.

Companies help each other use safer chemicals

NGOs and businesses formed BizNGO to promote responsibility about the chemicals used in products. They developed these steps:

1. Know what chemicals are used to make your products. If you require your suppliers to report what chemicals are used in their factories, you can know what chemicals are in yours.

2. Stop using the most toxic chemicals first.

3. Test and substitute for other problem chemicals.

4. Tell workers, customers, and consumers what is in your products and what your company is doing to reduce the use of toxic chemicals.

Companies making shoes, electronics, and other products have found these steps useful. BizNGO provides conscientious people working in industry a way to support changes to benefit families, friends, and neighbors—because we all share the same planet.

Machine injuries

Sharp, hot, or moving machine parts and materials are always dangerous. Many factory workers have been burned or lost fingers, hands, arms, legs, or eyes because they were not properly protected from the danger areas of a machine. Machine injuries can cause permanent disabilities and sometimes death. Broken machines can also harm workers by leaking dangerous chemicals, hot steam, or liquids that can make floors slippery or burn workers.

Most machine injuries can be prevented by installing and using proper machine guards, by training workers to use machines safely, and by keeping machines in good condition. Too many workers are injured because bosses disconnect guards and other safety features to speed up production, push people to work faster, and do not maintain or repair machines.

To prevent machine injuries:

- Give workers plenty of time and training to learn how to operate, adjust, and maintain their machines.
- Design machines and job tasks so a worker never has to put any part of her body near the dangerous parts of a machine.
- Provide workers with the necessary protective equipment that fits them well.
- Give workers the power to shut down a dangerous machine before it causes an injury.

Working safely with machines

Each worker should be trained to safely use every machine she operates. Because operating a machine often includes tasks such as maintenance, cleaning, and making adjustments to the machine, be sure you are trained to do this safely as well.

An experienced worker can train new workers to use machines safely.

Clearing jams and debris

If you must clear a jam or remove debris from inside a machine, be very careful. Use methods that prevent injuries. For example, use tools and avoid putting your hands or body in a dangerous area. If you do not have the right tool, or if you cannot clear the machine with the tool you have, be sure to disconnect and lock out the machine before you get near a dangerous area. If you are not trained to lock out and tag out the machine, do not try to clear the jam or debris yourself. Get help from a worker who is trained to safely repair the machine.

Use a tool, not your hands, to clear a machine.

Experienced workers know machine dangers better than anyone else. They can show the boss and other workers the dangerous areas of a machine that need guards or other protections.

Protect workers from machine injuries

Machine guards prevent a worker's body or clothing from getting caught or cut by moving parts, from getting burned by hot surfaces or materials, and from being injured by materials or parts that can break off or fly out of a machine.

Guard the dangerous areas of a machine:

- **where the work happens.** Guard where the machine does the work, such as the cutting edge of a saw or knife, the molds of an injection molding machine, or the needle of a sewing machine. If you have to put your hands inside the machine's working area, it should also have a mechanism to prevent it from operating while your hand is there, such as an automatic shutoff (see pages 193-199).

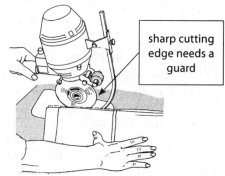

sharp cutting edge needs a guard

- **where the power is transferred.** Belts, chains, flywheels, pulleys, connecting rods, cams, spindles, gears, cranks, and any other parts that transfer power from one part of the machine to another need to be guarded. Workers' hair, clothes, or body can get caught and be crushed by these moving parts.

  The danger areas to be guarded are the nip points or pinch points where 2 moving parts meet. For example, the point where a drive belt meets a pulley, where 2 gears mesh, or where 2 rollers come together.

  You can help prevent injuries by not wearing loose clothes, scarves, veils, or jewelry such as rings, bracelets, long chains, necklaces, or earrings that can get caught in the moving parts of a machine. Keep long hair covered or gathered so it does not get caught in the machine.

nip points that can catch clothes or body need a guard

- **where debris is thrown into the air** from grinding and cutting equipment, including powered saws, grinding wheels, sanding belts, and riveters.
- **where parts can break or shatter.** Sewing machine needles or a grinding wheel can break and cause eye injuries and deep, even deadly wounds.
- **where machines and materials get hot.** Parts and materials that can burn a worker's skin or clothes, such as steam presses, curing ovens, injection molding machines, and

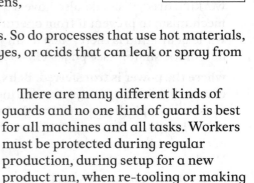

grinding wheel needs a guard

soldering equipment need guards. So do processes that use hot materials, such as molten plastic, metals, dyes, or acids that can leak or spray from equipment.

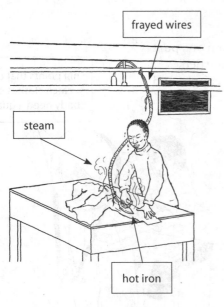

frayed wires

steam

hot iron

How would you change this workstation to protect the worker from injury?

There are many different kinds of guards and no one kind of guard is best for all machines and all tasks. Workers must be protected during regular production, during setup for a new product run, when re-tooling or making adjustments to machines during use, and when clearing parts that get jammed.

All machine guards should be inspected and tested regularly to be sure they are in place and working.

Fixed guards

A fixed guard prevents a worker's body from getting near dangerous areas of a machine, or from being hit by broken parts flying out of a machine.

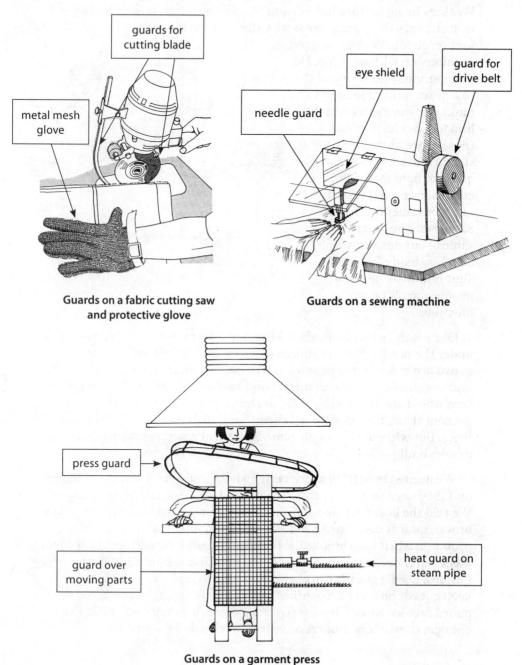

Guards on a fabric cutting saw and protective glove

Guards on a sewing machine

Guards on a garment press

Getting the boss to replace needle guards

My name is Cecilia. I work in a large garment factory in Mexico. Workers in my factory have organized for many years, and we have won changes that make our work safer and the workplace better for everybody. We have a good relationship with our boss. He understands that many of the things we have requested to make our work safer benefit him too. But he also sees that we are united and strong and that we are going to fight for better conditions even if they are not "convenient" for him. Sometimes he agrees to some of our demands right away instead of resisting. That is how we got new needle guards on our machines.

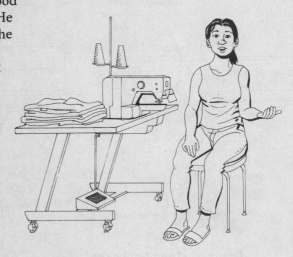

Our machines had guards to keep our fingers from getting caught under the needle. But the guards often broke. At first, when a needle guard broke, we just kept sewing. We have to meet a production quota and stopping can make us miss it and lose our bonus for that day. The boss would see us working without the guards and think, "they can work without them, they don't need them," and then he would not replace them. But without the needle guards, several workers injured their fingers badly.

We needed to act! We work very fast with powerful sewing machines and they need to have guards. The injured workers led the campaign. We told the boss that we would stage a sit-in if he did not replace all the broken guards and make a plan to ensure that guards were replaced promptly when they break. The boss knew a sit-in would cost him a lot of money and he did not want to pay the health costs for injured workers. Besides, needle guards are cheap and easy to replace. So he agreed to keep guards on all the machines and extras in stock. Now when a needle guard breaks, we can have it fixed the same day. Since we made this change, no workers' fingers have been seriously injured by a needle.

Adjustable guards

Some guards can be adjusted for different uses and materials. They protect workers only if they are adjusted properly and used. But because they can be adjusted, they are easy to remove. Don't let your boss remove or disable these guards to speed up the work and meet unsafe production goals. Take the time to make the adjustments and save your fingers — and your life!

clear guard over blade

saw blade

Saw for cutting wood with adjustable guard

Interlocking guards

An interlocking guard turns off power to the machine when it is not in place. A worker can remove the guard to safely adjust or clear a machine, and then replace the guard to safely restart it. Removing an interlocking guard does not make the machine safe to repair — you still need to lock it out and tag it out first (see pages 201 to 202).

Movable barriers

Some machines have a gate that opens to feed new material into the machine only when the machine is turned off. That way, the gate will not close, and the machine will not turn on, if a worker's hand or arm is in the way.

gate will not open if machine is on.

Metal press with movable gate

Automatic shutoff devices

Machines with doors or gates that open and close often have safety controls that cut off power to the machine when the door is open. Automatic shutoff devices must be regularly maintained and tested to be sure they always work.

Two-hand controls

Machines with 2-hand controls will start only when you push 2 buttons at the same time. These controls are separated so you must use both hands to push them.

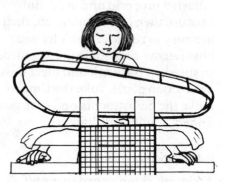

While excellent for the worker who uses the controls, this does not prevent other workers near the machine from getting caught by moving parts.

The worker must use both hands to close the press.

Light curtains and presence-sensing mats

A light curtain is made of many rows of light that sense when a worker gets too close to a machine. When you cross the light curtain, the machine automatically shuts off.

A presence-sensing mat shuts off a machine as soon as someone steps on the mat.

Light curtains and presence-sensing mats must be far enough from the machine so you cannot reach the danger zone before the machine stops moving.

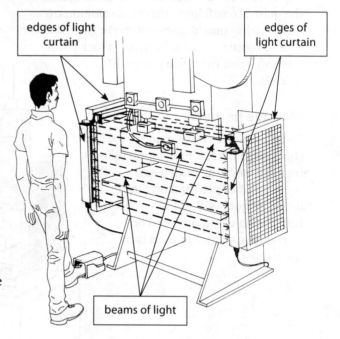

edges of light curtain

edges of light curtain

beams of light

Machine with light curtains

Covered foot pedals

Many machines start when someone presses a foot pedal. If a person presses the pedal by mistake or if something falls on the pedal, the machine can start while a worker's hands are inside. A protective cover over a foot pedal can help stop this from happening.

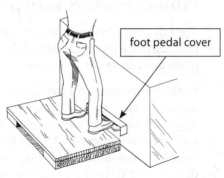

foot pedal cover

Restraints and pullbacks

A restraint is a strap tied to a worker's wrist or arm that keeps her hands away from the dangerous areas of a machine all the time. A pullback allows a worker's hands to enter a dangerous area to feed and remove material while the machine is stopped. When the machine starts, the straps pull her hands away from the dangerous area.

Restraints and pullbacks must be adjusted each time a different worker operates the machine.

Some countries ban restraints and pullbacks because they are unsafe in emergencies, making it difficult for the worker to leave her machine quickly. They are also humiliating.

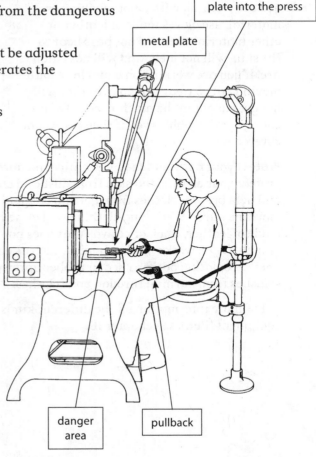

tool feeds metal plate into the press

metal plate

danger area

pullback

Protect workers with personal protective equipment

The boss must provide workers with equipment and clothing that can help protect them from machine injuries. These are not a replacement for having good guards on the machines.

Protect your face and eyes. Safety glasses and face shields protect you from flying debris, broken parts, and splashes of chemicals or hot materials. If you are working with hot materials, wear face shields made from material that will not melt, burn, or shatter from heat. When you remove the face shield or goggles, tip your head forward and close your eyes to prevent hot particles or debris from falling into your eyes. Hats, hair ties, and hair nets keep your hair from getting caught in moving machine parts.

Protect your hands. Use gloves. Wire mesh gloves are used to protect workers from being cut by blades. Leather or fabric gloves and sleeves protect your skin from sharp edges. If you are working with a hot machine or material, use gloves made of leather or other material that will not pass heat to the skin, will not melt, and will not catch fire. If you are working on a machine with moving parts, wear tight gloves that will not get caught in the machinery. Always change gloves right away if they get wet or covered with chemicals.

Use tools to handle hot materials.

Protect your body and feet. Coveralls and aprons protect your clothes and skin from dust and chemicals, and help prevent clothes from getting caught in moving machine parts. Wear long clothing and closed shoes made of leather, wool, or canvas that does not burn easily or melt. If you work with hot liquids, such as chemical or electroplating baths, a heavy rubber apron and rubber boots will keep splashes from burning through your clothes.

For more information on the different kinds of personal protective equipment (PPE), see chapter 18.

Lock out and tag out machines for safe repair

Workers who clear jams or repair machines need additional protection, because they must work inside the dangerous areas of a machine. To prevent a machine from starting or moving during repairs, workers need the time, training, and tools to:

- **Lock out** the machine so it cannot start or move. This means not only disconnecting the electricity from a machine but also disconnecting any belt or drive shaft from another machine that might drive the machine being repaired.

- **Block out** the machine so water, chemicals, or other materials that flow into it are completely blocked or shut off during maintenance and repair. Also, energy stored in springs, in electronic parts such as capacitors, and as water or air pressure in pistons, hoses, and pipes must all be released or blocked.

- **Tag out** the machine so other workers know the machine, power cord, and belts were disconnected on purpose and they should leave them alone.

Employers are responsible for making lock out and tag out required, easy, and routine.

Guidelines for lock out

Every factory should have a lock out program to prevent repair and maintenance workers from being killed or injured by a machine. A good lock out program will follow these guidelines:

- A worker never repairs or maintains a machine until all the energy sources to the machine are disconnected, blocked, and locked. This will prevent the machine from starting up unexpectedly.

- A repair worker attaches a tag to his locks that says why the machine is locked out, says who is responsible for the lock out, and shows other workers and supervisors not to reconnect and start the machine.

- The repair worker has the only key to his locks and is the only one who can unlock the machine, remove the blocks and tags, and reconnect the power.

- If more than one worker is repairing the machine, each must attach his or her own lock and tag and remove them when done.

- All workers are trained on why lock out procedures are used and why respecting these rules is important.

Lock out instructions for each machine

Some factories have many kinds of machines and several types of the same machine. To make each machine safe for repair, you need to know exactly how to disconnect it and block it. Putting individual lock out and block out instructions with pictures on each machine helps workers be sure they are doing it the right way for each machine.

Reinstall guards and other safety devices

Machine technicians and maintenance workers sometimes remove guards and disconnect safety devices while they work on a machine. Always reinstall the guards and reconnect safety devices before unblocking a machine and reconnecting the power.

Now that I know the machine is locked out, I don't have to worry about the supervisor on the next shift turning it on.

Always lock out, block out, and tag out a machine before beginning repairs.

First aid for machine injuries

First Aid

Most machine injuries are very serious and should be treated by a health worker right away. If no health worker can come quickly, transport the injured worker to the nearest clinic or hospital. Have him lie down on the way. In the meantime:

Watch for shock: A person who is bleeding heavily from any type of injury can go into shock and die. Bleeding inside the body — although you cannot see it — can also cause shock.

> **Signs of shock:** weak, rapid heartbeat; pale, cold, damp skin; weakness, confusion, and fainting.

> **To prevent or treat shock:** have the person lie down on his side with his feet a little higher than his head. Stop any bleeding. If he vomits, clear his mouth immediately. Cover him with a blanket. If he is awake, give him sips of water.

Protect your hands from blood: Wear rubber or plastic gloves, or plastic bags, on your hands. Blood can carry germs, including hepatitis and HIV. Clean gloves keep dirt, germs, and chemicals out of the wound. But the most important thing is to stop the bleeding and help the injured worker as quickly as possible.

First call a health care worker. Stop the bleeding while you wait.

Here are procedures for certain types of injuries:

Big or deep cuts, or part of the body cut off: Have the person lie down. Raise the injured part of the body. Press a clean, thick cloth directly on the wound with your gloved hand. Keep pressing until the bleeding stops. This may take 15 minutes or more. Never use dirt, kerosene, lime, or coffee to stop bleeding.

Deep wound in the stomach: Have the person lie down. Cover the wound with a clean cloth. Do not give food or drink, even water.

Part of body crushed: Have the person lie down. Watch for shock.

(continued)

First Aid

(continued)

Objects stabbed into the body: If part of a machine or another object stabs deeply into a worker's body, leave the object in his body while you wait for a health worker or transport him to a clinic. If the object is connected to something large or heavy, try to separate it but do not move the object or push it farther into his body. If he is bleeding, press a clean, thick cloth on the area. Keep pressing until bleeding stops.

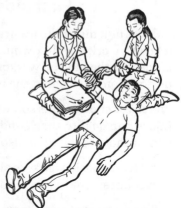

Direct pressure will stop bleeding of nearly all wounds. But be patient — it can take a long time.

Eye injury: Have the person lie down and cover the wound with a clean cloth. If you think there is something in the eye such as a piece of fabric, thread, plastic, or metal, rinse the eye with water for 15 minutes. If something is stabbed into the eye, do not take it out. Leave it in the eye until he gets to a clinic or hospital.

Head injury: Have the injured person lie down with his chest and head raised halfway to a sitting position. Support his head and chest with a cloth, blankets, pillows or clothing. Cover the wound with a clean cloth.

Cuts and scrapes: Wash the wound with lots of water. Dirt in the wound can cause an infection. Cover the cut with a clean cloth or bandage and change it each day. If the skin around a wound is red, swollen, and tender, or it does not heal, see a health worker.

Burns: Place the burned body part under running water for at least 15 minutes. Treatment for burns from hot machines or materials is mostly the same as for burns caused by fire (see First aid for burns, page 217).

Cleaning up after an injury: Once the injured person is cared for, make sure everyone in the area washes off any blood on their skin or hair with soap and water. Remove bloody clothes and put them in a plastic bag until they can be washed. Clean up blood in the work area using rubber gloves and a germ-killing cleaner, such as water with chlorine bleach. Put bloody rags and bandages in a plastic bag, tie it closed, and put it in the trash.

Tell the health worker if your skin or eyes were exposed to the injured person's blood. You may need a hepatitis vaccine or post-exposure prophaylaxis (PEP) for HIV (see chapter 30).

Electricity

Electricity powers the lights and machines that make factory production possible. But if wires are not properly connected and maintained, electricity can injure and kill people. Unsafe electrical equipment, uncovered wiring, overloaded circuits, and unsafe use of extension cords can cause fires, burns, and dangerous shocks. Workers can also trip and fall over cords lying on the floor. When poor maintenance damages machinery, the machines can give you dangerous, even deadly shocks. Also, sparks from exposed wires can start fires.

Protect workers from electrical dangers

- **Correctly wire and ground electric machines** and the outlets into which they are plugged. Grounding is a way of connecting machines and electrical wiring so they do not shock people. If the metal parts of a machine cause tingling or give shocks when touched, the machine is not grounded and can be very dangerous. A 3-point outlet on the electrical system does not mean the electrical system and outlet are grounded. Ask your employer to test every outlet and machine to be sure they are grounded.

- **Inspect electrical cords, wiring, and electrical equipment regularly.** If coverings are cut or frayed, repair or replace cords or wires. If equipment is damaged or rusty, it should be repaired or replaced.
- **Clean machine vents to keep them free from dust.** If air does not cool the wires inside, they can overheat, melt their coverings, and cause shocks and fires.

Dangers of wiring

Covering the wires inside the electrical system of a building or inside equipment protects the equipment and the workers. Keeping the wires and equipment dry also prevents shocks because water on or near the wires can carry electricity to anything the water touches.

Dangers from overloaded circuits

Electrical wiring can safely operate only a certain number of machines or lights. If too many machines are using one circuit, the wiring can become very hot and cause a fire. When a circuit box, machine, or wiring feels or smells hot, it is overloaded, and is a fire waiting to happen.

- Demand that the boss upgrade the electrical system to make it safe.
- Limit the use of multiple outlet power strips, often used to connect many electric tools or cords to a single outlet. They can easily overload the outlet and cause a fire.
- Do not connect one power strip to another.

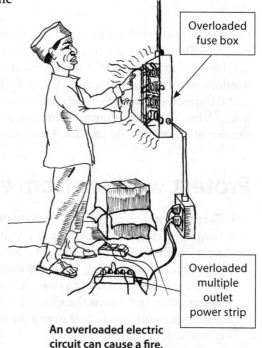

Overloaded fuse box

Overloaded multiple outlet power strip

An overloaded electric circuit can cause a fire.

A small fire sparks prevention

Liang grew up in a small farming village in China. When he was fifteen, he went to the city and got a job in a garment factory. He worked long hours every day, trying to save money.

Liang became a cutter in the factory. As his power knife moved, its electrical cord would rub against the table edge. This wore through the covering on the cord, and he was shocked many times. The manager said it was his fault for touching the wires. One day, while he cut cloth for shirts, the cloth touched the exposed wires and caught on fire. A worker near the wall grabbed the fire extinguisher and ran to Liang's table. They put out the fire before it spread to the piles of cloth nearby.

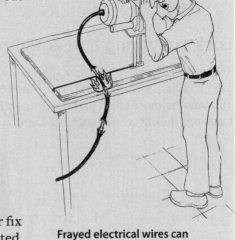

The manager yelled at Liang for letting the cloth catch on fire and for using so much of the fire extinguisher. But everyone knew that Liang had stopped the fire from spreading to the rest of the factory. The cutting room workers demanded the manager fix uncovered wires like the one that started the fire. Before the fire, the boss had said it was too expensive to repair Liang's

Frayed electrical wires can cause shocks and start a fire.

cutting knife and that he should just be more careful. But now he hired an electrician to fix all the wires and cords.

Encouraged by this success, Liang and his co-workers met to discuss other problems, like locked exit doors. They used the fire to make their factory safer. Liang hoped they could win more changes before any other accidents happened.

Dangers from extension cords

Extension cords are not sturdy enough to be used in place of permanent wiring. It is dangerous to run extension cords through walls, doors, or ceilings. When they are connected for a long time, extension cords can get hot and cause fires. Workers can also trip over extension cords, or a tangle of cords connected to a power strip, injuring themselves and damaging the cords.

- Extension cords are easily damaged. Inspect them often and repair or replace them if they are damaged.
- Fasten loose cords to the wall or floor with tape, or cover them with thick rubber mats.

Lock out wiring and equipment for repair

To prevent shocks and other injuries, workers should always tag out and lock out electrical systems and equipment before doing maintenance and repairs. This means more than just disconnecting the electricity from a machine. See Lock out machines for safe repair, on pages 201 to 202.

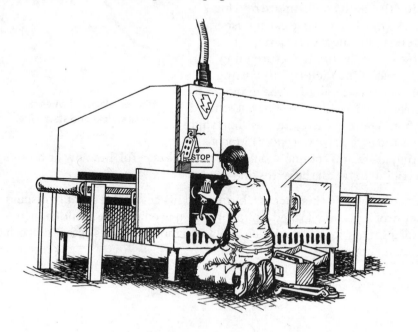

Maintenance and repair workers need time and training to prevent electrical injuries.

First aid for electric shock

A small electric shock may cause only a mild burn to the skin. But a big shock can cause deep burns and stop your heartbeat and breathing.

If a person is being shocked: Do not touch the person. The electricity can pass through his body and shock anyone who touches him. First, unplug or turn off the machine or tool causing the shock. If you cannot turn off the power, use dry clothing, rope, or a piece of wood, such as a broom handle, as a tool to separate the victim from the power source. Do not use anything wet or made of metal. If the person is lying in water, use the wood or cloth to drag him out, and do not step in the water yourself!

After a person has been shocked: Keep the person lying down. Carefully examine the victim for burns on the skin. Sometimes burns from electric shock do not look serious on the skin but are much worse inside the body. Cover burns loosely with a clean, dry cloth.

If he is unconscious, lay him on his side and cover him with a blanket.

If he has stopped breathing or his heart has stopped beating, start rescue breathing and CPR (see *Where There Is No Doctor,* p. 80).

For more information on first aid for burns, see page 217.

What should be available in your factory

- blankets to cover the person or to prop their legs up.
- clean cloth to protect burns or injuries caused by electrical shock.
- a well-marked breaker box, to shut off electricity if it is not possible to turn off the power to the machine or separate the person from it.
- training for all workers in rescue breathing and cardiopulmonary resuscitation (CPR).
- If a defibrillator is available in the factory, make sure someone knows how to use it correctly.

11 Fire

Fires are serious and often deadly for workers in factories and dormitories, and workers who do factory work at home. Of the many dangers workers face, fire is one that can easily be prevented, or contained and extinguished when it does happen. Most countries have laws that require employers to provide fire safety in their workplaces. Even though it is not very expensive for employers to comply, many factory owners continue to violate fire safety laws and put workers' lives at risk.

exposed wires and extension cords

smoking near burnable materials

burnable materials and chemicals

aisle and door blocked

locked exit

This factory has many problems that make fire a serious danger.

Prevent fires

International, national, and local laws and standards have been developed around preventing fires more than around any other workplace danger. Even if the authorities in your region will not enforce fire safety standards, there are things you, other workers, and factory managers can do to reduce the risk of fire in your workplace. Make a fire prevention plan and organize workers and managers to take responsibility to keep your factory safe.

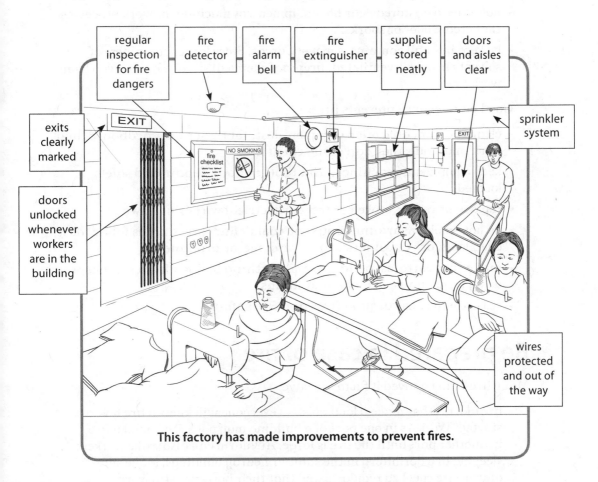

regular inspection for fire dangers

fire detector

fire alarm bell

fire extinguisher

supplies stored neatly

doors and aisles clear

sprinkler system

exits clearly marked

doors unlocked whenever workers are in the building

wires protected and out of the way

This factory has made improvements to prevent fires.

Store solvents safely

Because solvents catch fire more easily than almost anything else, store solvents safely to prevent fires. Solvents should:

- always be stored in tightly sealed, fireproof containers.
- never be stored in dormitories, stairways, or near fire exits.
- not be stored near other chemicals or materials that catch fire easily, such as fabric or foam insulation.
- not be used or stored near hot equipment, or machines or work processes that create heat or sparks.
- be kept in small containers in work areas. Store larger containers of solvents in a well-ventilated, fireproof chemical storage room away from work areas.

Good maintenance prevents fires:

- clean the work area often of paper, dust, fabric scraps, cardboard, and other materials that can easily catch fire.
- keep equipment, machines, and tools in good repair and safely located.
- replace or repair broken or frayed electrical wires right away.
- do not smoke near anything that could catch fire, such as fabric, dust, chemicals, or containers of gas, kerosene, or propane.
- make sure curtains, bedding, and clothing in dormitories are kept away from stoves, heaters, and lamps.
- raise awareness around fires and fire safety.

Be prepared in case of fire

Many lives can be saved if factories have:

- **fire alarms** that make a loud noise so everyone will know a fire has started. Workers in one part of a building may not see or smell a fire in another part until the fire is large. An alarm can also wake workers sleeping in a dormitory in the same or nearby buildings. Make sure alarms are checked regularly and that their batteries still work.
- **exits** that open outward and are always unlocked when people are in the building. Exits should be well-lit and marked with signs. In a multiple story building where stairs are the way out, stairways need to be well-lit, wide, and strong enough so workers can exit safely.

- **open passageways** that lead directly to exits. Passageways should be at least 1 meter wide, and even wider for large work areas. It is very important to keep passageways clear and free from boxes, racks, and containers.

Practicing how to get out of the factory or dormitory quickly and safely, and where to meet outside, helps keep people from panicking if there is a real fire. Organize a "fire drill" in your factory.

- **an overhead sprinkler system** with smoke detector, water pipes, and plenty of water. The sprinklers should start automatically when a fire starts.

- **fire extinguishers** should be provided by the factory. They should be well-marked and easy to reach, checked regularly, and replaced when expired. Fire extinguishers let you put out a small fire quickly and prevent it from spreading. Water buckets usually do not hold enough water to put out a fire and it is dangerous to put water on electrical, chemical, or grease fires.

Point the spray at the base of the fire.

A fire extinguisher can put out a small fire quickly.

Make sure all workers know how to use a fire extinguisher. When you use a fire extinguisher, make sure the fire is on one side of you and the exit on the other, so you will not be trapped if you cannot put the fire out. Use role plays to practice fighting a fire.

Fires need 3 things:

- a flame, spark, or something hot to start the fire
- fuel (materials) to burn
- oxygen to keep the fire burning

When you remove or block one of the things a fire needs, a fire cannot burn. It is important to know about and practice ways of stopping a fire, but also practice how you can get out of the factory quickly if a fire starts.

Factory fires: Preventable disasters

New York 1911

On March 25, 1911 about 500 immigrant women were working in the Triangle Shirtwaist factory in New York City, USA, when a fire started. They tried to escape, but the doors were locked. The fire escape was so weak, it collapsed. Other workers tried to escape the flames by jumping out windows 9 floors above the street. In just 25 minutes, 146 women workers died.

The Triangle fire made people realize how unsafe factories were, and workers' organizations in the USA pressured the government to pass and enforce fire safety laws.

Bangkok 1993

On May 10, 1993 a fire broke out in a storage area of the Kader toy factory in Bangkok, Thailand. The building's fire alarm did not sound and workers were told to keep working so they could finish an order. The fire spread quickly. Workers had been locked in to force them to work overtime, and there were no fire exits or fire extinguishers.

188 workers were killed and hundreds more injured. The survivors and the victims' families used their anger and sadness to fight for safety and helped form ANROEV, the Asian Network for the Rights of Occupational and Environmental Victims.

Dhaka 2012

On November 24, 2012 more than 100 people were killed when fire raged through the Tazreen factory in Dhaka, Bangladesh, which was making clothing behind locked doors for Walmart and other brands. Only a few months earlier, a Walmart representative had told the Bangladesh Garment Manufacturers and Exporters Association that it cost too much to put fire safety systems in garment factories.

Workers will continue to die in preventable factory fires until local factories and the big international brands that purchase from them place as much value on workers' lives as they do on low prices and high profits.

Who is to blame for factory fires?

*"The **sourcing departments of the brands** are to blame. They keep pushing everyone for lower prices. You have one department of the company supporting the campaign for fair wages, but then in the very next room the sourcing department is asking that workers work for 10% less wages."*

— Labor organizer

*"The **buyers for the brands** are to blame. They say we have to improve working conditions so they can tell their customers they are good companies. But when we ask to pay just a few cents — cents! — more per piece, which would go to workers' welfare, they refuse! They say the economy is bad, but we see that they are making a lot of money."*

— Ministry of Labor

*"The **Labor Ministry** is to blame. Nobody told me I had to install an emergency exit. I could have done it, but nobody ever suggested I do it. Why am I to blame for something nobody told me I had to do?"*

— Factory owner

*"The **owners** are to blame. The factories should be closed until they are safe. But the owners are very influential. They pay off the government."*

— Fire official

Prevent fires while working at home

A fire can spread quickly in a home where factory work is done. There is lots of material to burn and electrical connections may be poor and are often overloaded. If you do factory work at home:

- keep chemicals away from open flames and do not smoke inside.
- store solvents and other flammable materials in metal boxes or barrels and help neighbors do this too.
- keep windows and doors open for ventilation, and use fans.
- if a fire starts in a cooking pot, cover it with a lid to smother it.
- keep a bucket of sand or earth on hand to use to smother fires, especially fires caused by chemicals or electrical problems, and for wood or cloth fires when water pressure is too low to depend on a hose.
- ask your employer for a fire extinguisher. If he won't give you one, you can make a small one for home use (see page 216).
- make sure there is a clear exit path out of the house.

Prepare for fire. Plan with your neighbors what to do if a fire breaks out in your community.

- **Let people know there is a fire.** Bang on an iron pipe to sound the alarm and alert everyone to danger.
- **Plan how to fight the fire.** Organize people to work as a "bucket brigade," to bring pails of water, sand, or dirt.
- **Where to meet after.** Name a place, such as a park or large building, where people can agree to meet in case of an emergency, and later to make sure everyone is all right.

How to   Make a fire extinguisher at home

You will need:

- plastic bottle, half liter or more
- water
- vinegar (any kind)
- baking soda (sodium bicarbonate)

- small plastic bag, cut into a circle of about 3 inches or 15 cm in diameter
- a nail, screw, or pin
- tape

1. Fill ½ of the plastic bottle with water. Then fill most of the remaining space with vinegar, but be sure to leave about 2 inches of space at the top.

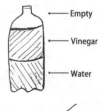

Empty
Vinegar
Water

2. Place the circle of plastic on top of the opening of the bottle. Use your finger to push the middle of the circle inside the mouth of the bottle. Put 2 to 4 spoonfuls of baking soda inside, using your finger to push the plastic farther into the bottle as it fills. Roll the ends of the plastic into a cone so the cap can be screwed on the bottle. Close the bottle as soon as the plastic packet of baking soda goes in.

Plastic →

Baking soda

3. Close the bottle tightly and store upright. The packet of baking soda will sit on top of the liquid. Tape the nail to the bottle.

Nail

Cap →

Prepare several of these in advance.

To use, shake the bottle hard and fast to mix the baking soda, vinegar, and water. When you start to see foam, use the nail to make a hole in the bottom of the bottle (feel for a thinner spot in the plastic) and point the spray at the fire. Continue shaking the bottle as you spray the fire.

Puncture the bottle to use

First Aid

First aid for burns

For any burn, take off clothing and jewelry near the burned skin and put the burned area under cool (not iced) water for at least 30 minutes.

Minor burns that do not form blisters: Put the burned area under cool water immediately. This will reduce pain and lessen the damage. Burns can hurt, so use a pain medicine if needed.

Burns from hot water or oil: Take off any clothing that has the hot oil or water on it. Immediately rinse the burn with cool water.

Burns that cause blisters: Put the burned area in cool water immediately. Do not break the blisters. If the blisters break, wash gently with mild soap and water, but do not use a disinfectant or iodine. Keep the burn clean and protect it from dirt, dust, and flies with antibiotic ointment or honey, and sterile gauze or bandages. If healing is slow or the skin stays red, swollen, or painful, see a health worker. You may need treatment for infection.

Burns from chemicals: See page 175 in chapter 8: Chemical dangers.

Go to a health center immediately for:

- **Large or deep burns:** Burns that cover a large area of the body or expose raw or charred flesh are always serious.
- **Burns that cover a joint, the face, or the genitals:** These can lead to disability.
- **Burns combined with other injuries.**
- **Burns on children:** It is harder for children to recover from burns than adults.

Note: Never put grease, fat, animal skin, coffee, herbs, or feces on a burn. They might cause an infection or prevent the skin from healing.

Breathing smoke

Breathing smoke can burn the lungs, which can be very serious. Go to a health care center immediately if there is difficulty breathing, a burning feeling in the lungs, a tight chest, or severe coughing.

When near a fire, cover your mouth and nose.

12 Dust

After so many improvements, why is there still dust in the factory?

Grinding, sanding, packing, sewing, handling, and cutting metal, plastic, fabric, leather, and other materials produces a lot of dust. Because it is so small, dust can easily go into your nose and mouth and onto your skin. And it can travel with you to your home in your clothing, hair, shoes, and skin.

Preventing dust from being produced is the best way of ensuring it does not pose any harm. Removing dust as it is produced is also good. Dust becomes a danger when it accumulates in the air and equipment.

Some signs that there is too much dust in the factory are:

- Workers wheeze or have difficulty breathing.
- Workers cough, sneeze, and blow their noses often.
- The mucus in workers' noses is the color of shop dust.
- Workers' hair, face, and clothes are full of dust.
- The floor, equipment, lights, windows, or walls are covered with dust.
- The air in the factory is hazy.

Yolanda's blue face

Yolanda worked in a jeans factory in Piedras Negras, Mexico. Every day, workers went home covered in blue jean dust. Their paper masks did little and the ceiling fan only moved dust around. Yolanda wondered, "If we're covered on the outside, what do we look like inside?"

At a union meeting, Yolanda agreed to work 1 day without wiping dust off her face to show how bad the problem was. By lunch, she was completely covered with blue fuzz. With other workers, Yolanda went to the manager. Yolanda's blue face embarrassed the manager.

The manager agreed to ask the boss to install exhaust vents. The boss was unhappy, but knew if the inspectors found out he would get in trouble. He agreed to add one vent a week. When he did not, the women had to pressure him again. But finally, all the machines had extractors.

Dangers from dust

The dust in factory air is mostly fine bits of the material workers use to make products. Factory dust can also include soot from burning fuels and from hot or burned materials. Dust often contains chemicals used in the manufacture of the materials.

The most common health problems caused by dust are breathing problems. Some dusts irritate your nose and lungs or cause allergies and asthma. Other dusts pass through your nose and can harm your lungs. Cotton dust, very common in garment factories, can cause a very dangerous lung disease called byssinosis (see pages 97 to 98).

Workers whose lungs are irritated by dust are much more likely to get sick from tuberculosis (see chapter 31).

When dust makes breathing difficult, it puts an added strain on the heart. Dusts also can irritate your eyes and cause skin rashes.

Dusts can explode!

I worked in the polishing workshop of the Foxconn factory. Our job was to polish the aluminum backs of iPads for Apple. The factory ran 24 hours a day and all of us worked overtime every day. We ended our shifts covered completely in aluminum dust: our hair, our hands, inside our shirts and shoes, everything was grey.

Early one morning there was a huge explosion in the polishing area. Everybody was screaming and running. We didn't know what happened, or what had exploded. Many people were injured, and 2 people died. The factory closed for a few days. They said it was so they could investigate. When it reopened, they told us one of the extractors was not taking out all the dust. But we knew the problem was not just one pipe — there was always too much dust! There had to be several extractors not working, not just one. The truth is they let all the dust accumulate until it exploded.

A few months later, the polishing area exploded at a different factory also making iPads. It was the same problem. After that, Apple said they had fixed the ventilation systems at all their suppliers and there would be no more explosions. We will see if that is true. We will see if more workers are killed in explosions, or if they will be saved only to have nightmares about explosions like I do.

Protect workers from dust

The best way to protect workers from breathing dust is to remove dust immediately from the source and to keep it out of the air.

A local extractor removes the dust as it is created.

Use ventilation

A good ventilation system pulls dusty air away from the worker and out of the factory, and brings in fresh, clean air. Workers breathe less dust, and less dust settles on equipment and other surfaces. To learn more about different types of ventilation, see chapter 17.

Clean up the dust

Cleaning on a regular schedule will prevent dust from collecting on floors and equipment. Cleaning should include hard-to-reach places, such as overhead lights, fan blades, and high windows. Regular cleaning removes dust that has settled so it does not get stirred up again.

Use a wet rag or mop, or a vacuum cleaner designed for dust. If you have only brooms for cleaning, first sprinkle water on the floor, and then sweep gently.

Cleaning should not add to the dust problem by stirring up the dust again.

Do not use compressed air or blowers to clear dust or debris from work surfaces, machines, floors, or clothing. It just blows the dust back into the air to be breathed in by workers. Compressed air can also send debris flying into workers' faces and eyes, causing injuries.

Wear face masks for dust

A dust mask can prevent some dust from going into your nose and mouth. But it will not protect you from chemical fumes or vapors in the air. See chapter 18: Personal protective equipment, for more information on dust masks and respirators.

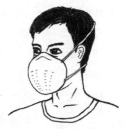

Make sure the mask fits you well around your face.

13 Noise

Loud noise can cause many hearing problems. The damage to your hearing depends on how loud the noise is, and how often and for how long you are exposed to it. The way you hear noise may also change. Sounds may become unpleasant or seem louder than they really are.

To protect workers' hearing, employers should:

- test workers' hearing before they start work and regularly during their employment.
- test the noise level at work.
- make changes to reduce noise.
- provide earplugs and earmuffs if the noise level at work can harm workers.

Health problems caused by noise

Temporary hearing loss: You may lose some of your hearing while you are in a noisy place. After you leave, you may not hear well, and you may hear a constant ringing or buzzing noise (called tinnitus). If you stay away from loud noises, these problems should go away. But if you spend a lot of time in very loud places, the problems can get worse or become permanent.

Permanent hearing loss: If you work repeatedly around a lot of loud noise, temporary hearing problems may become permanent. Also, as we grow older, our hearing naturally grows weaker. You may lose your hearing more quickly if you work where there is loud noise every day. An extremely loud noise, such as an explosion, can damage your hearing right away and cause permanent hearing loss.

Other health problems: Loud noise can cause other health problems, including feeling tired, headaches, stress, miscarriage, high blood pressure, heart disease, muscle tension, stomach problems, and dizziness.

Tania's hearing has been damaged by working in a noisy factory.
Now it is hard for her to hear her daughter's soft voice or to follow a
conversation when there is noise in the background.

Organizing against hearing loss

Batam Island in Indonesia is a big export processing zone. Small and large factories make electronics for some of the world's biggest brand names, from Panasonic to Philips.

But Batam is very different from most places where electronics are made because electronics workers in Batam can join unions. Electronics companies often say that unions hurt production, but Batam shows that when workers are paid decent wages and treated with respect and dignity, everybody wins. And these unions are not "yellow" unions, forced upon workers by the government or the employer. They are real, democratic, worker-led unions.

At first, Batam's unions focused on improving wages and benefits. But soon they realized that health, especially how work affected health, was very important. The FSPMI (Federation of Indonesian Metal Workers, part of the global union federation IndustriALL) is one of the unions in Batam with a strong occupational safety and health division.

The FSPMI started a campaign against noise when workers testing loudspeakers began to complain about hearing problems. The union asked labor and occupational health organizations to teach them how to measure and how to prevent hearing loss. They got an audiometer and learned to use it to measure hearing loss. They began testing workers during union meetings. Many workers showed signs of hearing loss, not just those who tested speakers. A few workers could hear very little.

Wages are important but our health is much more important. If we are sick, we cannot work and cannot earn our salaries.

With the audiometry test results in hand, FSPMI went to the factory owners. FSPMI said that the company needed to reduce noise and give workers earmuffs and earplugs. They also demanded that the companies start measuring hearing during the yearly checkups and before workers even started work. And for the workers who already had hearing loss, FSPMI demanded that the companies take responsibility and compensate injured workers.

The companies gave in and began a noise reduction and hearing loss prevention program. This happened due to workers' activism but also because hearing loss is one of the only occupational diseases recognized by the Indonesian government.

How to tell if noise is too loud

Signs that the noise in your workplace is too loud and can damage your hearing include:

- you have to raise your voice to talk to someone 2 arm lengths away.
- you have problems hearing at the end of the workday, but you can hear better after resting away from the factory.
- your ears ring at the end of the workday.

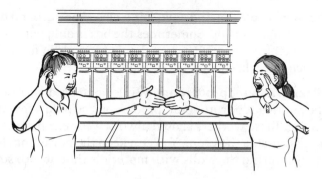

If you cannot hear someone talking 2 arm lengths away, the noise is too loud.

You may not notice you are losing your hearing right away. Most people notice it when they begin to have difficulty hearing conversations clearly. By the time you notice hearing loss, the damage is usually permanent.

The boss should not wait for workers to begin going deaf before reducing noise in the factory. You can prove that the noise at work is dangerous by measuring the sound level and by testing workers' hearing over time.

Measure noise

A sound level meter measures sound on a scale from very soft to very loud. The measure on the scale is called a "decibel." Working in areas with sound levels louder than 90 decibels will harm your hearing. Ask your union or your boss to have someone measure noise in your workplace.

Test workers' hearing

An audiogram is a test that measures the ability to hear sounds that are low or high and soft or loud. If a worker's hearing is tested every 6 months, the audiogram can show if her hearing is the same or getting worse. If you use earplugs all the time at work, the tests can show if the earplugs give enough protection. Hearing loss from noise is different than hearing loss from aging, and the test can prove if your hearing problem was caused by work.

How to make factories quieter

Even if each piece of equipment in a factory is not too loud, when all the equipment and people work at the same time, the noise can be very loud. There are several ways to make a factory less noisy.

Use quieter machines. Ask the boss to replace older machines with newer ones built to be quieter than older models. Sometimes older machines can be rebuilt to make them less noisy.

Put noisy machines in a box. Putting a wall or a closed box around a machine can keep some of the noise inside. Sometimes the box is only put around the noisiest part of a machine. The wall or box should be made of material that absorbs sound, such as cork, rubber, felt or foam.

Put noisy machines in a soundproof room. While not a great solution, loud machines can be put in a separate soundproof room, so only a few workers are exposed to the noise. These workers should always wear ear protection and take regular breaks outside the room. You can keep the noise from building up inside the room by covering the walls with materials that absorb sound.

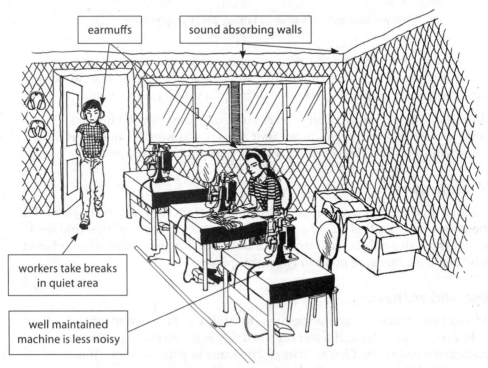

earmuffs

sound absorbing walls

workers take breaks in quiet area

well maintained machine is less noisy

Workers inside a soundproof room need protection from noise.

Absorb sound:

- **on walls, ceilings and floors:** To make the whole factory quieter, cover the ceiling, floor, walls, and work-area dividers with panels or curtains of sound-absorbing material at least 5 centimeters (2 inches) thick.
- **on metal work surfaces and tools:** Rubber-lined carts, bins, tumblers, and rubber-coated work surfaces and tools reduce the sound of metal parts and tools hitting metal surfaces.
- **on air-powered tools:** A muffler on the release valve of an air-powered (pneumatic) tool can reduce noise of air coming out of the tool.

Keep equipment in good repair. A machine may be noisy because it needs oil, adjustment, or a part is wearing out. Regular maintenance and repair can keep machines from getting noisier.

Good maintenance keeps machines quiet.

Turn down the music . Some factory bosses play very loud music to keep workers from talking and to keep them working fast. This often makes noise in a workplace even louder and more dangerous for workers' hearing.

I have a headache every day from the noise in here!

When the music stops, it is such a relief!

Share the burden. If you cannot make the machines less noisy, workers can rotate jobs so that no one stays in the noisy area all the time. This is not a good, long-term solution to noise problems.

Protect your ears

Workers in noisy areas should wear earmuffs or earplugs. These can help protect workers' hearing while you organize to make the machines and the work area quieter.

Earmuffs give good protection if they gently but firmly touch your head and completely cover your ears. Earmuffs should be cleaned often and replaced when they no longer fit snugly and keep out noise.

Disposable foam earplugs can protect your hearing if they are the right size and properly inserted in your ears. They should be small enough to fit comfortably and expand to fill the hole of the ear. See Protect your hearing, on pages 271 to 272.

Hearing protection can prevent you from hearing alarms or approaching vehicles. It is always better to get rid of the noise rather than to block it out.

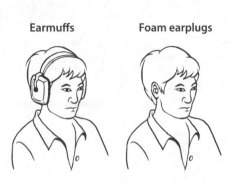

Earmuffs   Foam earplugs

Light 14

window shades
to adjust light →

→ overhead light

sunlight

task light

Many export factory workers must keep their eyes focused on small parts and details. To see well, your work area should be lit evenly and brightly. Too little, too much, or uneven light can harm your eyes and cause other health problems.

A factory without enough light in corridors and storage areas makes it harder for workers to see dangers and prevent accidents, harder to escape a fire, and can make people feel unsafe, especially women.

Make work safer

- Evaluate and install lighting in the work areas, storage room, bathrooms, stairs and hallways, around the entrance of the factory, and at emergency exits.
- Clean lights regularly and change broken or burned-out bulbs.
- Add general lighting if needed.
- Add task lights for work that is very detailed, such as sewing or cutting.
- Monitor glare and reflection and pay attention to any changes in the light that might be causing you problems.

How to know if light is a problem

The best way to find out if the lighting in your factory is harmful is to ask other workers:

- Do you need to bend over to see your work better because you do not have enough light?
- Do you have to work in uncomfortable positions to see well or to get away from a bright light?
- Do you often get headaches while working?
- Are your eyes tired, aching, dry, or irritated at the end of your shift?

Also pay attention to the lights in the factory:

- Are there lights or does light only come from outside?
- How far apart are the lights? Are they close together or too far apart?
- Are the lights bright enough?
- Does the light cause bothersome reflections or glare on windows, or shiny floors, tables, or equipment?
- Are the lights in good repair?

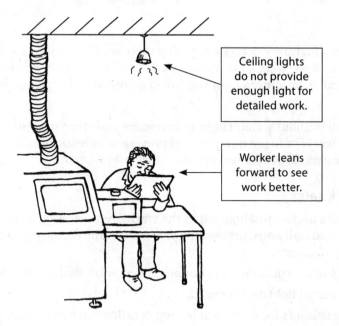

Ceiling lights do not provide enough light for detailed work.

Worker leans forward to see work better.

How to see better and protect your eyes

Add or change lights. Your factory may need more or different kinds of lights for different tasks. Lights that hang high above the work area should provide a soft, even light. Many workers need a task light they can adjust so there are no shadows on their machine or their work. Older workers may need brighter lights.

Use energy-saving light bulbs. Energy-saving bulbs give as much light as other bulbs. They may cost a little more, but use less energy, so they save money in the long term. Compact fluorescent bulbs contain mercury, so if one breaks, clean it up carefully (see page 71) and dispose of it as toxic waste.

Make sure the light is not pointed at your eyes or reflected from your work surface.

Repair lights. Get the boss to repair flickering and broken lights, and broken window shades.

Clean lights regularly. Lights are often ignored, because they are too high up to clean. But cleaning them regularly can help improve visibility in the workplace. Clean dust from your task light every day.

Move for better light. If you cannot change or move the light, you may be able to turn or move your workstation, or change the way you sit or stand as you work. Some workers wear a hat with a brim to keep bright overhead light out of their eyes.

Cover surfaces that reflect light. To reduce glare, cover shiny surfaces with fabric, paint, or other coating that does not reflect light.

Cover windows with cloth, curtains, or blinds when the sun is too bright or casts shadows.

Wear eye glasses. If your eyes are tired or irritated, or if you have trouble seeing your work, get an eye examination to find out if eye glasses can help. Each person's eyes are different, and lenses for eye glasses are made to fit one person's eyes. Eyesight changes over time. If you wear glasses and still have trouble seeing, you may need different lenses. Doing the eye exercises on page 75 can help keep your eye muscles healthy.

15 Heat and cold

If the temperature inside the factory feels hot or cold, it can make your work uncomfortable. But if the temperature gets too high or too low, it can also cause serious health problems. Many factories around the world are too hot.

Your employer is responsible for:

- monitoring the temperature in the factory.
- making sure the air in the factory does not get too hot. For many people, it is uncomfortable and sometimes unhealthy to do physical labor in temperatures over 27°C (80°F). Check your country's laws to see if they set maximum and minimum temperatures for work.
- installing, monitoring, and improving ventilation (see chapter 17: Ventilation).

Your boss should also provide fresh, safe water to drink and breaks to go to the bathroom (see chapter 29: Access to safe water and toilets).

Dangers from heat

When you get very hot, your body sweats to cool off. And when you sweat, your body loses liquid. To stay healthy, you need to drink enough water to replace the liquid you lose as you sweat. If you do not drink enough water or if you do not get regular breaks from the heat, you can get sick very quickly.

The first signs of too much heat are heavy sweating and a quicker heartbeat. If you begin to have a headache, feel weak or tired, have painful muscle cramps, or feel dizzy, confused, or nauseous, you are in danger of heat illness. As soon as you feel these warning signs, you need to begin cooling off or you could collapse.

If you keep working past these signs, you might suffer heatstroke. One sign of heatstroke is that you no longer sweat even if you are very hot. Heatstroke happens because your body gets too hot and it overheats your brain. It can cause permanent damage to the brain and other organs, and can kill you.

If it is very humid inside the factory you might not notice you are sweating or how hot your body is getting.

Other health problems caused by too much heat include:

- skin rashes, boils, or infected hairs
- heart problems
- vaginal infections, especially in women who sit most of the time, and whose clothing stays damp with sweat
- pregnancy complications and miscarriage
- fewer sperm in men, making it difficult to conceive a child

Too much heat is especially dangerous for people with heart problems, high blood pressure, diabetes, and for people taking certain tranquilizers or medicine for nausea.

When people start a new job in a hot factory, it affects them more. Watch co-workers for signs of too much heat, especially in the first few weeks.

Stand together, fan together

I work in a shoe factory in Reynosa, Mexico. After work, I meet with a group of women to talk about problems at work. When the air conditioning in the factory broke a few months ago, the manager said fixing it was too expensive. We started to talk about how sick we felt working in the heat. The manager did not listen to us when we asked him to fix the air conditioner, so our group decided to find another way to convince him. One morning we walked into the factory, but we did not start working. We sat down and started fanning ourselves. Other workers saw what we were doing and joined us. Soon all the workers in the factory had stopped working and started fanning. By the end of the day, the manager had fixed the air conditioning!

Cool the air inside the factory

The best way to protect workers from too much heat is to keep the air inside the factory cool and give workers time to rest, to cool off, and to drink enough safe, clean water. For more information about ventilation, see chapter 17.

Rest and drink water

- **Drink cool water** whenever you feel thirsty. It is better to drink a little bit of water several times a day than drink a lot at one time. Do not drink coffee or cola because they will dehydrate you. Policies that let workers take enough bathroom breaks help them stay hydrated and healthy.

- **Take rest breaks.** If your job makes you very hot, you should rest in a cool area for 5 minutes to recover. Take as many cooling breaks as you need.

- **Wear loose-fitting, lightweight clothes** that let air through to your skin to help dry your sweat and cool your body. Loose underclothes made of cotton, instead of nylon, can also help prevent skin rashes and infections.

- **Limit time working in very hot areas by rotating jobs,** so that nobody works in high heat all day or every day.

First aid for heat illness

Pay attention to people who act confused or delusional when working in a hot environment. The person is probably suffering from heat illness, though these are also signs of chemical exposure. Take action immediately. Do not wait until a person faints to give first aid.

1. Have the person lie down in a cool place.

2. Raise his feet and rub his legs.

3. Give him cool water to drink. You can give juice or other drinks if that is all you have, but do not give coffee or cola.

4. Place cold cloths on his face and neck.

5. If the person faints, get medical help right away.

Muscle cramps caused by heat

When you sweat too much and do not drink enough to replace it, your muscles will cramp. Drink fluids regularly during the day to prevent muscle cramps.

If you have a cramp in your legs, arms, or belly:

1. Every hour until the cramps are gone, slowly drink 1 liter of cool water or rehydration drink, juice, or any drink except for coffee or cola.

2. Sit or lie down in a cool place.

3. Gently massage the painful areas.

To make rehydration drink:

1. Pour 1 liter of clean **water** in a container.

2. Add ½ teaspoon of **salt**.

3. Add 8 flat teaspoons of **sugar** and mix well.

Give as much as the person will take. For more on rehydration drink, see *Where There is No Doctor*, page 152.

Dangers from cold

When you are cold, your muscles become tense and less flexible, which makes strain and injury more likely. When your body gets cold, you can also get sick with other illnesses more easily.

Working when you are too cold can also be dangerous because you think and move more slowly. Your hands and feet cannot hold or feel things as well as usual, so you may not notice if you are injured. Using tools that vibrate can make problems from cold even worse.

Warm up the workplace

The best way to protect workers from getting sick or injured due to cold is to keep the factory at a comfortable temperature.

- **Insulate the roof and walls** to keep warm air inside the building and cold air outside.

- **Heat the work area** with a hot air system, or with hot water or steam radiators that spread the heat evenly.

- **Insulate the floor** – especially floors made of concrete, stone, or metal – with rubber, wood, or carpeting. Anti-fatigue mats can be good insulation from cold floors.

A hat, jacket, and floor mat can help you stay warmer.

- **Insulate chairs** with cushions, cloth, or foam rubber, especially if the chairs are made of metal. Wood, plastic, and fabric chairs are warmer to sit on than metal chairs.

- **Heat vehicles** with electric seat warmers or hot air blowing on the feet.

- **Close doors and windows** to keep out cold air when the climate is cold. If open windows and doors help ventilate the factory, see chapter 17: Ventilation for information about other ways to keep chemicals and dust out of the air.

- **Open doors, windows, and window shades** to let sunshine and warm air in when the climate is warm.

Stay warm in a cold workplace

- **Wear warm clothing,** including socks, closed shoes, and boots with thick soles. Several thin layers are warmer than 1 layer of heavy clothes.
- **Cover your head and ears** with a hat or scarf. Just covering your head helps keep your whole body warm.
- **Wear gloves,** especially if you touch cold things while working.
- **Avoid getting wet,** it makes the body lose heat more quickly. If you do get wet, change into warm, dry clothes.
- **Move around to keep the blood flowing** to all parts of your body.
- **Take regular breaks** from the cold to warm up.
- **Drink hot liquids and eat often** to warm your body from the inside.

First Aid

First aid for being too cold

A worker who is too cold shivers uncontrollably, cannot think clearly, feels tired or sleepy, speaks slowly and unclearly, and stumbles when walking. This is a very dangerous condition. Often the person does not realize what is happening.

1. Get her to a dry, warm place.
2. Cover her whole body with blankets or any fabric or material you can find. If possible cover her head.
3. Give her warm, sweet drinks and sweet food, fruit, or candy. If you do not have anything sweet, give starchy foods like rice, bread, plantain, or potatoes.
4. If she stops shivering but still has signs of being too cold, or if she loses consciousness, get medical help.

Frostbite

When one part of a person's body is exposed to very cold temperatures, it can become numb and change color as it loses all feeling. This is called frostbite. Frostbite happens mostly on fingers, toes, and nose.

1. Wrap the numb part with a dry cloth and warm it against another part of the person's own body or someone else's.
2. Cover her to warm her whole body.
3. Get medical attention quickly if the body part becomes hard.

16 Falling workers, falling objects, and vehicle injuries

When a worker is hit by a tool or container falling from above, people usually say, "He had an accident." When a worker falls from a high place or trips and falls on the floor, he may be blamed for being careless or clumsy. If a worker is run over by a lift truck, both the driver and the worker are told they should watch where they are going. But these "accidents" are not the worker's fault. A factory should be designed and equipped for safe storage, clean floors, and safe traffic. Workers should be given the tools and time to make the workplace safe.

Who is to blame when this worker falls?

Prevent falls from high places

Working above the floor on a stable platform is the best way to prevent a worker from falling, and to prevent tools or parts from falling into the work area below. A platform can be moveable or fixed in one place. The platform should be large enough for a worker to do his job with room for tools and materials.

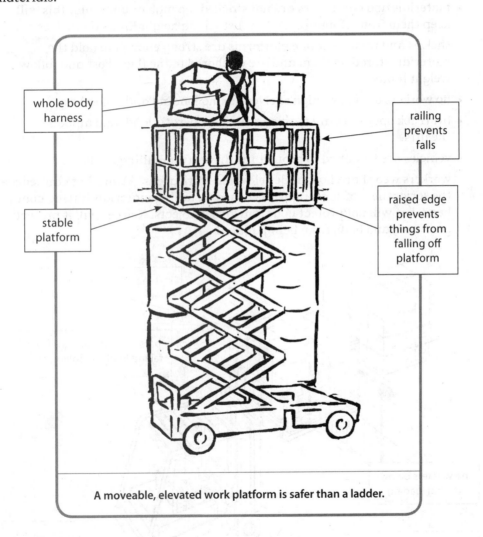

whole body harness

railing prevents falls

stable platform

raised edge prevents things from falling off platform

A moveable, elevated work platform is safer than a ladder.

Prevent injuries from falling objects

Workers can be severely injured or killed by tools or materials falling or dropped from above. To prevent things from falling onto workers, make sure:

- work areas and walkways are not directly below overhead rail systems, platforms, or stored materials.
- materials and containers are not stacked too high or unevenly. This will keep them from tipping over. Mark stacking height limits on shelves.
- shelves and raised storage platforms are strong enough to hold the materials stored on them and are anchored to the floor. Post and follow weight limits.
- no workers are below high shelves during loading and unloading.
- lift truck operators are trained to safely operate, load, and unload the lifts.
- vehicles are equipped to protect the driver from falling loads.
- workers wear hard hats under elevated work areas. A hard hat can reduce the seriousness of some injuries caused by falling materials hitting your head, but will not protect you from larger objects. Neither will it protect your neck and body from being injured.

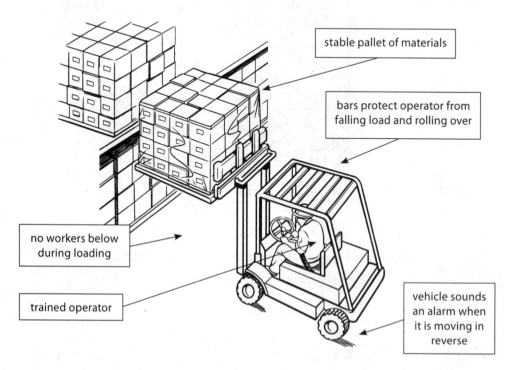

stable pallet of materials

bars protect operator from falling load and rolling over

no workers below during loading

trained operator

vehicle sounds an alarm when it is moving in reverse

Prevent slips, trips, and falls

Uneven floors, holes in the floor, changes in floor levels, wet floors, and wires and debris on the floor cause workers to slip, trip, and fall.

Many falls can be prevented by:

- repairing rough floors.
- keeping walkways clear.
- marking changes in floor level, such as stairs and ramps, with paint or different surfacing, so you can see them.
- cleaning up water, oil, and chemical spills immediately.
- cleaning up debris, dirt, and dust regularly.
- fastening loose cords to the wall or floor with tape.
- adding better and more light.
- wearing slip-resistant shoes.

good lighting so workers can see floor ahead

floor level change marked

clean, smooth floor

bins for debris

Trips, slips, and falls are common and can be prevented.

Prevent vehicle injuries

Some of the dangers from motor vehicles are the same in and outside factories. Injuries from motor vehicles on roads and in factory zones can be prevented by separating vehicle traffic from walkways and clearly marking each. Make sure workers are trained to operate vehicles safely, and that vehicles are regularly inspected and maintained.

When motors burn fuel indoors, workers breathe dangerous exhaust from the burned gasoline or diesel fuel. Propane-powered vehicles are safer, but electric vehicles burn no fuel so they are the safest.

To protect people from vehicles:

- Mark walkways and separate them from vehicle traffic lanes.
- Put a stop sign where vehicle traffic crosses a walkway, and post speed limits.
- Make walkways wide enough for the number of people using them.
- Leave vehicles space to move around work areas without colliding with machines, equipment, materials, other vehicles, or workers.
- Clear walkways of parked vehicles, stored supplies, and debris.
- Park vehicles where they do not block lanes or walkways.
- Store materials and place large machines so drivers and people walking can see ahead clearly.
- Train drivers to operate vehicles safely, including how to load and unload them.
- Maintain and repair vehicles regularly.

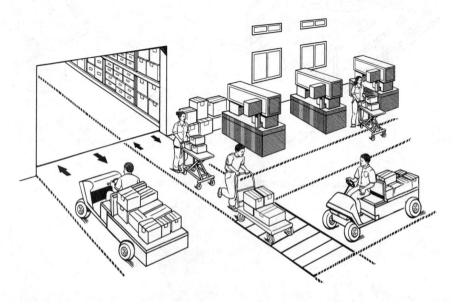

After a worker is killed, factory improves parking lot

Silvia used to work at Solectron in Mexico. Every day, she would catch a van to her factory. One morning as she was walking towards the gate after being dropped off, a van carrying other workers hit her and ran over her leg.

Her friends and the van driver tried to help. One ran to get the nurse from inside the factory. But the nurse just stood there, looking confused. She wanted to put Silvia in a wheelchair even though she could not move. Finally somebody brought a stretcher. They put Silvia in the van and drove very fast to the hospital.

After surgery, Silvia got a very bad infection. But nobody wanted to take responsibility for her injuries or medical care, neither the transport company who owned the vans nor Solectron. So the hospital refused to treat her. Without medicines, her infection got worse.

Her family contacted a lawyer from CEREAL, a labor organization in Mexico. They tried to get the transport company to make their insurance pay, but it was too late. Silvia died in a few days from a completely treatable infection.

After her death, CEREAL had a meeting with Solectron, the van company, and Silvia's family. Both companies agreed to pay the maximum compensation allowed by law for the death of a worker. This is how companies take responsibility, always too late.

But the question remained: Why did this happen? Many workers had complained about the vans and parking lot at Solectron. There was no system. Vans from different companies came and went, with no signals or safe crosswalks. Workers had to dodge the vans that competed to leave the lot first.

Solectron fought with the transport company over responsibility for Silvia's death, but they also began to change the parking lot at the factory. They installed lighting, which helped both drivers and people walking to see better and feel safer. They installed signals to direct traffic and placed speed bumps to slow the vans. Now there is also a safe walkway from the drop-off zone to the factory.

These changes came at a great cost for Silvia and other workers who had been injured trying to get to work. But change finally came.

17 Ventilation

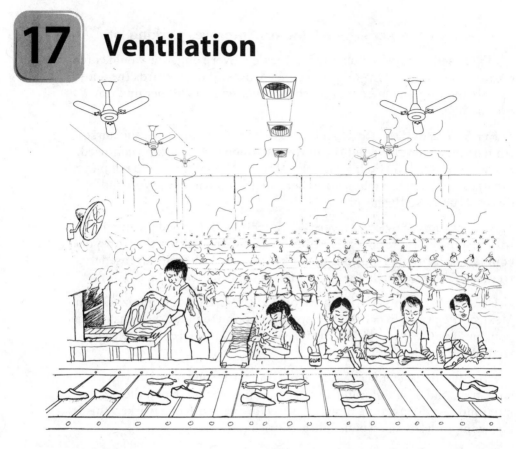

All buildings have ventilation—the way air moves in and out. But in many factories, bad ventilation harms workers' health by not moving air containing chemicals, dust, and heat out of the factory.

The factory owner is responsible for protecting you and the air you breathe by:

- making sure all workers have clean, fresh air in the factory.
- reducing the risk of exposure for workers and people in surrounding communities by using fewer chemicals and less of each one, and replacing harmful chemicals with less harmful ones.
- changing tools, machines, chemicals, and work processes so they produce less fumes and less dust. See pages 164 to 172.
- preventing the buildup of chemicals, dust, and heat and safely removing them from the factory.
- keeping the factory at a comfortable temperature (see chapter 15: Heat and cold) and giving workers enough breaks and clean water to drink (see page 414).

Bad ventilation makes you sick

When the ventilation systems in your factory are not working well, chemicals and dusts are likely to get into your body.

If chemicals and dust are in the air you breathe, you probably are exposed to them in other ways, too. Chemicals can be absorbed through the skin or get into your stomach if you touch food or drink, or smoke cigarettes after working with them. You might be exposed to chemicals and dust after you leave work, if the air coming out of the factory is polluted. For more information on how chemicals get in the body and how they can harm you, see chapter 8: Chemical dangers.

 Record any health problems in your health notebook . Ask other workers to do the same. Compare notes to find similarities and note special concerns.

Some chemicals and dust can harm the body right away, while others can take a long time to cause health problems. Watch for signs you are exposed to heat, chemicals, or dust in the air.

- **Headaches and tiredness:** Breathing chemicals often causes headaches or dizziness, but these are common problems and can be caused by many things. The same is true of being tired all the time.
- **Problems of the eyes, nose, and throat:** Red and irritated eyes, coughing, sneezing, a runny nose or nose bleeds, or mucus the color of the material you are working with can be signs you are breathing dust or chemicals. These signs may go away when you stop working, but they show one or more chemicals got inside your body and may still cause health problems.
- **Asthma or other chronic lung problems:** Breathing dust or chemicals may cause permanent damage to your lungs, or even cancer or death. Some damage can be managed with medicines. See pages 97 and 160, and Appendix B: Common chemicals and materials.
- **Heat exhaustion:** Workers can die from too much heat, especially if they have no time to rest or not enough clean water to drink. See chapter 15: Heat and cold.
- **Other health problems:** Breathing chemicals can cause many other health problems, such as damage to the kidneys and liver, and cancer. Babies and young children and the developing baby inside a woman's womb can be harmed more quickly by chemicals. See the chemicals that harm reproductive health on page 382 and Appendix B.

If you cannot breathe or suddenly feel sick, immediately leave the work area and go where you can breathe fresh air. See the First aid box on page 174.

General ventilation

General ventilation helps air move through the factory, reducing the concentration of chemicals in the air.

A good general ventilation system removes some of the dust, heat, and chemicals from the air and replaces it with safe, clean air to breathe. Good ventilation also keeps the temperature and humidity of the workplace at a healthy and comfortable level.

Good ventilation requires regular inspection and cleaning of all vents and filters to keep the system working well and prevent polluting the air outside the factory. This protects people in the community from being made ill from factory pollution.

Heating, Ventilation, and Air Conditioning (called HVAC) is a complex kind of general ventilation system used in electronics factories to better control air flow, temperature, and humidity (see page 249).

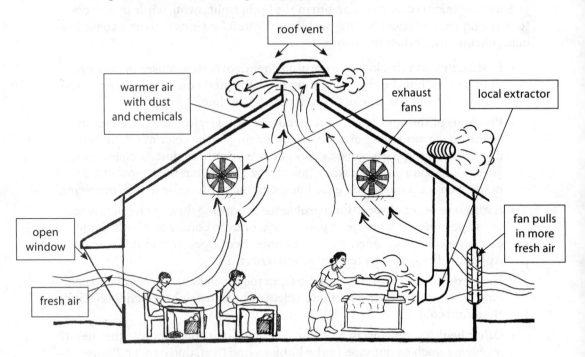

roof vent

warmer air with dust and chemicals

exhaust fans

local extractor

open window

fan pulls in more fresh air

fresh air

A ventilation system can improve air flow and health *inside* a factory. But if the air leaving the factory is not filtered, it hurts the health of the people *outside* the factory.

How general ventilation works

General ventilation should move fresh air into the workplace and move the dirty air coming from the work out.

Fresh air is important because it dilutes the amount of chemicals in the air you breathe so it causes less harm. Do the activity Follow the air! on page 253 to see how fresh air moves through your factory.

Windows and fans

Factory windows and doors bring in fresh air but this might not be enough to keep the air flowing and stop people from getting sick from chemicals in the air. Wall fans can move fresh air into the factory or dirty air out, but need to be checked and cleaned regularly to make sure they are working well.

Fans move air through the factory

Directional and ceiling fans help guide air through the factory and can help keep an individual worker cool. If the fans in your factory are not guiding clean air in and dirty air out, they are likely just moving dust and chemicals around in the factory.

If your factory is hot and fans blow hot air at you, drink lots of water and pay attention to health problems caused by heat.

Vents and exhaust fans move dirty air out

A roof vent lets the warm air out. This creates a draft that pulls fresh air in to replace it.

If they don't check it or clean it, they are not really providing good ventilation!

An exhaust fan will only pull air from the area close by and will not help general ventilation. The exhaust vents will not work well or may not work at all if there is not enough fresh air coming in from outside. An exhaust fan that is too weak will not pull out enough dirty air.

Air from local ventilation extractors should be filtered before it is released into the community or back into the factory, so it carries fewer chemicals that may make people sick. When local exhaust ventilation is not filtered, chemicals in the air being removed can cause health problems, especially for pregnant women and young children near the factory. See chapter 33: Pollution from factories.

Is air flow helping or harming you?

Martina works in a radio assembly factory in Mexico. She cleans plastic parts with a strong solvent in a small workshop. Her station used to be in front of an open window. When air came in through the window toward the exhaust fan behind her, she would breathe in chemical vapors as well as some fresh air. Martina got headaches and sniffled and coughed almost every day.

After a training about ventilation, Martina asked the boss to move her workstation across the room. Her boss agreed because she wasn't asking for anything new, like a local extractor. Now fresh air from the window comes from behind her and pushes the chemical vapors away from her. The exhaust fan is strong enough to pull all the vapors away from her and out of the building. Martina feels a lot better.

When the busy season came, more people were hired. Now Martina shares her workspace with Celeste. The boss put Celeste in front of the window, the spot where Martina had worked before. Even though the factory has a strong exhaust fan and a lot of fresh air, the way the air flows through the workshop is now unhealthy. Both Celeste and Martina are breathing chemicals that affect their health.

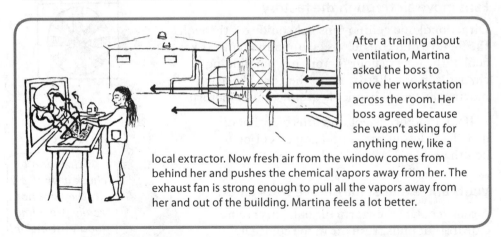

Special general ventilation

Heating, ventilation and air conditioning (HVAC) systems are used in work areas like "cleanrooms" that must be kept at the right humidity and temperature.

To work well, HVAC systems should:

- **balance air in and air out.** If the fans bringing air in are too strong, they overwhelm the vents extracting the air, and not enough dirty air will be removed. Dusts and chemicals will accumulate in the cleanroom.

- **clean and filter the air.** Dirty air, full of dusts and chemicals, is extracted, scrubbed, and filtered. Almost 70% of this air is sent back into the cleanroom after it is cleaned. If scrubbers and filters are not monitored and replaced, they might not remove all chemicals.

- **control the temperature and dampness.** Air conditioning keeps the work area cool and dry to lower the amount of fumes and vapors, and the flammability of the chemicals used in the cleanrooms. The temperature might be too cold. See chapter 15: Heat and cold.

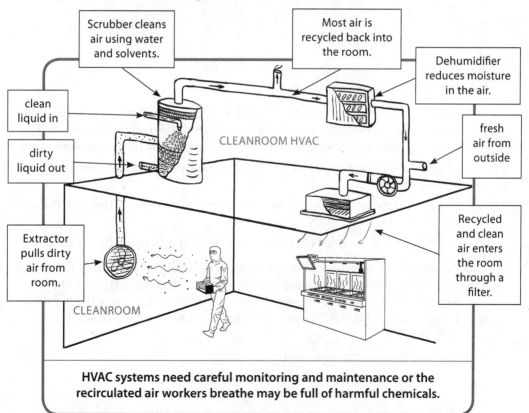

Scrubber cleans air using water and solvents.

Most air is recycled back into the room.

Dehumidifier reduces moisture in the air.

clean liquid in

dirty liquid out

CLEANROOM HVAC

fresh air from outside

Extractor pulls dirty air from room.

Recycled and clean air enters the room through a filter.

CLEANROOM

HVAC systems need careful monitoring and maintenance or the recirculated air workers breathe may be full of harmful chemicals.

Local ventilation

Local ventilation is placed close to the work being done to immediately remove most of the chemical vapors, dust, steam, and heat before they get into the air you breathe.

Local ventilation is sometimes called an extractor, an exhaust vent, or local exhaust ventilation. Local ventilation does not replace general ventilation. To protect workers, both systems need to be working.

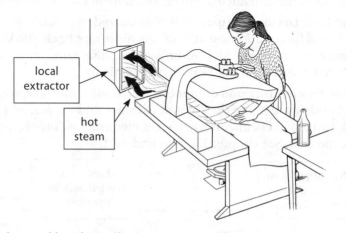

These jobs need local ventilation:

- grinding, sawing, and sanding, because they create large amounts of dust and debris. Workstations with a lot of dust should also be cleaned well with vacuums, wet towels, or sponges to prevent the dust from spreading.
- gluing, soldering, and spot cleaning, because the chemicals used for these release vapors.
- jobs that use mists or sprays, because these move quickly through the air and can be harmful to the lungs.
- jobs that use or produce chemicals or dust that can catch fire or explode.

Some work processes should be completely enclosed in a machine to prevent chemicals or dusts that are very dangerous to health from getting in the air. Maintenance workers must be especially careful about exposure to chemicals when they open and repair these machines. See Enclosed machines, on page 169.

Kinds of local ventilation

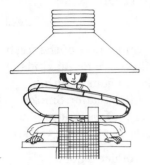

Extractor hoods are placed above or next to the work area. If hoods are close to the work, they will remove more of the hot and dirty air. If they are too far, some of the fumes might get in the air you breathe. Fans, or people walking by, opening doors or windows, can change the direction of the air. Do the activity Follow the air! on page 253.

Local extractor vents are placed very close to the work or on the tool itself. Vents should be downwind from the work you are doing, so they pull the air away from your face instead of towards it.

Dust and fumes are extracted through here.

Local exhaust booths protect workers by putting a protective barrier between the worker and the work, and then use ventilation to remove most of the dust or fumes from inside the booth. Workers need the right kind of gloves to protect their hands. See Gloves on pages 262 to 265.

All local ventilation systems need regular cleaning and maintenance. Regularly check and replace filters, fans, motors, belts, and gauges. When the filters or air ducts are blocked with dirt, more dust or chemicals stay in the air workers breathe. Filters should be cleaned or disposed of safely.

If the local ventilation is not working or not working well enough to extract all the dust and chemicals being produced at your workstation, you will breathe them in. Demand that the boss fix the ventilation. In the meantime, use masks and gloves to protect yourself from these dangers. See chapter 18: Personal protective equipment.

| How to | **Check your local ventilation** |

A smoke test is an easy way to see the direction, flow, and power of the fresh air coming into a work area and the dirty air leaving. There are many kinds of smoke testers. Some produce a lot of smoke that can harm your health. Some are as small as a match and produce less smoke, which is safer. Smoke tests can be done with smoke bottles, smoke pens, powder puffers, and smoke matches. (Where ductwork contains smoke detectors, this test will not work.)

If you do not have any of these, use other things that produce a good amount of smoke. Do not use fire around flammable or explosive chemicals, dusts, or processes. Another way to check how the air moves around you is to attach tissue to a stick that will not bend and move it close to the extractor.

1. Use several sticks of incense, cigarettes, cigars, or a bundle of leaves or paper that burns slowly and creates a lot of smoke, like a bundle of sage. If you are working with flammable or explosive chemicals or processes, do not use anything burning. Instead, fill a bottle that has a small nozzle with baby powder that will drift in the air like smoke.

2. Turn on the extractor closest to your workstation.

3. Stand or sit where you do your work.

4. Make smoke. Where does it go? How does it move? Does anything change when people walk by and block the ventilation?

5. If the smoke goes directly to the extractor and all of it goes inside, it is probably working well.

6. If it moves towards your face, towards other workstations, or in other directions, something is probably wrong. Maybe not enough air is coming in, maybe movement around you affects the direction of the smoke, or perhaps the extractor vent is not powerful enough. Have your co-workers do this activity, too.

7. If all the smoke does not go in the extractors, you and your co-workers can pressure your boss to find someone qualified to fix the problem.

Activity	Follow the air!

1. Draw a map of your factory's ventilation

If you work in a large factory or if you work inside cleanrooms, it might be useful to also make a map of your work area.

- **Where does air come in?** Draw every source of air, even if it is "when a door opens and closes." Do some sources of air bring in more or less air? Is it fresh air from the outside or air from other parts of the factory?

- **Where does the air go and how does it move inside the factory?** Air is hard to track. But try to draw where the air goes after it comes in. Show fans and which way they move air. By making a steady stream of smoke or powder and following it, described in Check your local ventilation on page 252, you can see how air moves in the factory.

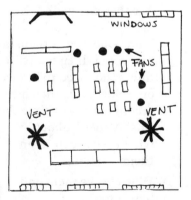

- **Where are the vents or extractors that remove the air?** In some factories, windows and doors might be the only way air goes out of the factory.

- **Where are the work areas where people are getting sick?** Areas where there are problems may not have good ventilation. See Bad ventilation makes you sick, on page 245.

(continued)

| Activity | **Follow the air!** *(continued)* |

2. Inspect the ventilation system in your factory

Ask maintenance workers for help. They can tell you about the ventilation system or take (or let you take) photos of it. Work with them to understand how poor ventilation harms their health too, and let them know you are not blaming them for any problems.

3. Find out how the ventilation system is maintained

Fans, extractors, and vents get dirty and can break. Cleaning, inspecting, and replacing blocked or broken fans, vents, and extractors should be included in a good ventilation plan.

- **Are they cleaned?** Ask maintenance workers if they know who cleans them and how often. They may also have filters that need to be cleaned or replaced. Do they have any record of the last time they did this? Also ask about what they use to clean them.

- **Who checks them and how often?**

- **How quickly are parts or units replaced if they are broken?**

Is there anything blocking the air coming in or going out of vents?

How dusty are the vents?

Can you see or smell dust or chemicals?

Is there anything outside the factory blocking air from coming in or going out?

Is the ventilation system on all the time, or just sometimes?

Are fans and extractors strong enough?

I told the boss that the vent was not working a year ago! He is only having me change it now because auditors are coming next week.

Let's set up a meeting with the safety committee and the boss.

The right to healthy air at work

The **ILO Working Environment (Air Pollution, Noise, and Vibration) Convention (No. 148)** says employers are responsible for:

- designing workplaces and installing systems to reduce air pollution.
- changing how work is done to reduce air pollution.
- providing and maintaining personal protective equipment, and ensuring it fits workers, if it is not possible to reduce all of the air pollution.
- providing a baseline medical examination for workers when they start work, as well as regular examinations free of cost to the worker.
- finding suitable alternative employment if the medical examination finds the job harmful to a worker's health.

The **Working Environment Convention** also says workers can:

- receive training and information about air pollution and protection from it.
- receive medical examinations.
- present proposals to improve ventilation without fear of retaliation.
- Inform government officials of processes, substances, machines, and equipment that cause air pollution and expect they will encourage the employer to repair, improve, or replace them.

The **ILO Protection of Workers' Health Recommendation (No. 97)** says that employers should ensure:

- workers have safe and sufficient air.
- air temperature and humidity is comfortable in the workplace.
- frequent testing of work areas where dangerous chemicals are used.

The roles of the UN, ILO, and other international organizations that promote workers' rights are explained in Appendix A.

Better ventilation improves everyone's health

Workers are not the only ones who are healthier when they can breathe air free of chemicals and dust. The well-being of their families, communities, and even factory management depends on them staying healthy.

Some changes to ventilation systems are very easy to make and maintain. Some cost more. You may also come up with other ideas to improve ventilation that might not require the boss to be involved.

Form a workers' ventilation committee

Invite your co-workers to build a team of workers that can focus on ventilation problems. Anybody can join the team, because every person in the factory will benefit from better ventilation.

Find out what ventilation issues there are in your factory through surveys, inspections, and mapping activities (see chapter 3: Organizing to improve worker health). Share any information you gather with all workers.

Seek support from people who know about ventilation, such as maintenance workers, ventilation installers, health organization staff, occupational safety and health professionals, and others.

Reach out to your co-workers, supervisors, and the boss.
Ventilation requires constant attention. Getting an extractor may be a great step forward, but it will not protect your health if it is not regularly checked and cleaned. Keep pushing for monitoring, testing, maintenance, cleaning, as well as worker involvement at every step.

The boss gave us masks and said ,"Now you are protected." He refused to make any changes to the ventilation until we complained to the company that buys from him.

Think of ways to improve ventilation while workers organize to win bigger changes. For example, moving workstations to improve air flow while demanding that the boss install extractors. When discussing what changes to make, make sure to include all workers.

Talk with people in unions, worker centers, and NGOs to learn about how others have campaigned for better ventilation (what worked or did not work), to get help reviewing information you have collected, and for advice on how to improve your workplace.

Reach out to government officials and learn about laws about ventilation in your country, and research the ways in which you can push to enforce them. If your current laws are weak or leave ventilation regulation to the companies, seek support from legal clinics and organizations about how to influence or change laws. See if you can find support in international conventions (see Appendix A: Laws and the struggle for decent, healthy work) or the "Codes of Conduct" for the brands being made in your factory.

Talk with community groups working against air pollution in your community. The polluted air extracted from the factory can affect the health of everybody inside and outside the factory. Join campaigns to reduce and prevent air pollution and increase pressure on government officials to monitor and regulate ventilation in the factory.

A cooler factory

The Ocean Sky factory in El Salvador got very hot in the middle of the day. Managers always locked the doors and windows to "reduce theft" so no fresh air could come in. Workers would sweat right onto the clothing they were making for Puma and Adidas.

But ventilation was not the only problem at Ocean Sky. When workers got together to talk about the things that needed to change, they realized there were so many! With the help of several unions, the women's group Mujeres Transformando, and international organizations, they decided to fight for all of them at once.

To create a good ventilation proposal, workers collected research and involved experts and the government. When the government official came to test the temperature at the factory, he was shocked at how high it was. The official told the boss he needed to open windows and doors, install extractor fans, and place cooling fans around the factory. By now the united effort with unions and NGOs had gotten the attention of the brands that gave the factory contracts. They pressured the boss to make these changes.

A few months later, another organization came to check on the changes. All the windows were open, but the air flow was still bad. Shelving units blocked air flow through the factory. The boss moved them to a better place.

Now workers do not sweat as much as before, but many still have allergies and breathing problems. They are discussing how to get the boss to install local extractors for the machines that produce dust.

Personal protective equipment (PPE) 18

When workers complain about dangerous materials and chemicals, the boss may tell them, "Wear these gloves. They will protect you." When personal protective equipment (PPE) is part of a system of preventative measures (see page 9), it can help protect workers from getting sick or injured from work. But PPE should never be the first or main form of protection. The general rule, "Change the workplace, not the worker," puts the responsibility on the employer, where it belongs, and usually provides more and better protection. For example, replace a dangerous chemical with a safer one, enclose a machine to limit noise or vibration, or improve ventilation in the factory. It can also cost less over time for management to eliminate dangers than to provide protective equipment.

PPE may provide extra protection for an individual worker, but it should not be a substitute for changes that protect all workers.

One size does not fit all

Personal protective equipment is "personal." To protect you, PPE has to:

- fit you correctly and be tested for fit.
- be different for women and for men (their bodies are different).
- be clean if it is PPE you reuse, or new if it is PPE you use only one time.
- be in good condition, with no holes, cracks, or ripped in any way.
- be the right kind for the danger you face.
- be replaced regularly and at any time it no longer works.
- be used as a last resort after other, safer, controls are in place.

PPE must also be comfortable enough to use all the time. Gloves that make it difficult to move your fingers, masks that are hot, glasses that are scratched or fog up — these may make it harder to work, make you work slower, and, if not well-chosen for the job, create problems such as heat stress and heart strain.

Do not let these difficulties lead you to work without the equipment you need to stay healthy. Instead of listening to the boss blame you for not wanting to protect yourself, organize to get the boss to provide better PPE, adjust piecework rates, or slow the speed of the line if necessary. Even if you feel you are strong or tough enough to work without PPE, it is better to protect your health than to risk it.

Finally, do not let PPE make you think you are protected when you are not. Wearing PPE does not mean you are safe. The only way to make sure you are protected is to fight for safer chemicals, safer conditions, and safer production schedules for everyone in your workplace.

The boss hired a specialist to train us to use new PPE. He showed us how to put it on and take it off, and how to clean and store it. But he never asked us how the PPE felt. Wearing it was hot and uncomfortable, and it made it difficult to do the job as quickly as the supervisor wanted us to do it. Some people stopped using the PPE right away. When the boss saw people working without PPE he didn't ask why we didn't wear it, he just said that if we got hurt it would be our own fault. When one of the workers was working without goggles, a hose on a machine broke, squirted solvent into his eye and he had to go to the hospital. Even then, he lost vision in that eye. The company refused to pay him compensation because he wasn't wearing PPE. That's not fair.

Eye protection

Your eyes can be quickly and permanently damaged by chemicals, dust, bright lights, or sharp objects. Safety glasses, goggles, and face shields provide some protection. If a chemical or dust gets in your eye, immediately rinse it with running water for at least 15 minutes. See First aid on page 175.

If you work in an area that uses UV lights or radiation, use safety glasses, goggles, or face shields that filter out UV rays.

Do not wear contact lenses if you might be splashed with a chemical, if chemical vapors are common where you work, or if you do not have safety glasses. Contact lenses can keep a chemical on your eye longer and the material they are made of may react to some chemicals. Always wear eye protection if you use contact lenses, even when working in areas where there are no chemicals.

Safety glasses: Safety glasses provide some protection from splashes and some objects. Regular glasses that you use to see better will not protect your eyes like safety glasses do. Safety glasses with side shields are best.

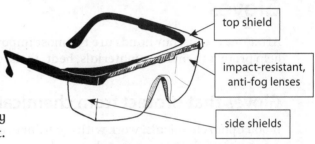

top shield

impact-resistant, anti-fog lenses

side shields

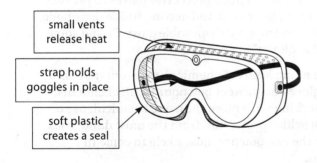

small vents release heat

strap holds goggles in place

soft plastic creates a seal

Goggles: Wear chemical-resistant, vented goggles if you work with acids, alkalis, and other chemicals that can quickly burn, or in areas where chemicals are sprayed. Goggles provide more protection than safety glasses because they make a more complete barrier around your eyes.

Face shields: A clear face shield can protect your mouth, eyes, and face from many splashes. This type of shield is easy to take on and off, and is easy to clean. Even though it covers your mouth, a face shield does not stop chemical vapors from going into your nose and mouth. If there are chemical vapors, wear a mask or respirator (see pages 266 to 270).

Wear chemical goggles or safety glasses underneath a face shield. You really need both.

When you use eye protection:

- Check that it is not broken, cracked, or scratched.
- Make sure it fits snugly, comfortably, and won't fall off as you work.
- Get a new pair if yours are so scratched or dirty you cannot see well through them.
- Safety glasses or goggles must fit over your vision glasses comfortably, or you can get special prescription safety glasses.

- Disinfect shared eye wear after each use.
- If you are working with corrosive chemicals such as acids, make sure your eye protection resists those chemicals.

Gloves

After our brains, our hands are the most important tools in the factory. Gloves help protect them from materials, heat, tools, and machines.

Gloves that protect from chemicals

If you apply chemicals, work with containers of chemicals, or touch, carry, or move materials that contain chemicals, you need protective gloves to prevent chemicals from irritating and burning your skin and getting inside your body. Some gloves are thrown away after every use ("disposable gloves") and some are used more than once ("reusable gloves").

There are many kinds of chemical-resistant gloves, but no one glove can protect you against all chemicals. If you are working with more than one chemical, use a glove that provides protection from the most dangerous chemical or the one you are most likely to come in contact with.

Look at the box to find out the kind of gloves and the chemicals they protect you from. The wrong gloves might absorb chemicals and hold them against your skin, making problems worse.

Wear 2 gloves on each hand if you might be splashed with hydrofluoric acid (HF) or if you are working with a very harmful chemical. If the 2 pairs of gloves are different colors, it will be easier to see if the outer one rips. Change the outer glove as needed. If you work with large amounts of HF, use a heavy nitrile glove outside and a thinner one inside. Also wear 2 pairs of gloves if you work with nanoparticles.

If you work with machines, wear gloves that cannot catch in moving parts.

Disposable gloves

Natural rubber (latex) gloves are the most common. They can protect you from mild chemicals. They are cheap, flexible, and easy to use. They also provide some protection from heat and irritation, or injury from rough surfaces. If you are allergic to latex gloves, use nitrile gloves.

Neoprene gloves can protect you from alcohols and some acids. They are also good protection for glycol ethers found in cleaners. They are very flexible and are commonly used instead of latex gloves.

Nitrile gloves are a good general glove. They protect you from some solvents, acids, and bases, but not from solvents such as benzene or methylene chloride. They are flexible and can be used for doing very precise work. When they are damaged, they rip open, so it is easy to know if it is time to throw them away.

Butyl gloves can protect you against some strong acids and some solvents (alcohols, ketones, esters), but do not protect you against other solvents such as aromatic hydrocarbons or halogenated hydrocarbons. They offer some protection against gases. They are flexible even when cold.

Discard used gloves as dangerous waste.

Reusable gloves

Thick gloves will protect more against chemical spills but they are not good to do very precise work because they prevent your fingers from moving as easily as with a disposable glove.

If you are working with a lot of chemicals, a chemical that can burn you quickly (such as an acid), or one that is very harmful, wear a thicker glove on the outside and a thinner glove on the inside for extra protection.

Norfoil gloves can be used to protect workers from many dangerous chemicals. They can be loose and big, making it harder for you to use your fingers to do precise work.

Viton gloves are used to protect workers from chlorinated and aromatic solvents and can resist some cuts.

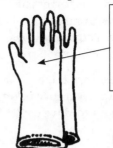

Some glove material is not stretchy and does not mold to your fingers.

You can make thick gloves fit better by putting a tight nitrile glove over them.

Polyvinyl chloride (PVC) gloves are used for protection from strong acids, bases, and alcohols. They **do not** protect you from most solvents.

Polyvinyl alcohol gloves are used for protection from aromatic and chlorinated solvents, such as methylene chloride and toluene, but are not a good choice for water-based solvents.

When you wear gloves that protect against chemicals:

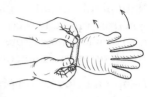

- Look and check all gloves for rips or holes before you use them. Some holes might be too small to see. For reusable gloves: Fill them with air by holding the opening and flipping the glove over itself quickly and closing off the opening. If you feel or hear air, there is a hole. Get a new pair. Use scissors to cut off the fingers so no one else will use them.

- If a chemical spills or splashes on them, rinse and remove them and safely dispose of them. Get a new pair.

- Use a new pair if the gloves are stiff or have changed color.

- Remove them before touching phones, doorknobs, shared objects, food, or anything you put in your mouth.

- Wear a thin glove inside a reusable glove for more protection. A washable cotton glove liner can reduce problems from sweating.

To take them off:
Use your gloved finger to roll the glove off the other hand so it is inside out. Then use the inside-out glove to remove the other one. Make sure your bare skin does not touch the outside of either glove.

We demand gloves!

My hands were red after the first day of working with an automatic ironing machine. When I asked my supervisor for gloves, he refused. So, I brought my own canvas gloves. When the other women saw my hands got better right away, they started using gloves, too.

But the gloves were too big. One day, my glove got stuck on the iron, trapping my hand. My co-workers turned the iron off before it crushed my hand. The boss said we couldn't wear gloves because they were "unsafe."

Without gloves, our hands got red again. We were angry. We decided to turn the machines off and yelled at the supervisor, "The cloth makes our skin red. We won't work until you give us gloves." He had a big order to fill, so he agreed to buy us gloves. Now we have to get him to buy gloves that are different sizes, to fit women with smaller hands.

Allergies to latex gloves

Some people are allergic to latex gloves and cannot wear them. A rash is usually the first sign that you might be allergic to latex, but pay attention to any signs that appear when you wear latex gloves. Report a rash to your employer right away. If the rash does not improve in a few days, the cause might be something else.

The rash can appear in any part of the hand and fingers.

The next time you wear latex, the allergic reaction can be the same or worse. Your allergic reaction could include problems breathing, or even going into shock. If you have an allergic reaction, remove the gloves and immediately stop using latex gloves. Tell your boss you need nitrile gloves instead. To protect you and others with latex allergies, it is best to have all the workers switch to a non-latex glove.

If you must use latex gloves:

- Use "powder-free" ones, with no talc inside.
- Wash your hands with mild soap as soon as you take them off.
- Use water-based lotions on your hands after washing them.
- Remove the dust that comes inside the gloves.

The risk of an allergic reaction is less when other workers help reduce the spread of latex powder.

Gloves that protect against cuts and heat

Gloves made from leather, metal mesh, or canvas can protect you from some cuts and heat. They may not protect you from needles or other objects that can pierce the skin. They will not protect you from cuts from large power tools. If you also work with chemicals, use a chemical-resistant glove under your cut-resistant gloves.

Fabric gloves coated with plastic might protect against some chemicals. Fabric gloves made with aluminum thread protect against heat and cold, cuts, and some diluted acids.

Leather gloves protect against some cuts, heat, and sparks.

Metal mesh gloves can protect against some cuts from cutting tools.

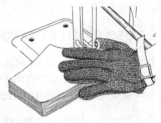

Always use metal mesh gloves in the cutting area.

Masks and respirators

A mask or respirator can provide some protection from dust, germs, fumes, mists, and chemicals in the air if it fits you well and is the right kind for the dangers of your job and workplace.

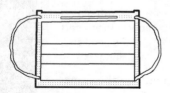

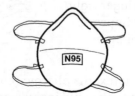

Loose masks only protect you from germs. They do not protect from dust or chemicals.

Particulate masks protect you from some dusts. They do not protect you from chemical vapors or very small dust.

Respirators with filters protect you from chemicals and dusts only if they use the correct filters for those substances.

If you have asthma or other breathing problems, it might be difficult to breathe using a mask or respirator. If one is required, ask to be moved to a different job. If your boss will not make changes, let your co-workers know you have breathing problems and tell them what they need to do in case you have difficulty breathing. The factory should have doctors examine all workers who use respirators to make sure they are healthy enough to do the work.

Some dusts are more dangerous than others. Cotton dust can cause byssinosis (see page 97), silica in sandblasting can cause silicosis (see pages 101 to 103) and lung cancer, and asbestos dust can cause severe lung problems and cancer. Wear a respirator with a HEPA filter (High- Efficiency Particulate Air), labeled N-100, if you work where there is very fine or small dust. A HEPA filter can filter almost 100% of the particulates and is the best for small particulates. The finest dusts are the least visible — and the most dangerous.

When you wear a mask or respirator because there is enough dust or chemicals in the air to harm you, also wear gloves, eye protection, and protective clothing to protect your skin and eyes.

Loose cloth or paper masks

Loose-fitting masks offer very little protection from dust and do not protect from chemical vapors. Since they do not seal around your face and mouth, they let dust in.

Chemical vapors pass right through the paper or cloth. Only masks with filters will protect you from breathing in chemicals (see page 268).

Make sure your mask covers both your nose and mouth.

| How to | **Make a cloth mask for dust** |

Instead of covering your face with a cloth that lets dust in through the bottom…

…make a mask that fits more closely over your nose and mouth.

1. Cut 2 strips of cotton fabric about 10 to 12 cm wide and long enough that you can tie them around your head comfortably. Stitch the edges, or at least take all the threads off the ends.

2. Place the center of one of the strips on top of your nose. Tie the ends behind your head.

3. Then put the center of the other strip over your mouth and tie the ends behind your head. Make sure the edge of the cloth on top of your nose is underneath the seam of the one covering the mouth.

You can make a more permanent mask by sewing the pieces together. Or make many! Wash the mask by itself, not with other clothes.

Dust mask

Tight-fitting paper or plastic masks, also called "particulate masks," catch dust and germs but they do not protect you from breathing many chemical vapors or very fine dust.

Different kinds of particulate masks are categorized with numbers and letters. The higher the number, the more particulates the mask will filter. Standard particulate masks often look the same so find out their number and what they are good for. These often clog quickly and cannot be used more than one day.

The "95" means that this mask filters out 95% of particles.

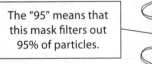

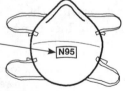

N95

Check the mask and its box or bag to make sure the mask is the right kind for the substance you are working with.

Respirators with filters

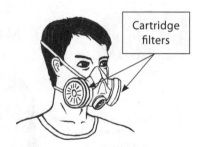

Cartridge filters

Also called rubber masks or masks with filters, respirators have filters that prevent some of the chemicals or dusts in the air from getting into your lungs.

Respirators protect you when:

- they fit you well.
- they have the right filters for the chemicals you and others are using in your workplace.
- the filters are replaced when necessary.

Respirators can have 2 filters on the sides or one in the center, and can cover parts or all of your face.

Respirators can cover the nose and mouth or the entire face. If they are too large or too small and do not make a seal against your skin, you will be breathing air that is not filtered, which can harm you.

The filters stop certain chemicals and substances from passing into your lungs. After a certain amount of time (see the box or instructions), filters are used up and no longer work. Your factory should have a system for cleaning and changing the filters regularly, before they stop protecting you. Changing filters also makes it easier to breathe using the respirator. Read the box to know how long the filter should be used and to be sure it is the right one to use in your brand of respirator.

Countries have different laws regarding the use of respirators. Look at the label and Safety Data Sheets (SDS) of the chemical and seek support from health officials, unions or other organizations to get this information. Also find more information in Appendix B: Common chemicals and materials.

Respirators with their own air supply

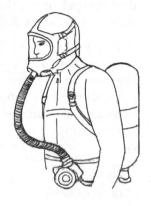

These masks have tanks of air so the person does not breathe outside air at all. These respirators fit more loosely, but they cover the entire head. Respirators with their own air supply are used when there is no other way to reduce the exposure, such as a chemical spill or accident. They might be necessary for maintenance workers opening or entering machines, or when the chemicals in the air are likely to harm you. They can be heavy and make work more tiring.

Respirators with supplied air need careful cleaning after every use.

How to	Check that your respirator fits and works

Look at it. Move and touch all the parts to make sure they are put together correctly and there are no holes, cracks, or damage.

Try it on. Make sure it fits. Turn your head from side to side and up and down. Check that it does not bump against your shoulder or chest. Speak for 30 seconds to see if moving your jaw and lips changes the fit. Facial hair (mustaches, sideburns, or beards) might not fit in the mask or might not let the mask seal around your nose and mouth. If you will wear goggles or other eye wear, they must fit well when you wear your respirator.

Breathe normally first and then take a deep breath. Can you smell or taste the chemical you are working with? If you can, then it is not working properly. However, some chemicals do not have a smell or you might not be able to smell them. Try to test your mask around chemicals you can normally smell.

Check the seal. Test the respirator every time you put it on. Even if the respirator fits well one day, it might not the next. Always take the time to test the fit of any respirator you wear.

You can check the seal in 2 ways:

The first way is to do a **"negative"** pressure test by trying to pull air into the respirator. If no air from the outside comes in, it means the seal is probably good. To do this test, put the respirator on. Put your palm or a cover on top of all the entry points of air from the outside to close them. Take a breath and hold it for a few seconds. The respirator should tighten around your face, and collapse in a little. If it stays like this during the time you hold your breath it is probably sealing well.

 The second way is to do a **"positive"** pressure test, where you add air to the respirator. If no air escapes, it means the seal is probably good. Cover the exhale valve and breathe out inside the respirator. If the air stays inside the respirator, it is probably a good seal. Use the positive test only when the exhale valve is small enough that one finger or your palm will cover the valve completely.

(continued)

How to Check that your respirator fits and works (continued)

Clean it. After using it, remove filters and other parts and clean the respirator with mild soap and water. Rinse well with water and mild soap. Any residue left might irritate your skin later. Let it air dry. If you do not have soap, you can also use a cloth with a very small amount of IPA to clean it. IPA might damage the rubber over time, so do not use IPA often.

Protect it. Put the respirator in a bag and store it where it will not be stepped on, crushed, or get dirty.

Replace filters often. Filters may last for a few minutes or a few days, depending on how much chemical is in the air where they are used. Maintenance and other workers exposed to high amounts of chemicals need to replace the filters more often than workers doing other kinds of work. Replace straps, valves, or anything else that does not work properly.

Pay attention to your health. Notice any changes in your health that might be a sign that your respirator is not protecting you.

- You have difficulty breathing or your breathing problems are worse when you wear the respirator.
- You smell or taste chemicals while using it.
- You find dust or chemical residue inside it.
- You feel effects from chemicals while wearing it.
- You feel sick during or after work with signs of problems that come from chemicals in your work area.

Let your employer know immediately if your respirator is not working well or if you have signs of exposure to chemicals.

Wear PPE that keeps chemicals off of and out of your body.

Protect your hearing

Loud or constant noise can harm your hearing permanently. It can also prevent you from hearing other people, raise your blood pressure, and cause stress. The best way to protect workers is to lower the noise levels. See chapter 13: Noise for more information.

Earmuffs

Earmuffs give good protection if they gently but firmly touch your head and completely cover your ears. They are best for really loud noise or for sounds with very low frequency.

I said, Work faster!

At least I can't hear him yelling anymore.

Clean earmuffs often and replace them when they no longer fit snugly and keep out noise. If you cannot maintain a good seal because you wear glasses, have long hair or sideburns, or because the earmuffs move when you talk or chew, it might be better to use earplugs.

Earplugs

Earplugs are made from cotton dipped in wax, rubber, or foam. Earplugs can protect your hearing if they are the right size for your ear and are properly inserted in your ears. They should be small enough to fit comfortably and expand to fill the entry into the ear. Most foam earplugs are inexpensive and are made to be used only 1 time.

If you reuse earplugs, make sure they return to their original shape after you pinch them. If they do not expand to fill your ear, they will not protect you. Molded earplugs can be reused. Clean them after every use with soap and water or alcohol. Let them dry completely before using them again.

Plain cotton or cloth earplugs do not protect you well from noise. If you do not have access to rubber or foam earplugs, you can make better cotton ones by dipping them in petroleum jelly. Make new ones each day because reusing them might cause an ear infection.

For some kinds of noise, you might have to use both earplugs and earmuffs.

How to	Insert earplugs so they work

To block noise and protect your hearing, earplugs need to get into the right part of your ear. To make sure earplugs fit well:

1. **Clean your hands and the plugs** when you insert the plugs. This will help prevent ear infections.

2. **Roll the plug between your fingers** to make a long, thin cylinder.

3. **Open the ear.** To put the plug in your left ear, hold the rolled plug in the fingers of your right hand. Reach your right arm over the top of your head and grab the top of your left ear. Gently pull your ear up and back a little. This opens up your ear canal to make it easier to fit the plug in.

4. **Insert and hold the plug.** Insert the narrow tip of the rolled plug into your ear canal as far as it will go. Press the earplug gently into your ear and hold it there with the tip of your finger while it expands to fill your ear canal. This takes about 30 seconds. You should feel the foam expanding to fill your ear and notice noises become much quieter.

5. **Check the fit.** Cup your hands over your plugged ears and notice how loud noises are. Remove your hands from over your ears and notice how loud noises are. If they sound about the same, the plugs fit your ears. If the noise is louder when you remove your hands, then the plugs do not fit your ears well and you need to pull them out and try to put them in again. If you still cannot make them fit well, they may be the wrong size for your ears or the foam may be too worn to work well.

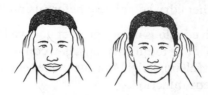

Clothing and shoes

Cloth or plastic protection over your clothing can protect your skin and clothes from some dusts and chemicals. Chemical-resistant clothing, such as aprons, suits, and boots, are necessary if you work with dangerous chemicals, especially acids. These chemicals can hurt you quickly and permanently.

Coats, aprons, and suits

Coveralls on top of your clothes will protect your skin and clothing from dust and splashes. But protective clothing, such as rubber aprons, long sleeves, and other PPE, can make you feel very hot, especially if your workplace is hot. Drinks lots of water, take breaks, and pay attention to signs of heat stress (see page 233). Keeping the factory cooler will help reduce heat stress.

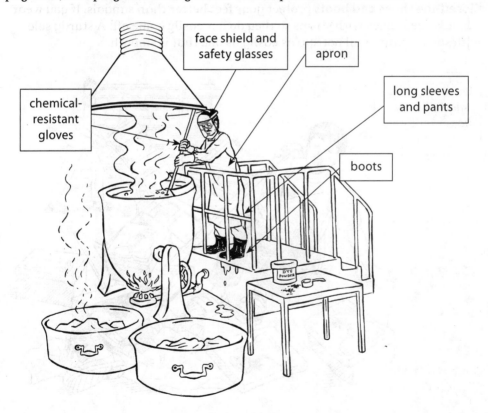

face shield and safety glasses

apron

chemical-resistant gloves

long sleeves and pants

boots

Cotton cloth coats and aprons will not protect you from many chemicals, but they can provide a barrier from dusts and small splashes from mild chemicals. They might give you some protection from sharp or rough materials. They should be washed in the factory. If you take them home to wash, wash them separately from your clothes.

Many body suits are made with a material that is thin and looks and feels like paper. They are meant to be worn only one time. Body suits used in cleanrooms, also called "bunny suits," protect the product, not the worker (see page 65). They do not offer real protection from chemicals.

Chemical-resistant clothing is made from rubber, neoprene, or other plastic. These protect you from chemical splashes when they are the right kind for the chemical you are working with. If you work with corrosive chemicals, wear chemical-resistant protective clothing.

Closed-toe shoes and boots protect your feet better than sandals. If you wear sandals, wear ones with straps so they do not easily come off. A sturdy sole with some texture will not slip as easily as one that is smooth.

Shoe covers or strap-on protectors are often made of a plastic or paper-like material. They may prevent dust and dirt from coming into the work area but provide only a little protection to you. If they cover the whole shoe and you throw them away after using them, they may prevent you bringing home dusts and chemicals on your shoes.

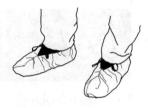

Most disposable shoe covers are slippery. Ask your employer for non-skid shoe covers that have texture on the bottom.

Safety shoes are made of leather or a heavy material that will not melt. Wear safety shoes if you work in an area where things might fall on your feet. They might need chemical-resistant or strong soles that will not slip, and have metal or other material in the toe area to protect against something heavy dropping on it. If you work in an area where electrical static is common, shoes that conduct electricity will prevent you from making sparks while walking. However, if you might be exposed to electrical dangers (see chapter 10), you should not wear shoes that conduct electricity.

Shoes with laces or other closures are better than slip-ons.

Heavy plastic boots protect you best in areas where chemicals splash.

When you wear safety shoes and boots:

- Make sure they fit you well. Your toes should be comfortable without too much space. If you trip when you wear them, they are not the right size.
- Look for tears, cracks or holes, or any area where the shoe might be breaking or coming apart.
- Check the bottom of the shoe every day to make sure there are no metal or objects stuck on it.
- Wear long pants over boots and shoes so chemicals do not get on your legs or in your boots.
- Keep safety shoes at work or wear shoe protectors so you do not bring dust or chemicals home with you.

If you wear plastic boots, wash your socks and feet every day to prevent fungal infections. If your feet itch, air your feet as often as you can and use a foot powder.

The right to personal protective equipment at work

The **ILO Occupational Safety and Health Convention (No. 155)** says employers must:

- Protect workers from dangers at work by designing the workplace better, testing dangers regularly, choosing safer materials and systems, and installing and maintaining ventilation to reduce harm to workers.
- Reduce dangers at work.
- Provide workers with adequate protective clothing and safety equipment after all the other systems of protection are in place.
- Provide workers with training and instruction for proper use of the equipment.
- Provide first aid for emergencies and accidents.

The **ILO Working Environment (Air Pollution, Noise, and Vibration) Convention (No. 148)** says if it is not possible to reduce all of the air pollution employers must:

- Provide and maintain personal protective equipment and ensure it fits workers.

The **ILO Chemicals Convention (No. 170)** says that the boss is responsible for protecting workers from chemicals by first using safer chemicals and then by making changes to the workplace.

If personal protective equipment is needed, bosses are responsible for giving workers personal protective equipment and clothing at no cost to the worker, creating the right conditions to allow workers to use PPE correctly, and maintaining and replacing PPE when needed.

The roles of the UN, ILO, and other international organizations that promote workers' rights are explained in Appendix A.

PART 4

Social Dangers and Solutions

19 Working too much, too fast, for too little

I iron over 100 shirts in 1 hour. The standing is very painful, but it is my work...

It takes 2 days to travel home. I haven't seen my children for 3 months.

I used to attend night classes, but I do not have time anymore.

Bosses in export factories want workers to produce the most they can for the least amount of money. To do this, they pay workers as little as they can get away with and make them work long days, including overtime hours, at a dangerously fast pace. Workers often feel they have little choice but to do this if they want to keep their jobs and make enough money to survive.

But jobs are designed by people and can be changed by people. Workers, their supporters in the community, and the companies and people who buy their products can demand that employers fulfill their responsibility to:

- pay a living wage, enough so workers don't need overtime to live well.
- give rest and meal breaks during the day.
- prohibit mandatory overtime.
- pay workers for sick time and pregnancy leave.
- give workers at least 1 day off weekly and all legal holidays and vacations.
- eliminate injuries from too-fast line speeds and high production quotas.

In many countries, rules covering wages, hours, and working conditions are already part of the law. Too often, governments fail to enforce these laws.

We are not robots!

Every person needs time to rest, relax, and take part in family and community life. But employers want us to work like robots that never feel pain nor fall in love, do not have families, never get sick, and have no lives outside the factory. They want workers to be like robots and never complain, question, challenge, or change a factory system that makes them poor, sick, and tired.

Workers are parents too.

Working too fast or for too long leads to more stress and more injuries, including overuse injuries of muscles and joints (see chapter 7: Ergonomics).

Stress

Long working hours do not leave us enough time to take care of personal or family needs. Pressure from work comes home with us and can make us feel tense and nervous. Feeling too much "stress" can lead to a variety of physical and mental health problems.

Women are especially affected by stress from long working hours because after a day of work even more work awaits them in taking care of their families. (See chapter 21: Discrimination.)

Exhaustion

Exhaustion occurs when your body and mind can no longer cope with pressures at work and home. It is not just feeling tired, which is common after a long day at work. People who have reached the point of exhaustion may feel extreme fatigue that does not go away with sleep or rest. You might feel pain in muscles and joints, have stomach problems, skin rashes, sore throats, and headaches. Women often will have problems with their monthly bleeding, miscarriages, or other problems with pregnancy. Exhaustion also weakens your body's defenses against infection and illness. It can make you less able to think clearly, solve problems, or enjoy being with family and friends. Having time to rest and relax can help reduce and prevent exhaustion.

Poor nutrition

People who work long or unpredictable hours have less time to buy fresh food and cook meals. They often cannot afford to buy prepared meals.

If the factory does not provide meals, a place to store food, or time to eat, workers are likely to go hungry or fill up on highly processed "junk foods." (For more about the importance of food, see chapter 28: Eating well for health.)

> *I don't eat breakfast because that's the only way I can get a little more sleep.*

Finding ways to buy fresh food

In the Las Mercedes export zone in Nicaragua, we work 12 to 14 hours a day just to earn enough to survive. Working late in the evening meant

we could not go to the market to buy fresh food. A few years ago, a group of merchants began a weekly night market near the zone. We liked it so much it now is a daily market. The market stays open a few hours after most workers get out, which allows us to buy better food for ourselves and our families.

Drugs

Tired workers sometimes take or are forced to take stimulant drugs so they can keep working and not feel so tired. Some bosses give workers pills or put drugs in drinking water to keep them awake during long shifts. These drugs make your heart beat faster and raise your blood pressure. Drugs that keep you awake may keep you from feeling hungry even when you need to eat, make your mouth dry, and make it difficult to pass stool.

> *The company gives us pills and an 'energy drink' to keep us awake during the overnight shift once a week. The boss told us the pills were vitamins, but we know they are drugs to keep us awake. Even when I am awake, I have no energy. And when I get home, I can't sleep even if I am tired.*

The right to fair working hours

The **UN** and **ILO** have set standards but each country has its own laws on hours.

The **UN Universal Declaration of Human Rights** says you have the right to holidays with pay, rest time, and limits on working hours, while the **ILO** says workers should have a 40-hour work week, rest, paid holidays, and limits on night work. But each country makes its own rules, so check the laws in your country.

The **ILO 40-Hour Week Convention (No. 47)** gives workers the right to:

- an average work week of 40 hours.
- regular working hours and rest periods.
- the same wages and benefits if a longer work week is reduced to 40 hours.

The **ILO Weekly Rest Convention (No. 14)** gives workers the right to 1 day of rest (at least 24 hours) every 7 days. Rest days should be on traditional days of rest.

The **ILO Holidays with Pay Convention (No. 132)** gives workers the right to at least 3 weeks of paid holiday every year, beyond sick days or national holidays:

- Workers should earn regular pay and be paid at the beginning of the holiday.
- The employer decides when you take a holiday, but should talk with you first.
- If you have not taken all your holiday when you quit or get fired, the employer must pay for earned holiday time.

The **ILO Night Work Convention (No. 171)** says that a shift of 7 hours or more that includes time between midnight and 5 in the morning is hard on workers.

- Night workers should be paid more, work shorter shifts, or get other benefits.
- Workers under 18 years old must not work at night.
- Pregnant workers should have an alternative to night work before and after childbirth, such as day work, social security, or longer paid time off.
- Employers must protect night workers' health, help them meet family and social responsibilities, and provide opportunities for promotion.
- First aid facilities must be available for night workers, including arrangements for quickly taking workers to a clinic or hospital.
- You have the right to see a health worker free of charge before starting night work and while working. If you are unfit to work nights, you cannot be fired.

The roles of the UN, ILO, and other international organizations that promote workers' rights are explained in Appendix A.

Low wages keep people in poverty

If the harder you worked, the more money you earned, then export factory workers would be among the richest people in the world. But workers in export factories live in poverty. Employers pay workers as little as they can, and lobby governments to keep the minimum wage as low as possible. Though it may be illegal, factory owners often pay less than the minimum wage, and refuse to pay bonuses, overtime, or social security benefits. Since governments want companies to build factories and stay in their countries, they rarely enforce laws regarding wages, hours, benefits, or working conditions.

When companies pay workers barely enough money to survive, they deny them the right to a healthy, dignified life.

I can't afford to live in a place with clean water, schools, and clinics nearby. I can barely feed and clothe my family!

Not paying full wages and benefits

Many employers do not fully pay even the low wages the law requires. Some do not pay minimum wage or a higher wage for overtime hours, for all the hours worked or all the pieces made. Legally required bonuses for attendance, holidays, and festivals may be unpaid. And workers are fined for breaking factory rules. Sometimes factories schedule vacations during holidays to avoid giving holiday pay — this is not legal.

Some employers deduct health or other social security payments from workers' pay but do not pay it into the social security system. This means workers take home less money but also cannot get the health care and other benefits they have paid for and deserve.

I took 1 day off and lost almost 3 days of pay because they illegally deducted my attendance and punctuality bonuses and food vouchers. I took 1 day off and the next week didn't even have enough money to eat.

Mandatory overtime

Even where workers' pay is not set by the piece, high production targets must be met before the shift is allowed to end.

If an employer requires workers to work overtime, punishes workers by forcing them to work extra hours, or locks workers in the factory to finish a job, this is forced labor. Forced labor violates national and international human rights laws and worker rights agreements.

In the factory where I work in Kenya, if you do not meet your target, you are not allowed to leave. Sometimes we work all night with only short breaks.

International companies (brands) force overtime on factories they contract by demanding production schedules that are almost impossible to meet. In search of ever lower costs, they drive a system in which factory owners keep wages as low as possible to ensure their profits. Most of the time, wages are not enough to support one person, let alone a whole family, so workers are forced to depend on extra pay from overtime work and bonuses.

Ban on forced labor

The **ILO Forced Labor Rights Convention (No. 29)** and **Abolition of Forced Labor Convention (No. 105)** say that it is illegal for companies to force people to work without pay and/or with the threat of violence, debt, or other forms of coercion.

The roles of the UN, ILO, and other international organizations that promote workers' rights are explained in Appendix A.

Piecework hurts workers' health

A piecework pay system, where employers pay workers by the piece instead of by the hours or days worked, allows employers to pressure workers to work faster and longer than may be legally allowed, even if they are tired, injured, or ill.

Piecework pay is often set so low that workers must work overtime just to make enough money to survive. If workers complain, bosses threaten them with losing their overtime or their job. They punish workers by not letting them drink water, eat, or go to the toilet. Sometimes, they even lock the doors or gates to force them to keep working!

Paying some workers less than others

Bosses discriminate against some workers — women, indigenous people, migrant and child laborers — by paying them less than others doing the same work. Although women workers are often a majority, they may not be promoted to better paying jobs, even if they can do the job well. (See pages 305 to 306.)

Contract and temporary workers

Another way employers keep people in poverty is by hiring workers for only a short time. They may hire workers when there is a lot of work and fire them when there is not. Employers often contract temporary agencies to provide these workers to avoid the legal responsibilities of being the direct employer.

This system stops workers from getting benefits the law may give to permanent workers. Because contract and temporary workers come and go, it also hides illnesses and injuries caused by work, and makes it harder for workers to organize for better, safer conditions.

Working to pay off debt

Getting paid too little means workers do not have enough money to save, for emergencies, or to pay for things they need. Stores in and around the factory often let workers purchase goods on credit but charge high interest rates. Employers, banks, and loan sharks charge high rates for loans. Workers owe so much in interest that when they settle accounts they have even less money to live on. Then they have to buy more on credit or take out another loan!

Migrant workers also become victims of the debt system. Recruiters charge a lot of money to get them jobs in other countries. Workers begin paying their debt when they arrive. But recruiters and employers often demand more money, charge high interest, or change the rules. Some workers get trapped in a system that never lets them pay off their debts. This is called "debt bondage."

Savings groups help workers get out of debt

Kavita had been working for a long time to pay off a loan from the boss, but her debt did not seem to go down. Many women were in the same situation. One day, an organizer from the group Sankalp talked with them about their debts and about finding a way to pay them off. The organizer proposed that they start a savings group. If 10 women worked together, they could save up to 1 rupee a week, she said. The organizer would help them set up a bank account. If they saved regularly, the bank could also give them a loan, with much better conditions than the boss.

The women got organized and saved 1 rupee a week. After 3 months, they had enough to pay the debt of 1 woman and chose Kavita. The women, including Kavita, kept saving and every few months they paid somebody else's debt. After paying all 10 women's debts, they kept saving money to give loans to each other instead of going to the boss or the bank. Now they are better prepared to pay for emergencies than ever before.

Activity	**Examine your pay**

You should be able to find out if you have received all the pay you have earned. This activity will help you to:

Know what you should be paid. Find out what the employer is supposed to pay for each piece, or hour or day, and for overtime. Find out if they are required to pay for holidays or increase pay for each year of work.

Know what should be deducted. If part of your pay is deducted for taxes, social security, savings, or housing, make sure the employer is subtracting the correct amounts. Ask co-workers if their tax or social security deductions are the same as yours. Ask your union or a lawyer to help you contact the government to ensure your employer is paying the correct amounts.

Keep records. Write down all your working hours, the number of pieces you make, the price for each piece, and any other information that might be useful, in a notebook or on a calendar. Keep copies of pay stubs, deposits, and any other information about your pay.

Calculate your pay. With the record of pieces you made, or the days and hours you worked, you can calculate how much money you are owed.

Make a time log

Create a form (or use a calendar) to record hours worked and time off. Add columns (see the example below) to fit your situation. For example, add a column to record the number of pieces you made or for bonuses.

Day	Date	Time In	Time Out	Regular Hours	Overtime Hours	- OR -	Pieces Made
Monday	June 4	7:00	17:30	8	2		160
Tuesday	June 5	7:00	19:30	8	4		220
Wednesday	June 6	7:00	19:30	8	4		220
Thursday	June 7	7:00	17:30	8	2		170
Friday	June 8	7:00	17:30	8	2		170
Saturday	June 9	7:00	11:00	4			60
Sunday	June 10	—	—	0	0		
Total paid hours				**44**	**14**		**1000**

(continued)

Activity	**Examine your pay** (continued)

Whether you are paid by the hour or by the piece, your employer must pay you **at least** the legal minimum wage plus extra pay for overtime hours. The pay rates below are only examples.

If you get paid by the time you worked:

1. What is the legal work week in your country? How much did you work?

In our country the legal work week is **44** hours. I worked 58 hours.

2. Divide the number of regular hours by the pay you should receive.

I was promised $110 a week. So, $110÷44 hours = **$2.50** an hour.

3. Multiply the number of overtime hours you worked by the overtime pay rate.

Overtime is paid at 1 1/2 times regular pay, so $2.50 x 1.5 = **$3.75**

4. Add your weekly regular pay and your weekly overtime pay.

I worked 14 hours overtime, so, 14 x $3.75 = **$52.50** (overtime pay)

$110 (regular pay) + $52.50 (overtime pay) = **$162.50**

5. Add bonuses earned this week, such as bonuses for meeting production goals, attendance, or food stipends.

$162.50 + $20 attendance bonus + $20 production goal bonus = **$202.50**

6. Subtract taxes and fees for things such as health care and other social insurance. For example:

$202.50
- $20 for taxes
-$25 for social security
= **$157.50** weekly pay.

If you get paid piece rate:

1. Multiply the number of pieces you made by pay per piece.

1000 pieces x $0.15 = **$150**

2. Add bonuses earned this week.

$150 + $20 production goal bonus = **$170**

3. Subtract taxes and fees for things such as health care and other social insurance.

$170 - $30 for social security = **$140** weekly pay.

Get your full pay

Compare your time log and pay sheet with your paycheck every pay period. If you find that you are not getting as much as you calculated:

- **Talk to the bookkeeper** (or your supervisor) and ask about the difference between your records and theirs. It is helpful to bring the contract or written agreement that defines your salary and deductions, but your time log will be even more useful when confronting the person who pays you. Have a co-worker go with you for support and to be a witness.

> *The boss says he'll pay what he owes me next week. He has said that before. What should I do?*

- **Seek advice and support from unions, worker groups, or other organizations.** Bring as much information as possible about the factory (name, address, owners) to make it easier to start a legal process. The boss might be within the law in what he is paying you, but if it is not what he promised in writing or verbally, you may be able to demand the correct pay through social pressure, worker unity, or the legal system.

- **Talk to other workers.** If you are not getting paid correctly, it is very likely that other workers are in a similar situation. Together you can talk about solutions and support each other.

The minimum wage is not enough!

I work in a TV factory in Ciudad Acuña, Mexico where I earn a little above the minimum wage. During one of our trainings with the Comité Fronterizo de Obreras (CFO) we did an activity to determine our sustainable living wage. We looked at our weekly expenses, divided into "things we need to survive" such as basic foods, clean water, and hygienic products, "things we need to pay each month" like electricity, rent, and transportation, and "things that we need to have a dignified life," which included more nutritious and varied foods and school fees. When we compared how much we needed each week with how much we earned we saw that even if we bought the cheapest brands of everything and did without a lot of things, we only earned about 25% of what we needed! We actually need 4 to 5 times the legal minimum wage in order to cover our most basic monthly expenses. The CFO is now working to raise the minimum wage so that working full time at minimum wage is enough for a worker to sustain her family and live a healthy life.

How much do *you* need to cover all your expenses?

A living wage is a human right

The minimum wage should be enough money to cover basic needs — a place to live, water, and food for a worker and her family. But people need to do more than just survive. We need a decent home, enough healthy and nutritious food for our families, and to earn enough to pay our monthly bills as well as save for bigger purchases or emergencies. A living wage allows workers and their families to break the cycle of poverty and illness and live a healthy life.

 Standard of Living

The **UN Universal Declaration of Human Rights** says everyone has the right to a standard of living that allows for their health and well-being, including food, clothing, housing, medical care, and social services.

The **ILO Minimum Wage Fixing Convention (No. 131)** says governments must:

- set a minimum wage for all workers, considering the needs of workers and their families.
- enforce the law to ensure workers are paid properly.

While the ILO requires governments to set a minimum wage, each country decides what that is. Check your country's labor laws.

The roles of the UN, ILO, and other international organizations that promote workers' rights are explained in Appendix A.

The Asia Floor Wage Campaign

To lure international companies with low prices, factories move from city to city and country to country searching for places where regulations are lax and they can pay the lowest wages. Tired of this "race to the bottom," workers all over Asia got together to launch the Asia Floor Wage Campaign.

They calculated how much a worker in each country must earn to support her family by working no more than 48 hours a week. They set the Asia Floor Wage to be the same for all of Asia so large companies would no longer move in search of the lowest wages. Some workers and unions have used the Floor Wage to negotiate for better pay with factory owners and managers, and to pressure the brands to change policies that strive only for low cost instead of the well being of workers.

Organizing when long hours make it difficult

How can you organize against working too many hours when you have so little time already? Here are some strategies that work:

- **Find times and places that are convenient for workers** and do not conflict with their duties at home. Plan meetings for workers' days off. Hold several smaller meetings instead of trying to find one time or place that works for everyone. Organize meetings by shift, job, or neighborhood.

- **Organize outside of meetings.** Speak with workers during breaks. Sit with different groups during lunch and encourage other organizers to also make new friends. Connect with workers before or after work — on the bus, at social gatherings, or in neighborhoods where workers live.

- **Involve women.** Because women often work a "second shift" caring for their families, sometimes it is harder for them to get involved. Offer childcare at the meetings, as well as food and refreshment, to make it easier for them to attend.

Workers win a day off

We make Nike shoes at the Sinotex factory in Sri Lanka. The boss had us working 7 days, with no days off even though the labor law in Sri Lanka entitled us to 1 day off every week.

When the union and other members of the Workers Council demanded our rightful day off, the boss refused!

We told all the workers about the law and Nike's code of conduct, which also said we had the right to 1 day off every week. We got organized and threatened to report the boss to Nike. The Nike auditor had visited our factory and didn't give it a good score, so the boss didn't want to lose any more points. He was scared of losing the Nike contract, so after 1 month of campaigning, he agreed to give us the 7th day off.

Some workers are happy we get Sunday off, but some aren't because wages are still too low. We agreed to organize to raise our wages!

Fighting for fair hours and better pay

In factories where workers have fought for and won a collective contract, they are often able to bargain for better salaries and fairer working hours. Forming a union or worker association is often the best way to get a good collective contract, overtime, and fair pay.

When you negotiate a collective contract, you and the employer agree to honor it.

Enforce labor laws

Labor laws in many countries set limits on working hours and overtime. Unfortunately, many export factories may be exempt from these laws, especially inside special export processing zones. Whether the laws apply to your factory or not, a campaign for fair working hours might bring enough pressure to make the factory honor them.

If the labor laws are weak or there are none regarding wages or working hours, your campaign might pressure the government to create and pass laws to protect workers and limit working hours. International agreements your country has signed on labor and human rights standards can be useful to your campaign, even if these standards have not been implemented. See Appendix A: Laws and the struggle for decent, healthy, and fair work.

Community campaigns

Workers organizing their factories often gain strength by joining with community groups and non-governmental organizations (NGOs), such as women's, religious, environmental, or human rights groups. Discussing problems in the community caused by low wages and long workdays can help build support for workers and help generate ideas to improve conditions for everyone in the community. Use the But why? activity on page 20 to help figure out what the underlying problems and solutions are. Worker and community groups have organized many kinds of projects.

- **Legal aid clinics:** Staffed by volunteer lawyers and law students, they offer free legal advice on many issues, especially labor law violations.

- **Low cost childcare, after school activities, and tutoring:** They keep children safe and learning, even if you are working overtime or at night.

- **Night or weekend free adult schools:** They teach what you want to learn and are available when you are.

- **Community-based health care and referrals:** They make it easier and less costly for you to get medical attention.

- **Night markets, community gardens, and buying food in bulk:** They can help you reduce your costs and eat more nutritious foods.

- **Cultural activities:** They can help you relate to other workers and enjoy life more.

International campaigns

Because employers and the brands sell their products all over the world, many worker organizations have involved groups in other countries in campaigns to increase wages, force companies to pay the wages and benefits they owe workers, and recognize their unions. (See page 59 for more information.)

How we won against forced overtime

Workers from other garment factories ask us how we got the freedom to leave at 4:30 pm and not work forced overtime. When people find out that we organized our own union and that we were successful, they feel like it is possible to fight for better conditions, and they want to know how we did it.

Share experiences with other workers

We work at the Choi Shin and Cimatextiles factories in Guatemala. Both of these factories are owned by the same Korean company and are right next to each other. Many people worked there under bad conditions. Besides the low pay and the mean bosses, they also forced us to work overtime, even when we did not want to. Some of us got together outside of work to talk about the conditions in the factory. We talked about everything, from how the bosses treated us at work, to how much we are paid, to how often we were forced to work overtime. After everybody got a chance to talk, we decided that the biggest problem we shared was forced overtime and low pay.

Organize a workers' group

At first most of us did not want to take action against the boss because we were afraid we would lose our jobs. But when we found out that forced overtime was illegal in Guatemala, we started organizing small groups of workers in neighborhoods outside the factory. After 1 year, we had organized 1,250 workers from the two factories. We all agreed to form an independent union.

(continued)

(continued)

Bring attention to the problem

We made the community aware of what was happening in the factory. The bosses responded with death threats, violence, bribes, and even rape to intimidate the leaders and break our unity. Twice, supervisors led non-union mobs to threaten and attack us, but we found support and protection in the community.

Build national and international support

Our union reached out to other unions and organizations in Guatemala and other countries. We wrote to the brands. They put pressure on the boss to improve our working conditions. To keep his customers, the boss had to sign an agreement acknowledging our union.

Pressure for legal enforcement

But the boss went back to harassing the union leaders, threatening to close the factories and move to China. But we kept working and organizing. After 2 years of struggle, the government was pressured by local, national, and international organizations to enforce the law. The government told the factory owner that he had to sign a collective bargaining agreement with us, rehire fired union workers, and address our complaints.

Win some, lose some

Although we won higher pay and no more forced overtime, we still struggle with the boss who hates our union and threatens to close and move the factories. But we are proud to be among the first unions in Guatemala to have a collective contract!

For a step-by-step description of how to organize a campaign, see pages 53 to 58.

Doing factory work at home

Some women do factory work at home because they or their husbands do not want them to leave home, or so they can care for their families while still earning money. Some workers bring work home for extra pay. Others are forced to work at home because factory owners cut costs or close the factories.

Workers work more hours and face different dangers at home than in the factory. Homeworkers are often paid less and absorb many of the costs of production that should be the boss's responsibility, such as:

- fans and protective equipment (if they have them at all)
- light and electricity
- tables, chairs, and work furniture
- waste disposal
- storage of parts, supplies, and finished goods
- transporting the work between the home and factory

Homeworkers are usually paid less than factory workers, even after taking into account that they may not pay for childcare, meals away from the home, daily transportation to the factory, or other things factory workers must spend money on.

How to   Calculate your real pay

To find out how much you really earn after paying all your costs of doing the work:

- **Multiply** the pay per piece by the number of pieces you made. Do this for different pieces, if they are paid differently.

> OCTOBER ORDER
> 60 hoods at 20 cents each
> 60 x 0.20 = $12

- **Subtract** the cost of materials, how much you pay family or neighbors who help you, and costs for electricity, water, and other things used while working. If you do not get your bills every month, make an estimate from previous months. (**Subtract** corrections you have to make if your boss does not pay for them.)

> $12 pay, minus
> - $2.00 for materials
> - $1.50 to Mary for helping
> - $1.00 for electricity
> - $0.50 for water
>
> = $7.00 total

- **Calculate and compare** this amount every month or every few months to see how much your pay changes. When you know how much you are really paid, you can better demand that your boss pay more of the production costs and pay you more money.

> January $8.50
> March $7.50
> June $7.50
> October $7.00

You are paying less for this batch than the last one! This is not fair!

If your husband earned more, you wouldn't need this extra money! Don't blame me!

Working for "extra money" or to "make a living"?

Homeworkers work more hours

Women who work at home do more than just factory work. They cook, take care of children or family members, buy or collect food, water and fuel, clean, and do other tasks. Doing factory work while caring for their homes and families means women work longer hours, spread out over a longer period in the day. They usually work more hours than they would at a factory.

No matter where you do the work, too much work always leads to more injuries, health problems, stress- related illnesses, poor nutrition and other problems.

To reduce the impact of working double on women's health, find ways for the whole family, especially men, to take part in caring for the home and family. Caring for the home is a skill men and boys can learn.

The whole family put to work

When work is moved into the home, the whole family is affected. One person may bring the work home, but often the whole family does the work, including the children, because every piece made means more money is earned. Sometimes the whole family must help in order to meet a production quota that is impossible for one worker to meet alone. Work may go late into the night, with no extra pay for the long hours worked by the family.

I try to give my children money to help me. I want them to know that work should be paid fairly, but when my pay is low, I cannot give them anything!

Work dangers are worse at home

Although homework is similar to work in a factory, working at home is more dangerous. Homes do not have enough space to create safe workstations or to store materials and chemicals safely. They often lack the lighting, ventilation, and safe electrical wiring needed for work to be safe. And if there is a health or safety problem, it can affect everyone in the family.

Fires

Materials near kitchen fires or stoves, outlets or other sources of heat (lamps, heaters, or cigarettes) can burn. Homes often catch fire more easily than factories, and even a small fire can spread quickly. Prevent fires in your home:

- Keep materials away from heat, flames, or electricity sources.
- Keep electrical wires dry.
- Unplug machines when you are not using them.
- Avoid overloading wires by not using many machines and appliances at the same time.
- Keep chemical containers tightly closed when not in use and make sure there is good ventilation to get rid of fumes.
- Do not smoke in the home or near materials that can burn quickly.

If a fire does start in your home, be prepared to put it out:

Eliminate one of the things fire needs to burn. Fires need material and air (oxygen) to burn. Small fires can be smothered by removing one of those elements. For example, if a fire starts in a cooking pot, covering it with a lid will stop it because it will not have air.

Extinguish fires with dirt, sand, or water from a container that you keep by your work area in case of fire. For electrical or chemical fires, use sand or dirt to put it out, not water. For cloth fires, use water or a fire extinguisher (learn how to make one on page 216).

Protect yourself. If you try to put out a fire, always stay between the fire and the door so you can leave if you must. Cover your nose and mouth with a cloth or mask to keep some of the smoke out of your lungs.

As a community we decided that every home would store 2 buckets of water.

Prepare your family and community about what to do in case of fire:

Practice escaping from the house with your family, discuss how to get help, and where to meet afterwards.

Write down the phone numbers of fire stations in your community and make sure people have these numbers.

Decide on a community alarm (like banging on a steel pipe) to let others know there is a fire, to get out, and to get help. Choose fire spotters to sound the alarm.

Work together to stop a fire. Make sure you know where to find water, sand, or other materials to stop the fire, and which to use on different types of fires.

Chemicals

Chemicals used at home may get in your food, water, and air. Commonly used cleaners (solvents) and glues can cause both short- and long-term health problems, including dizziness, breathing problems, skin and eye irritation, cancer, and even death. See chapter 8: Chemicals, and Appendix B: Common chemicals and materials, to find information about the chemicals you are working with. If you find no information, treat them as if they are dangerous.

- Limit contact with the chemical. Use personal protective equipment (see chapter 18) to keep it off your skin and out of your eyes.
- Wash your hands and work areas, and afterwards do not use those cleaning cloths or water for anything else.
- Do not use household containers to store chemicals. If you do, remove all labels and write the chemical name on the container. Label all containers with words like "DANGER" and "DO NOT TOUCH" to remind yourself and your family that it is dangerous.
- Never use a container that held a chemical for another purpose. Even if you wash it really well, the container can still have chemicals.
- Keep chemical containers covered and inside shallow containers to catch spills and leaks.
- Store chemicals away from children's reach.
- Store chemicals in a locked cabinet or outside shed.
- Do not smoke, eat, drink, or cook near chemicals.

chemicals for work

Dust

Small threads and dust from garments can cause difficulty breathing (see page 97), allergies, coughing, and skin rashes (see page 158). Sometimes dust is too small to be seen. Protect yourself with good ventilation (see chapter 17) and by using a face mask to cover your mouth and nose. See pages 266 to 270 to learn about face masks and how to make one.

Dust buildup on exposed wires can catch fire. Keep electrical boxes closed.

Strain and overuse

To reduce injury and pain from doing the same movements many times:

- Place tools and materials you need close by your workspace. Reaching repeatedly for them can hurt your body.
- Support your wrists, elbows, back, legs and feet while you work. If a part of your body hurts while working or after, try a different position.
- Take breaks. Look away from your work to let your eyes rest, and move and stretch your body.
- Get a comfortable chair with back support.

For more on strain and overuse problems, see chapter 7: Ergonomics.

Noise

The constant sound of a machine, especially if it is loud, can harm your hearing. See chapter 13 to learn more about noise and how to make earplugs.

Stress

It is normal to feel stressed, anxious, or sad when you are overtired and overwhelmed from pressure at work and at home. Feeling stress is not only uncomfortable, but over time it can lead to high blood pressure, headaches, weakened immune system, and muscle tension. You can reduce the harm from stress to your body and mind. See pages 403 to 404.

My contractor wants the order finished, my husband wants dinner, my mother has to go to the clinic, and the children need attention! But at least no supervisor tells me what to do!

With so many demands on your time, when do you take care of your needs?

Find support with other homeworkers

Doing factory work at home can be very isolating, and competition for work can be intense. Bosses encourage this competition, because it keeps costs low.

Invite other homeworkers in your community to talk about common problems, learn about each other's successes and failures, and find ways of working together for better conditions. Some homeworkers share space, buy supplies in bulk so they are cheaper, and share childcare responsibilities. Working as a group also lets you take bigger orders, bargain for better pay, or even become your own boss.

Our homeworkers' group

When I started sewing at home I didn't know how many women worked at home in my community. So I went around and spoke to most of the women who did factory work at home in my neighborhood. At first they didn't want to talk, but it was easy to share with someone who knew the work. Soon we would meet regularly to talk about our children and home life, as well as work.

After a chemical cleaner caught fire in the home of one of the women, we talked about how to prevent fires and what to do when fires happen. One woman explained that she had taught her children how to escape in case of fire. I learned a lot and felt much happier after the meetings.

Five of us decided to form a workshop together, and we work in my house. One of us takes care of the children while the rest sew. We share the profits equally, so we all get paid for our work sewing or caring for the children. When there is a lot of work, some of us stay up all night sewing together. The work is still very hard, but we now have some support.

Now that my husband has a large truck we are going to see if we can get larger orders directly from the factory owner, instead of the middleman. If we do, we can earn more money and be able to negotiate directly with the owner about pay, supplies, and tools, such as scissors. My hope is to organize more homeworkers in our community, so we can support each other and improve our conditions.

Homeworkers deserve recognition as workers

When homeworkers are recognized as workers, they can be covered by local and national laws and have access to social protection programs such as health insurance, maternity protection, and disability, injury, and unemployment compensation.

> Now that the boss has been forced to recognize our association, we can make work safer for all of us and our families.

> Why don't we invite workers from other neighborhoods to join our association?

The rights of homeworkers

The **ILO Home Work Convention (No. 177)** says homeworkers should be protected by the same national laws on health, safety, and labor rights that protect factory workers. Homeworkers should be:

- allowed to form or join organizations of their own choosing.
- protected in the field of occupational safety and health.
- protected against child labor.
- protected against discrimination.
- provided access to training.
- offered maternity protection.
- offered social security protection.

The roles of the UN, ILO, and other international organizations that promote workers' rights are explained in Appendix A.

Unions help homeworkers win rights

In the 1980s, many Australian garment companies started to hire homeworkers instead of factory workers. The Textile, Clothing and Footwear Union of Australia, which protected the rights of garment workers, realized that even though the homeworkers did the same job as factory workers, they often were paid less. They were also not covered by labor laws, which meant that the employers got away with not fixing bad working conditions. So the union tried to recruit and organize homeworkers. But many were too scared to make a complaint against their bosses. They did not want to lose their jobs. They thought nobody would believe them or support them because they did not have anything in writing and were immigrants who did not speak English.

The union worked with homeworkers and community partners to initiate the FairWear campaign. This national and international campaign brought together many community organizations to support home-based workers' rights. Women's groups, churches, and community organizations joined with the union in calling for companies to respect homeworkers' rights. They invited people from the radio and newspapers to the events and demonstrations they held outside the companies' stores. The media attention showed consumers which companies were making their clothing but not paying fair wages. With the support of consumers, the union forced the companies to sign an agreement to make sure homeworkers were protected by labor laws and received fair wages. Garment homeworkers are now protected by the Textile, Clothing and Footwear Union of Australia.

Discrimination

Divided we lose.

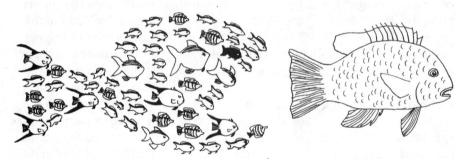

United we win!

All workers deserve respect, a healthy and safe job, and a living wage. No matter what our differences may be, we all should have the same rights. But some people are treated badly because of who they are. Women, migrant workers, people with disabilities, and people of different ethnic or religious backgrounds are often treated in unequal and harmful ways by the government, the law, our bosses and supervisors, and even co-workers and community members.

Focus on finding out what challenges all workers face, especially women workers. The activity on pages 310 to 311 can help you find ways of learning about each other in a respectful way while working towards common goals to improve conditions in the factory. Joining together in a struggle does not mean you all share the same challenges, but it can help build unity and understanding as you tackle the problems you do share.

My boss harasses me every day. Some days he tells me I am pretty. Some days he says I'm dumber than a donkey.

I have 10 years' experience and do good work, but I can't find a job. They say I'm too old, they only hire young people.

Dark-skinned people are loud and dirty! I'm glad the supervisor keeps them where they belong: in the cleaning room!

I can't talk to anyone at work. My co-workers make fun of my accent and my boss says he will fire me if I speak my own language.

Discrimination in the factory

It is no coincidence that most workers in export factories are young women. Because society teaches women to obey and serve men, bosses think they will accept the low salaries and harsh conditions of the factories. They also know that many young women were denied education, so factory work is one of the few opportunities they have. This makes bosses believe that women are less likely to cause "trouble." The same is true for people who migrate to find work.

Denied better jobs and promotions

Young and women workers get hired for low-skilled jobs with the promise of promotions later. But after they learn the skills necessary to change jobs or become supervisors, bosses might still pay them starting salaries.

Women are usually not promoted, even when they are qualified.

Lower pay

Wages are low in export factories. Yet women, indigenous people and ethnic minorities, workers who migrate, and people with disabilities are usually paid even less.

Wage discrimination means some workers are less able to afford nutritious food, decent housing, health care, and basic services such as clean water. Wage discrimination means they have to work longer and harder to make ends meet, and are exposed to toxics and repetitive movements for longer amounts of time.

What good will it do to organize for a higher minimum wage if, as women, we are not guaranteed equal pay?

Humiliating treatment

Insults and harassment by the boss are intended to make workers feel worthless and fearful and can lead to physical and mental health problems. Women, people who migrate, indigenous people, people with darker skin, and people with disabilities are often treated in ways to make them feel they are more stupid or worth less than other workers. Women are often humiliated and harassed because they are seen as less than men.

When workers' self-esteem is harmed by the discrimination they face at work and in their community, they might feel they have no power to fight against unfair and unhealthy working conditions. However, even when we do not think so, we all have power in one or many parts of our lives (see We have power, too! on page 317).

Dangerous jobs

The dirtiest, most dangerous, and lowest-paid jobs in the factory go to workers with the least power in the factory or community, or are given out as punishment to workers involved in organizing to keep them isolated, harass them, and force them to quit. When equipment and tools are not designed to fit women, they can lead to serious health problems caused by poisoning (see pages 269 to 270) and strain and overuse (see chapter 7: Ergonomics). Women who get pregnant should be moved to less difficult, less dangerous jobs, with no reduction in pay. When this does not happen, it puts them and their babies in danger (see chapter 26: Reproductive and sexual health).

Violence

Bosses use violence and the threat of violence to control workers. But often, the workers who are the most discriminated against are the ones that face the worst kinds of violence. Women and migrant workers are targeted most often. The violence inside a factory is often a reflection of the discrimination faced in our communities.

Blaming workers instead of the boss

Millions of people migrate from rural areas of China to work in factories in the big cities. In fact, the Chinese government encourages companies to hire workers from poor regions in China where most of the ethnic minorities live. Bosses know migrants left poverty and hardship in their home towns and are desperate for jobs. Employers take advantage of their desperation and say, "There are others just like you outside the door waiting for a job, so don't complain or we'll just fire you and hire someone new."

Workers who migrate face different hardships than local workers, but inside the factory walls, all are hurt by unfair and unsafe working conditions.

In Guangdong factories, the majority Han group clashed with the Muslim minority Uyghur people. The Han resented the new group for many reasons. When the boss started firing Han workers and replacing them with Uyghur workers, many Hans blamed the Uyghur, instead of blaming the boss. When false rumors about Uyghur men raping Han women began to spread, the Han put all their frustration and anger into fighting Uyghurs. Fights broke out among hundreds of Han and Uyghur workers and riots lasted for hours. Two people were killed. Fights between Han and Uyghur broke out in other communities as well.

In the end, the police had to intervene, arresting and beating many workers. But nothing changed. The workers who were fired were not rehired and the conditions in the factories only got worse for both Han and Uyghur.

Divisions among workers

When society believes in the superiority of one group over others, this carries over into the workplace. Workers with lighter skin may look down on workers who have darker skin. In racist societies everywhere, even the poorest people with lighter skin usually have privileges that darker skinned people do not. People with HIV, a disability, or qualities that make them visibly different are often abused the most.

> I don't want them to join our union. They are taking our jobs!

> But with them, we would have a bigger and more powerful union.

> They are backward. They should go back to where they belong.

> They treat us like we are less than them.

> I'm scared of them beating me up.

> They told everyone I have AIDS. I don't, but it doesn't matter. The boss will fire me when he hears this.

No representation in the union or worker committees

Unions and groups that support workers should represent and fight for the needs of all workers in the factory. But sometimes unions are led by one group of workers who have more power or privilege than others. They might fight for issues that affect only them and their group or not know (or care to know) about the issues that affect other workers.

UNION MEETING EVERY WEDNESDAY 8pm-9pm

> If there was childcare maybe I'd have a chance to stand up and talk.

Unions are often led by men, even if women are a majority in the factory.

The right to equality

The **UN Universal Declaration of Human Rights** says **every person**:

- has equal rights and freedoms no matter their race, sex, language, religion, political opinion, national or social origin, property, birth or other status.
- has the right to work, choose a job freely, fair work conditions, and protection against unemployment with no discrimination.
- has the right to receive equal pay for equal work with no discrimination.
- has the right to fair and adequate pay for their work with no discrimination.
- has the right to form trade unions.

The **UN International Convention on Elimination of All Forms of Racial Discrimination (ICERD):**

- prohibits discrimination based on race, color, or national or ethnic origin.
- guarantees everyone freedom of movement, freedom of opinion and expression, and the right to peaceful assembly and association.
- gives workers the right to form and join trade unions.
- provides equal access to public health, medical care, and social security, as well as education and training.

The **ILO Discrimination (Employment and Occupation) Convention (No. 111)** bans discrimination based on race, color, sex, religion, political opinion, or national or ethnic origin in getting a job, type of occupation, and exercise of worker rights. The ILO specifically supports the rights of vulnerable groups including: indigenous and tribal peoples, migrant workers, women workers, and children who work.

The **ILO Equal Remuneration Convention (No. 100)** says all male and female workers should receive equal pay for equal work.

The **UN Convention on the Elimination of All Forms of Discrimination Against Women (CEDAW)** says:

- Women have the right to job security and job promotion.
- Women have the right to equal access to health and safety protections.
- Women have the right to special protection during pregnancy.
- Employers cannot fire women for being pregnant.

The roles of the UN, ILO, and other international organizations that promote workers' rights are explained in Appendix A.

Discrimination is everybody's problem

It is easy to see the inequality we experience ourselves. It is harder to see how others are hurt by inequalities we do not experience, and to see the ways we discriminate against others. When our organizing challenges unequal access to opportunities, resources, and power in factories, we have to look at the roles that everyone, including ourselves, plays in continuing discrimination.

Activity	Who has the power?

1. In a group, brainstorm who has more power in your factory. Ask participants to consider what qualities people may have, or what positions they may be in that allow them to use their power to treat others badly. Do not use people's names. Focus on the positions or qualities they have. Write these down on the left side of a board or a large piece of paper under the heading More Power.

2. Then, ask people to think about the qualities people have or positions they are in that give them less power and make them subject to discrimination. Write these down on the right of the previous list, under the heading Less Power. Have people give examples of how these people are discriminated against: what happens, what do people feel, how do others treat them?

MORE POWER	LESS POWER
Owner	Supervisor
Supervisor	Worker
Contract worker	Temporary worker
Men	Women
Operators	Cleaners
Young	Old
Native-born	Migrant
Lighter skin	Darker skin
Majority	Minority
Not married and no babies	Married with a family
Educated	No education

(continued)

Activity	Who has the power? *(continued)*

3. Ask about how power is used in the factory: do people with more power use it to help or harm others in the factory?

4. Assign each person in the group a position and a few qualities from the More Power or the Less Power column. Make sure to assign equal numbers of roles from each column and to assign them randomly.

5. Now ask people to stand up and stand side by side. Make sure there is enough room for people to move forward and backward.

6. Using any of the qualities or positions in the More Power list, say, "Take a step forward if you are a man," or "Take a step forward if you are a worker with a contract." Then say, "Take a step backward if you are a woman," or "Take a step backward if you are a temporary worker," using the list in the Less Power column. Continue alternating between the 2 lists until everyone has taken several steps and people can see they are in different places.

7. Ask people to tell the group what mix of qualities and positions they have that contributed to their place in the power march.

8. Have a prize or prizes prepared (a piece of fruit or other snack), but give it first to the people who "lost" the power march, saying, "Why should the people with power always win?" Then give a snack to everyone.

9. End the activity by discussing what has to change to make work and power in the factory more equal. What should people in different roles do differently? You can also do the activity on page 317.

I can share my prize.

Improve women's status in the community and at work

Discrimination against women at home and in the community is brought, often without thinking, by workers and management into the factory and strengthens discrimination in the workplace. But by working to set rules in the workplace that prohibit discrimination, attitudes about what women can and cannot do might begin changing. These changes might be brought out of the factory and into the community as well. It's worth trying, and the activities in this chapter can help you make these changes.

The second shift

Before and after long days and nights in the factory, many women workers continue working: women cook, clean, and care for their families. Working outside the home and then coming home to more work means that women work 2 jobs, one of which is not paid enough and the other is not paid at all!

Overworked in the factory and at home, a woman's double work often gives her double stress. The demands of meeting family emotional and caregiving needs, combined with the economic demands of providing for the family through factory work, make many women's lives seem like production lines that move too fast and have unachievable production quotas. What is produced with great efficiency is unhappiness and stress, which can cause physical, mental, and emotional health problems. See chapter 27: Stress and mental health.

With all her family and work duties, it is hard for a working woman to find the time to prepare healthy meals, to care for her own needs, and to rest, much less to participate in community, women's, or workers' groups.

Support women to join organizing efforts

Because many women work a second shift and because factory areas are often dangerous, women face barriers getting involved in worker movements. Your group can make worker events more welcome to all if it:

- holds meetings near where workers live. Make sure safe transportation is available to get there and get home.
- calls meetings for times that do not conflict with women's work at home. Women have many time-consuming home duties such as washing, cooking, and gathering water, fuel, and food. Many women care for children, parents, or other family members.
- provides childcare at meetings. If you can, also offer food.
- creates gender policies to guide the work of the union. Set goals for the number of women in union offices and launch programs to increase the activity of women in the union.

What do you do in a day?

When women workers have to spend all their free hours doing all the work at home, they have no time to rest, take care of their needs, eat well, have fun, participate in the community, or join organizing campaigns.

This activity helps make visible all the duties that women have at work and at home.

1. Ask the group about all their duties and responsibilities during the day. On the board, write women's answers on one side and men's on the other.

2. How do they compare? What kind of responsibilities does one group have that the other does not? Why do you think that is the case?

MEN	WOMEN
Sleep	Sleep
Wake up	Feed the children
Go to work	Take them to school
Union meeting	Make all meals
Visit mother	Wash clothes
Eat	Iron clothes
	Make the beds

Take mom to clinic
Sweep and mop
Wash dishes
Go to work
Eat

If men share family responsibilities, men and women can both have some time to do things they like.

3. Ask each group to say what things they like or would like to do during the day. They can list as many as will fit on their side of the board. Ask: Do they have time to do the things they like?

4. Discuss how men and women can share some of the work involved in taking care of the home and children more equally.

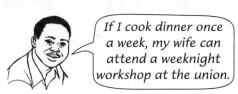

If I cook dinner once a week, my wife can attend a weeknight workshop at the union.

Include all people in organizing efforts

Unions, health and safety committees, and other worker groups should represent and fight for the needs of all workers in the factory, focusing particularly on the groups that have usually had less power, such as women.

One way in which unions can ensure that the voices of those most oppressed are heard and represented is to make sure that their leadership includes people from those groups. Representation, however, does not mean that women's voices will be heard. Male leaders need to make a commitment to women's equality too.

Our factories, like our communities, are now very diverse, so why shouldn't the union be diverse too? Fighting for equality in the union is just a small step, but when we achieve it, we open the doors for solidarity, unity, and a better life for all in our communities.

Organize activities with a group or union to talk about the ways in which gender affects women and men differently. Some women's groups organize to challenge discrimination by sharing information about women's rights through workshops and meetings, posters, flyers, newsletters, and even through songs and theater.

Gender issues for unions to bargain with the employer

- No sexual harassment
- No violence against women
- Equal pay for equal work
- Access to the same jobs – no sex discrimination in the workplace
- Safe transportation to and from the factory
- Parental rights and childcare facilities, including time during the day for breastfeeding
- No forced pregnancy tests or firing workers who become pregnant
- Flexible work hours to allow workers to care for family members

Use the law to fight against discrimination

Most governments have laws that ban discrimination at work and in the community. If you decide to report discrimination — to your boss, the brands your factory is producing for, the government, or a human rights group in your community — you should:

Have as much information as possible about the incident or incidents of discrimination. Write or ask someone to help you write the facts of what happened, including the date, time, location, names of witnesses, and other details. If it happens often, keep a running list of it all. It will also help to record what was said to you. Use a cell phone to take video of any incident.

Connect with other workers who might be experiencing discrimination. Working with groups that have something in common, for example, having women organizers talk with women workers, might make people more comfortable speaking about the discrimination they face. Add their experiences to a log of discrimination events in your factory, but do not reveal the names of workers unless they give their permission. Even if you decide not to report discrimination to your boss or government officials now, this information can be helpful in organizing workers or showing how long such situations have been occurring if things get worse.

Seek support from workers, human rights, women's rights, or other community groups. Discrimination affects people in many parts of their lives. NGOs in your community might already be organizing to fight against discrimination. They can help you decide what strategy might work best for you and the workers in your factory.

Find your power

The discrimination workers face at the factory and in the community can make them feel they do not deserve to be treated well — to earn a living wage, to be protected against safety dangers, to have decent benefits. They are being told, "just be glad you have a job." Self-esteem is further harmed when these ideas are repeated by co-workers, especially those who do not face all the same challenges. Sometimes we feel we have no power to fight against unfair and unhealthy working conditions. However, even when we do not think so, we all have power in some parts of our lives. We have:

Power within ourselves to hope and fight for a better future and to recognize and believe in ourselves.

Power with other workers. Even though we are different, we face many of the same challenges in the workplace. Working with other workers allows you to share the responsibility (and risk) of organizing, but it also allows you to reach for bigger goals!

Power to take action and change our circumstances. Whether we work with a group of people or not, nobody can take away our power to stand up for our rights.

<table>
<tr><td>Activity</td><td># We have power, too!</td></tr>
</table>

Activity

We have power, too!

1. Break the group into pairs. Ask each person to tell the other about an event or experience in which they feel powerless. Then ask them to tell about an experience that made them feel powerful or respected.

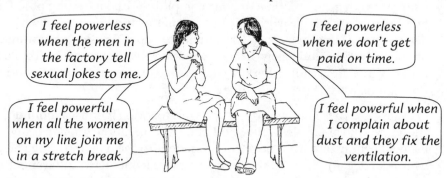

I feel powerless when the men in the factory tell sexual jokes to me.

I feel powerless when we don't get paid on time.

I feel powerful when all the women on my line join me in a stretch break.

I feel powerful when I complain about dust and they fix the ventilation.

2. Bring the group back together, and ask one person from each pair to tell one of the stories about feeling powerful or respected. Use a large piece of paper to make a list of the things that make people feel powerful.

3. Then ask one person from each pair to tell one of the stories about feeling powerless. Discuss each story.

   • What could you do or say to make a person feel supported in this situation?

   • What could we do as a group to support that worker?

   • What could we do to change the situation?

4. Add people's ideas of what makes people feel powerful to the list.

5. Conclude by discussing how we can include these ideas in our organizing and the ways we relate to each other.

What makes you feel powerful?
Learning about my rights
Creating a plan for difficult situations
Meetings
Working with the community
Learning to become a leader
Organizing a group of workers
Talking to workers from other factories
Singing together

They divide and rule; we unite and conquer!

Our small factory in Los Angeles, USA, had only 20 workers but we came from 5 different countries and spoke 5 different languages. We could not talk to each other, not even about what was happening at work. Another problem was that many of us were working without legal working papers. When anyone complained about getting paid for only 35 hours when we worked 50, the owner would threaten us with deportation. There was also a lot of racial tension. We didn't know much about each other and when the boss would tell us that a person from one group worked less than others, it was easy to blame all the people from that group. It was hard to organize.

An NGO in our community reached out to many factories that had the same kind of problem. They had materials in many languages and brought organizers who spoke our languages to the meetings. They helped us talk to one another. After hearing workers from all the different ethnic groups talk about their experiences and about how the boss was trying to divide us, we realized we needed to work together instead of against one another.

It took many months to learn to trust each other and to build up the power within our group. With the help of the worker organization we learned that even workers without legal papers have the right to organize and demand fair pay. Finally, one day we went on strike. The boss was so surprised! He never thought we would work together. It wasn't an easy battle and many times the boss's men would come to our homes and communities and try to provoke hate among the different groups. But we knew we had to stand together in order to change conditions in our factory.

Violence

Violence, both as a threat and as an act, harms the physical and mental well-being of workers, their families, friends, co-workers, and communities. Bosses sometimes use threats and physical, verbal, and psychological violence to keep factory workers fearful and docile, and to stop workers from demanding change. Workers may also face violence from other workers or community members who use violence to impose power over others. Whether attacks come from other workers, supervisors, paid thugs, or the police or military, stopping violence is rarely achieved by one worker alone. Organization is the one essential element of every successful struggle against workplace violence. When workers are unified they can:

- improve interactions among workers and supervisors in the factory, minimize yelling and public humiliation as management practices, and end hitting and physical violence as ways to control workers.
- demand that employers respect workers' rights to organize unions and to improve working conditions, pay, and benefits.
- form committees to train workers in self-defense, to travel home from work in groups, and to document violence and demand justice.
- stop the boss and other workers from sexually harassing or attacking women and men employees.
- create a workplace free from violence, where finding solutions to disagreements is done respectfully, involving workers and management equally.

Violence in the factory

There are many forms of violence. Sometimes we do not recognize them as violence because we are used to them and they feel normal. But the bad effects violence can have on our mental and physical health are not something that we should get used to. We do not think that injuries from dangerous machines are normal. Likewise, why should we think violent behaviors are ok?

Everyday abuse

Constant yelling, name calling, rude comments and insults are forms of emotional and psychological violence. Sometimes workers do not even recognize this abuse because it is so common. Constant abuse damages self-esteem and trains us to accept bad working conditions and other types of violence as well.

Look at you! You are so clumsy, stupid girl!

An abusive supervisor is a workplace danger.

Physical violence

Physical violence is the most visible kind of violence. Workers are beaten, cut, slapped, shoved, pinched, hit, and burned. (To treat these injuries, see First Aid on pages 203 to 204.) Some employers hit in places that cannot be seen, so the worker cannot report and prove it. When workers live with the constant fear of being struck by their supervisors, it also creates stress and other mental health problems (see chapter 27).

Murder

In too many countries, factory owners pay thugs (sometimes other workers or corrupt union officials) to murder workers, organizers, and union leaders to stop them from demanding better wages or conditions. Sometimes they count on the police or military to carry out this work for them. To create more fear and gain more control, they also threaten and kill workers' families.

Activity   # Facing fear together

Bosses use violence to instill fear in workers and shut up union leaders. Many workers are reluctant to talk about their fear of violence and instead let the violence do just what it was meant to: prevent people from participating in organizing. For a group to withstand violence, it is important to talk about people's fears and come up with ways  to support each other. When you can call a meeting to discuss fear of violence:

1. **Remind people of their reasons for organizing.**

   - **Issues:** Restate why the issues are important to each and every worker and what your organizing will achieve.

   - **Strength in unity:** The fears each person faces appear smaller and less overwhelming when people feel part of a larger, supportive group.

2. **Give workers space to talk about their fears.** Encourage people to talk freely. Sometimes social or political reasons prevent people from being open about their fears. Be compassionate and find creative ways to encourage people to participate. The goal is not to get rid of fear, but to learn how to face fear and not let it stop your organizing efforts.

3. **Identify fears shared by the whole group.** Make a list of the fears people raise, and ask which fears are the most serious or widespread.

Some male workers might not want to admit to a large group they are afraid, since men are raised not to show fear.

4. **Make a plan for dealing with these specific fears and threats of violence**. By talking about the most common fears of violence, workers can begin to make plans for dealing with them. You can talk about ways to reduce risks, prevent leaders and organizers from being identified, increase support from other workers and organizations, and campaign against violence.

If the climate at your factory becomes extremely violent, the group might consider temporarily hiding their organizing efforts. This may not stop the violence, but it can give workers a chance to regroup and decide how to continue the struggle in ways that feel safer.

Sexual violence

Although it would seem that sexual violence is caused by men's sexual desire, it really has more to do with power over others than it does with sex. Women are often blamed for the sexual violence they suffer. But as with other kinds of violence, the person who chooses to use violence is the person who is guilty.

Just as violence usually includes a mix of behaviors, from yelling and humiliation to beatings and murder, sexual violence can include behaviors from unwanted attention and touching to rape and murder.

Sexual harassment

Sexual harassment is a big problem in many factories where most supervisors and managers are men and most workers are young women. In the community, women workers are also harassed by other workers, neighbors, and strangers. Often the harassment happens around the factory, particularly at the start and end of shifts or at lunch time.

People do not always agree about what sexual harassment is. One woman may be offended by a joke that makes another woman laugh. Some women feel harassed when strangers make comments about them on the street. Other women do not mind very much. Each person knows when she feels harassed, and how she feels is what matters.

When we leave the factory at night men are always hanging around at the gate. They stare at us and make sexual comments about our bodies. The guard does nothing.

Sexual harassment is any kind of unwanted, unreasonable, or offensive sexual attention. Sexual harassment can be:

- **touching**: patting, stroking, grabbing, pinching, hugging, or leaning against another person's body;
- **words or sounds**: comments, whistling, or noises that suggest sex;
- **body language**: standing too close, pointing, facial expressions, or gestures with any part of the body intended to suggest sex;
- **pictures**: making someone look at sexual photographs, drawings, or videos, or having these images in public spaces; photographing or filming someone during sexual acts;
- **writing**: sexual graffiti on walls and other public places; sending someone notes, letters, or poems that suggest sex.

In factories, the person who is harassing might demand sex in exchange for a job or a promotion. Harassers are often supervisors or other bosses who can fire a worker or make her job harder if she objects to being touched or refuses to have sex. Men harass women because they know they have more power than women. But men also harass each other, using jokes, insults, and threats intended to place another man in a woman's role, so he will be considered to be less than a man.

Men might suffer sexual harassment at work, too.

Some people say, "Sexual harassment is no problem."

We say, "Sexual harassment is wrong!"

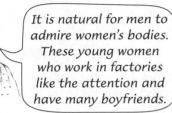

It is natural for men to admire women's bodies. These young women who work in factories like the attention and have many boyfriends.

Would you want your daughter or sister or mother treated like that?

If a man tries to become sexual with a woman, she must have done something to tempt him.

Harassment has nothing to do with what women do, say, or look like. It is never justified.

A woman's world is inside the home of her family and husband. Women should serve their husbands and children. If a woman leaves the protection of her family to go into a man's world, she should expect trouble.

We work to support our families. If we did not work we would not have enough money to survive. We should not be treated badly for trying to survive.

Factory responds to sexual harassment

Apolinar had been harassing me at work for a few months. At first it was easy to ignore what he said to me, but after he became my supervisor he said we were going to marry and I would have his children. I was very clear that I was not interested, but he kept insisting that soon we would be together and he kept asking me out.

One day he tried to move me to an isolated job. When I refused, he got really angry and started yelling at me. I reported him to his boss, who said I had misunderstood Apolinar. Realizing he wasn't going to help me, I went to the personnel manager. First he said, "You must stand up to him." Then he blamed me, saying he had seen me encourage Apolinar.

Since nobody at the factory would help me, I went to CEREAL, an organization that helps workers in Guadalajara, Mexico. They called the factory, but the managers did nothing to stop the harassment. So I resigned. When the people from CEREAL heard that I quit, they contacted the factory management again and this time they did something. They fired Apolinar and offered me a job at another plant.

He did it!

I have worked in a toy factory for 5 years. My supervisor would lean over me and touch my back and arms. I hated it but I was working and could not escape. It made very angry and uncomfortable. One day, when he came over to me, I reached my arm around him like I was patting him on the back. He did not realize I had put a sign on his back that said "Harasser!" I was so afraid he would get angry and fire me. But, when all the other workers and supervisors saw the sign and laughed at him, he got very embarrassed and stopped bothering me at my station!

If you are being harassed at work:

- Let the harasser know clearly and directly that you do not want his attention. If you are being harassed in public, respond by speaking loudly to the harasser.

- Ask co-workers to help you post signs in bathrooms naming the harasser.

- Keep a record of when and where you were harassed, and what happened. Write what the harasser said, what you said, how you felt, and what any witnesses did or saw. Keep things the harasser gives you as proof.

- Report the harassment to your boss, supervisor, union representative, worker or women's group. Many countries, factories, and companies have laws and policies against sexual harassment but as with other labor rights, you often have to organize with others to have them enforced.

Activity | # Role playing builds confidence

It can be difficult to confront a harasser and tell him to stop. You can feel more confident by practicing what to say with other people. A conversation with one person playing the role of another person is called "role play." You may also want to role play how to tell your husband or family about the harassment, or how to report it to your boss or the police.

Come here, girl.

Leave me alone!

Rape

Many policies in the factory put women at risk of being raped. Working alone in isolated parts of the factory, night shifts or leaving work late, lack of safe transportation to and from the factory, and an overall acceptance of domination and violence put women in danger. Rape is one of the worst kinds of sexual violence, because it affects women physically, sexually, emotionally, and psychologically, and it also affects their families and communities. Rape happens when men want to have power over women — it does not matter what women wear, how they act, or what they do. Rape is never the woman's fault.

If you know someone who has been raped:

- **Reassure her** that it was not her fault.
- **Be supportive.** Listen to her feelings, help her decide what she needs, and reassure her that she can go on with her life.
- **Respect her wishes for privacy and safety.** Do not tell anyone unless she wants you to.
- **Go with her** to see a health worker, to report the rape to the police, to talk with someone who is trained to listen and support her, to see a lawyer, and to go to court if she wants to do those things.
- **Do not protect the rapist** if you know him. He might do this again.

Health exam after rape

Someone who has been raped should see a health worker as soon as she can after the rape to get medical help and to record as much evidence as she can, especially if she is going to report the rape to the police. It is important that the health worker marks down everywhere that she is hurt. It may be helpful to document evidence of forced sex with photographs of bruises and other injuries.

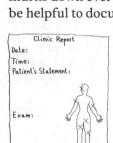

A drawing of a body like this one can be helpful for the health worker to note injuries she sees during the exam. Both the health worker and the person who was attacked should keep a copy.

First aid after rape

Get medical and emotional help if you are raped or assaulted.

First, talk with an understanding friend, someone you trust. Ask her to go with you to get medical care. Even if your injuries are not serious, a medical exam can document them, which may be useful later.

A health worker or doctor who understands the trauma of assault and rape can be will make the visit easier. Later you may want to talk with a counselor or support group of women who have been sexually assaulted or raped.

Tears and cuts

Sometimes rape damages the genitals by causing tears and cuts. These usually cause pain, but will go away in time. If there is lots of bleeding, you may need to see a health worker trained to stitch tears. For small cuts and tears:

- Soak your genitals 3 times each day in warm water that has been boiled and cooled. Putting chamomile leaves in the water can help soothe torn skin and help with healing. Or you can put gel from an aloe plant on the cuts and tears.

- Pour clean water over your genitals while passing urine so it will not burn. Drinking lots of water makes the urine weaker so it will burn less.

- Watch for signs of infection: heat, yellow liquid (pus) from the torn area, bad smell, and pain that gets worse.

Preventing pregnancy

You can prevent a pregnancy after rape if you act quickly. Use emergency family planning (see page 387) as soon as possible, no later than 5 days (120 hours) after sex. The sooner you use it, the better it works.

In some countries, abortion is safe and legal if a girl or woman has been raped. Ask a health worker or women's organization for more information.

(continued)

First Aid

First Aid

(continued)

Bladder Infection

After violent sex it is common for women to have a bladder infection. Treat a bladder infection as soon as you notice it so you do not also get a kidney infection. (See page 416 for more information.) See a health worker right away if you:

- need to pass urine very often,
- have pain, especially in the lower belly, or a burning feeling while passing urine, or
- your urine smells bad, looks cloudy, or has blood or pus in it.

Sexually transmitted infections (STIs)

Sexually transmitted infections pass from person to person during unprotected sex. After violent sex, the skin in the vagina or the anus may be torn, allowing an infection into the body. Since you cannot know if the person who raped you was infected with an STI, you should take medicine for gonorrhea, chlamydia, and syphilis right away. These infections often show no signs of illness, but cause serious health problems if they are not treated. (See *Where Women Have No Doctor*, chapter 16.)

HIV

If rape exposes you to HIV, a health worker can help you prevent HIV infection by prescribing 1 month of treatment with antiretroviral medicines (ART). Start treatment as soon as possible. Because HIV does not show up in tests for about 3 months, you should wait to take an HIV test. Even though you used the ART, the test is important to make sure you were not infected. During this time, use a condom if you have sex so you will not pass HIV to someone else in case you are infected.

Hepatitis B and C

Hepatitis B and C are viral infections that harm the liver. Both infections can pass from one person to another during sex. You can have one of these viruses and not get sick. But some people with hepatitis B or C become very ill with serious liver problems. Get tested right away, and come back for a retest after 6 weeks. Use a condom if you have sex during the time between when the rape happened and when you get the second test.

The right to live free of violence and sexual harassment

Violence and sexual harassment undermine individual and collective freedom and dignity. Also see The right to equality on page 309.

The **UN Universal Declaration of Human Rights** says:

- Every person has the right to life, liberty, and security of person.
- No one shall be subjected to torture or cruel, inhumane, or degrading treatment or punishment.

Governments are responsible for ensuring that workers are protected against all forms of physical, verbal, sexual, psychological, and emotional violence.

Sexual harassment is recognized around the world as a form of violence that hurts women and denies their right to live a healthy, dignified, violence-free life.

The UN includes "sexual harassment and intimidation at work" in the definition of violence against women. The Conventions that protect women against violence (see treaties.un.org) can be used to organize to stop sexual harassment at work.

The ILO says sexual harassment is a form of discrimination that undermines the integrity, dignity, and well-being of workers from many different communities, including women, youth, LGBT, and ethnic and racial minorities. Sexual harassment also violates workers' right to a safe, healthy workplace.

The **Inter-American Convention on Violence against Women (A61)** says:

- Women have the right to a workplace free from violence.
- Governments must penalize harassers and help victims of sexual harassment.

Unions that belong to the the **International Trade Union Confederation** (ITUC) have an Action Program to combat sexual harassment in the workplace. All their member unions have agreed to:

- include language against sexual harassment in their contracts.
- create rules about how to handle complaints and investigations.
- ensure regulations against sexual harassment are included in collective agreements.
- develop and provide trainings about sexual harassment to all members.

The roles of the UN, ILO, and other international organizations that promote workers' rights are explained in Appendix A.

Casa Amiga fights to protect women in Ciudad Juarez

In Ciudad Juarez, a Mexican city with many garment factories on the US-Mexico border, around 400 young women have been raped and murdered in the last two decades. The police have investigated very few of these killings. For all these crimes, only 3 men were ever arrested; 1 died in the hands of the police and the other 2 were tortured to get them to confess.

Esther Cano Chavez, founder of Casa Amiga Crisis Center, believed the murders and the lack of government effort to solve them or protect women was predictable. "As women start to take factory jobs and become independent, men use violence to punish them for breaking social rules. Women organizers are particularly targeted." Although Esther died of cancer in 2009, Casa Amiga continues to offer hope for the future by helping and supporting women victims of violence.

Casa Amiga offers a 24-hour rape and sexual abuse hotline, medical services, legal advice, and psychological counseling. They also work to prevent violence in the home and to challenge inequality and discrimination. Casa Amiga campaigns for safer streets, safe public transportation, and police patrols of areas where women have been abducted. They also organize self-defense classes for women workers.

Protect yourself and others

Do not be caught alone. Many times, thugs target workers when they are alone. Walk with others to and from the factory or bus station. If it is possible, have someone meet you at your bus stop. If you know of any worker who is being harassed or who you think might be hurt, find ways of accompanying him or her so that he or she is not alone.

If a worker is threatened by the boss, a supervisor, or another worker, do not leave her alone with the person who threatened her. Organize other workers to stay close to her at the factory and going to and from work. A worker alone is more likely to be attacked than a group of workers together.

To help yourself or others, learn where first aid and medical services can be found. For first aid information on treating injuries when you cannot reach a health worker, see pages 203 to 204. Also see *Where There Is No Doctor*, chapter 10: First Aid, for more information.

Record and report violence

Write down as much information about each violent incident as possible. Make a detailed description of what happened. Include:

- When did it happen (date and time)?
- Where did it happen?
- Who did what?

- Who witnessed it?
- Did you report it? To whom? What did they do?

If possible, take a photo or video of the incident. This record will be helpful whether you keep it or use it to make a report to the boss, the police, or any agency that can help you.

If you know of other workers being attacked, help them record attacks. Use a survey, workplace map, or community map to help you find out which workers are being threatened or attacked, where the attacks occur, when they occur, who committed the violence, and what kind of violence was used. This can give you better information to report or to use in planning how to prevent and resist violence against workers.

This street is safer. There are people around all times of day and night.

Collect information for a community map.

Respect workers' decisions. If a worker does not want to report the abuse for fear of retaliation or further violence, respect her decision. But ask her if she would allow the incident to be recorded without her name or other identifying information. This information can be helpful in mapping where, how often, and in what situations violence happens.

Get the local police to start a women's desk, staffed day and night by women police officers trained to take action on sexual violence cases.

Protest assaults against workers, demand appropriate compensation, bring abusers to justice, and prevent future violence. Build alliances between your union, women's organizations, community groups, and churches.

Activity	Learn self-defense

Practicing self-defense in a group can help you learn ways to defend yourselves if you are attacked. Invite someone from a local martial arts school to offer a workshop. The most important thing to learn is how to stop someone long enough for you to get away. If you continue with martial arts after that, you will be surprised at how quickly your skills increase. Self-defense groups are a good way of reaching out to more people and helping them gain self-confidence, as well as reducing the chances of being assaulted.

If you are assaulted, hit the attacker as hard as you can. Do not be afraid to hurt him — he is not afraid to hurt you.

Hit him hard in the stomach with your elbow, and run.

Step down hard on his foot with your heel, and run.

Lift your knee, and push it as hard and fast as you can in the groin.

Make your hands into fists and hit him as hard as you can on the nose.

Making harassment a work issue

When women workers in your factory are being harassed by other workers or men in the community it might be harder for them to seek support from workers or worker organizations. Your group can take a stand against harassment even if nobody has reported a case to you.

Talking about harassment makes many people uncomfortable, especially in groups that include both men and women. Hold separate meetings to help women open up about their experiences. Ask the other participants to think of ways to support women who are dealing with harassment and violence individually, but to also make a plan to work collaboratively to reduce and stop violence and harassment at work and in the community.

Telling everybody

There was a problem in our factory. Some men regularly made sexual remarks and jokes around the women workers. It was not just 1 or 2 men — it was a problem in most departments. Since the men are our co-workers, we wanted to take care of it ourselves, not get them in trouble with the boss.

We knew the men would not come to a meeting to discuss this. So we decided to bring it up at the next union meeting without putting it on the agenda. Because sexual harassment affects workers in so many ways, we knew we could find a way to raise it during debate on another issue.

I started with a story about how the jokes made me upset and sad. Two other women also had their stories ready. We did not accuse any worker by name. We focused on how the harassment affected us personally, and how disrespect divides workers and weakens the union.

After we told our stories, both men and women talked about harassment without feeling so guilty or defensive. Some of the men also confessed the sexual jokes made them uncomfortable. Many of us now feel we can bring issues of sexual harassment to the group and the union will support us if we file a claim. Knowing other workers support us and understand the issues is important to us.

Organize for a "no violence" policy

Some factories have a policy that bans violence in the workplace but do not enforce it. Companies that purchase from your factory may have codes of conduct that ban or penalize violence in the workplace. Try to find out what the policy is or involve the companies in setting up a no violence policy in your factory. A no violence policy should include:

- **clear definitions** of the threats and forms of violence that will not be tolerated.
- **an education program** for managers and workers explaining the policy. All new workers and managers should be told about the policy.
- **signs and posters** about the no violence policy that describe how employers will respond to complaints.
- **a complaint system** that is confidential for workers to report concerns, threats, and violence.
- **a fair and timely process for responding to complaints**, addressing unsafe areas of the factory, and preventing future intimidation and violence.
- **safety from retaliation** against workers who report unsafe areas or complain of fear, threats, or violence.

Just having a policy does not mean that violence will not happen. Working with other workers, labor groups, and government agencies can help you figure out the best ways to enforce a no-violence policy.

Find support in your stand against violence

Groups that organize against violence in the home and the community can help workers and unions build anti-violence campaigns in the workplace.

Other groups provide legal, social, and emotional support to victims of violence and their families. Ask them to help you and your co-workers. They may also have experience with medical and psychological recovery, dealing with authorities, and preparing to return to work. In addition to offering individuals emotional support, they may have ideas about how to build ongoing support groups to deal with violence at work and in the community.

We can overcome violence

My name is Chernklang Kreetha. I grew up in a rural area in Thailand but moved to Taiwan to find a job in a factory. The work conditions at that factory were not very good. After almost 3 years of working there, I got together with other workers in the factory to demand that the boss pay us for all the unpaid overtime, un-refunded taxes, illegal deductions from our wages, and forced savings that he kept. We thought we were going to win.

But a few days later, when we were leaving the factory for dinner, we were attacked by 8 thugs with clubs. The other workers managed to escape but I was trapped and beaten badly. They left me unconscious, lying in the street in front of the factory.

The other workers were shocked and scared, but more than anything, they were outraged that our boss would treat us like this. So the next day, they walked out of the factory, carrying signs that said "No to Violence," and "We want our rights now!" in Chinese, English, and Thai.

We knew this would upset the boss more and he would try to hurt us again. So we asked for help at the Hope Workers' Center. The Center protects and supports migrant workers in Taiwan. They housed us for a while to protect us and helped us organize to demand our rights.

After a lot of pressure, the company let us return to work and when we finished our 3-year contract, they gave us our back pay, taxes, and all the savings they had taken from us.

I did not think I had the courage to risk my life to get the rights I deserved, but the support from my co-workers, the community, and the Center helped me see that I was not alone and that we could win.

23 Workers who migrate

Many men, women, and children move to different cities or countries in search of better jobs, wages, and opportunities for themselves and their families. What they often find are new challenges and risks. Although they work as hard or harder than other workers, people who migrate face discrimination inside and outside the factory, legally and illegally, in ways that ultimately hurt all workers, not just migrants.

Like other workers, migrant workers deserve and need:

- safe living and working conditions, and a living wage
- access to health care, social services, and education, for themselves and their families
- the right to organize in unions, with materials in their own language
- freedom from violence and threats of displacement or deportation

Most important, people should have the right **not** to migrate, to stay in their ancestral homes, participate in the social and political life of their regions, and find ways to make a decent living in the place they or their families were born.

Learn about migrating before you leave

To better prepare for the challenges ahead, find out ahead of time what to expect while traveling and then arriving in your new city or country. If your arrangements are being made by another person, find out as much as you can about what is being planned. If possible, ask for a written agreement and leave a copy with your family or friends at home. Learn about migration and work laws, culture and behaviors, and how they might affect you. Ask about what is important to bring with you and what should be left behind for safe-keeping.

Recruiters and smugglers

Recruiters work for the large export factories that need workers. They charge the worker to get her a job, and charge the owner to find workers. Recruiters sometimes work with smugglers, who move people from one country to another, usually without legal permission. Dishonest recruiters and smugglers often lie about the conditions of work or travel, saying it is much better than it really is. They might change their fees as soon as you leave home, and they might put you in dangerous situations.

Getting into debt to get a job

I was so excited to have a chance to work in a factory in Taiwan. The recruiter promised more than I could earn at home in the Philippines.

I borrowed money from my family to pay the labor broker to take me to Taiwan. There, I was met by another recruiter who wanted even more money to get me work at a factory. I did not have much choice, so I agreed to pay him a little each week. Then I found out the factory also charges expensive room and board for the dormitory, deducts taxes, and withholds "savings" for when I finish my contract.

Each week after I pay the bills, I am left with little money to live on. I have to stay here and work until I can pay all that I owe. But it will take years to pay off this debt! I tell my sisters, brothers, cousins, and everyone back home to stay away from the labor recruiters. They promise a wonderful life but it is a lie.

Activity   Gather information about recruiters

Sharing information helps protect people from dishonest recruiters.

1. Ask other workers and their families about the recruiters and smugglers who work in your community:
   - Are they local or from other communities? Are they easy to find?
   - Who do they work for?
   - How are they paid?
   - How much do they charge the worker? The company?
   - What do they promise and what do they deliver?
   - Have they hurt or lost anybody?
   - Can they be trusted?

2. Share information with others so that everyone in your community can make better decisions when choosing a recruiter.

3. Make and post a list of recruiters who hurt or cheat workers.

Collect information about migrating

If you or someone you know is planning on migrating, gather as much information as you can about your destination from people who have migrated or their families, community centers, churches, health centers, NGOs, and the Internet. This can help you anticipate and avoid problems.

Try to find out about:

- **jobs available** in other parts of your country. Begin by asking in government offices, looking at newspapers, and talking to people. Maybe you do not have to migrate so far.

- **the real benefits and challenges of migrating,** including working conditions, costs, income, dangers, and how long you might have to stay.

- **recruiters, traffickers, and employers,** their honesty and helpfulness. Knowing what might be causes for concern can help you make better decisions. For instance, if the recruiter offers you a job that seems too good to be true, you should be cautious about accepting the job.

RADIO REALIDAD

Tell us about your experience migrating north to find work.

- **the destination city or country,** including type of jobs available, working and living conditions for migrant workers, local customs, and language.

- **the process for travel** to the destination country, fees to be paid, permits to be obtained, and waiting periods required.

- **how to get medical attention.** Make a list of low-cost or free services that are available to migrant workers on the way and at your destination.

- **how to manage money,** from opening a bank account and understanding basic banking processes, to learning how to save for the future, how to send money home, and how to help family members understand how you want them to use the money.

- **contact information** for resources in the new country such as embassies, migrant groups, unions, and human rights groups. Memorize some phone numbers of family members or friends in case of emergency.

Prepare for challenges in your new place

One of the reasons workers are encouraged to migrate is that employers find that migrants, who may not understand local languages or customs, or may not be protected by national laws, are easier to control than local workers. So migrant workers face more social dangers than other workers.

Sharing our stories

The Rural Development Foundation (RDF), an NGO in Indonesia, holds workshops for people interested in migrating. They learn about migrant worker rights and explore some of the dangers of migrating. If a person decides to migrate for work, they prepare him or her for life in the new place, focusing on family relationships, learning to resolve problems during long separations, and how to manage money.

When and if workers return, the RDF encourages them to share their stories with others who want to migrate, so that they too can prepare for the challenges of migration.

Returned workers can also receive trainings on managing businesses, credit unions, cooperatives, learning to invest, and using money wisely so they do not have to leave again.

Violence against immigrants

Moving to a new country without legal papers puts workers at the mercy of smugglers and other people who want to take advantage of them. Workers are often alone, afraid of being caught by the police, and in unfamiliar places or situations. For reasons that have nothing to do with the immigrants themselves, local groups often stir up anger, fear, and hatred against migrants. See chapter 21: Discrimination.

Women who migrate are most at risk for violence, not only because they are doing something risky — migrating — but also because recruiters, smugglers, labor contractors, employers, and even law enforcement think they can get away with hurting women. Sometimes women are told they will be given factory jobs but are instead forced into sex work. Women's organizations often provide help and shelter to migrant women in danger. See chapter 22: Violence.

Deportation or forced repatriation

Many countries have built their economies on the labor of migrant workers. Bosses try to get away with paying very low wages, following few or no safety regulations, and providing no protections or benefits. If workers complain or demand better conditions or pay, bosses threaten them with deportation.

Even workers who have legal documents to work in a new region or country are sometimes threatened with deportation. Usually, legal aid groups or clinics offer services in places where there are a large numbers of migrants. Ask around to find out which do the most affordable and responsible work.

Language and culture

If you do not speak the local language, it may be hard to make friends and fit into the community. Learning the local language and customs makes it easier to protect yourself, talk to other workers, and get and give support. But it is also important to have spaces to celebrate your own culture and language.

Ask the union and worker organizations to translate written materials into the different languages that workers in your factory speak, so that all workers can participate. Having interpreters in your meetings can help migrant workers participate more actively.

Housing and transportation

Factories that offer housing make it easy to find a place to live, but factory dormitories can have many disadvantages. See chapter 32: A decent place to live for ideas on how to organize for better housing.

In Bangladesh, workers have formed hostels that are cheaper and safer than factory dorms.

Access to health care

Some factories have medical services, but they are often very basic and the company-paid doctors often refuse to recognize work-related health problems. But using medical services outside of the factory can be difficult for migrant workers. Workers without documents might fear that by going to a health facility they will be reported to immigration authorities.

Even when health services are run by the government, that does not mean that they will report you. Low-cost or free medical services for migrant workers, regardless of legal status, in your language and respectful of your cultural and religious beliefs may be available. Ask other migrant workers and unions, social services, and churches about where to get care.

Some health programs offer migrant workers particular services, such as reproductive and sexual health information. Other organizations that work with migrant workers may not generally offer health services but do provide free tests for sexually transmitted infections (STIs) and HIV, as well as free condoms and medicines. Do not be afraid to ask.

Meaningful contact back home

Living without the support of the family and community you left behind can be lonely, stressful, and exhausting. The pressure to send money home can create tension and sometimes make family relationships more difficult. Finding ways of connecting to family back home can help reduce stress and other mental health problems. See chapter 27: Stress and mental health.

We offer many free workshops for migrant workers. A popular one shows them how to use the computers in internet cafes to connect with their families. It is very cheap and easy to set a regular call schedule with their families. We also help them set up money transfer accounts. That way they can send the same amount of money at the same time each month. If they have more money to send, they save it for the times when they have less. Their family knows how much to expect so it is a little less stressful.

Life in your new place

Tips to protect yourself in your new community:

- **Keep originals and copies of important documents.** Always keep your passport, work permit, and other personal papers. Do not turn them over to your employer or recruiter. Leave a copy of your ID and other information in your home country and have an extra copy with you as well, in case the employer takes your documents.

- **Do not sign a document** you do not understand or do not agree with.

- **Learn basics of the local language** and if you can, teach other workers the basics of your language.

- **Make sure the employer tells you the duties and conditions of the work.**

- **Keep track of your hours, payments, and deductions.**

- **If you are told you owe money,** ask why and check if the information is correct. Seek help from groups that support workers if you feel the amount is wrong.

- **Do not sign for pay you have not received.**

- **Do not let your employer "save" your wages** or transfer your pay to your home country for you. Ask to be paid in cash or with checks you can cash or deposit at a local bank.

- **If you are abused or attacked,** write down the place, time, who was involved, and anyone who saw the abuse. The important thing is not to be alone: go to a church, a community organization, the union, or any network that you feel can help you and accompany you if you decide to go to the police.

- **Make new friends** to reduce feelings of loneliness and anxiety.

- **Keep your money safe** and learn to manage it: save some for your future or an emergency, do not send it all home, and teach family back home to manage money.

Remember: You have the right to return home permanently and take your income, savings, property, and family members back to your country of origin.

The right to organize

Some governments and unions do not allow migrant workers to join unions. Local workers might feel migrant workers are not interested in organizing because they do not plan to stay in the area. But migrant workers can contribute to the collective effort and might even have helpful personal experience from organizing in their own countries.

Learn about your rights and resources

Each country has labor laws that affect migrant workers, even those who do not have legal papers. Learn about your rights from worker organizations, unions, other workers, the government, or research on the Internet. These might also be good places to find out what organizations can help you to get medical care, to learn the language, or, for example, if you get fired.

 The rights of migrant workers

The **UN Universal Declaration of Human Rights** applies to all people, including migrant workers.

The **UN Convention on the Protection of the Rights of Migrant Workers and their Families** says every migrant worker and every member of his or her family:

- has the right to protection by the law.
- will receive the same treatment as nationals regarding conditions of work (hours, pay, and overtime) and social security.
- is entitled to cultural, religious, and freedom of association rights.
- will be protected against violence, threats, intimidation, and forced labor.
- has the right to join trade unions and the right to organize.

The **ILO Conventions on Migration for Employment (No. 97)** and **Migrant Workers (No. 143)** say governments should offer:

- free assistance and information services to migrants.
- facilities for the departure, journeys, and reception of migrants.
- medical services for migrants and the members of their families.
- the same labor and human rights as local workers.

The roles of the UN, ILO, and other international organizations that promote workers' rights are explained in Appendix A.

Talk with other workers about common problems

Although there are things that may cause workers to experience the workplace differently, such as gender, age, and ethnicity, there are many dangers in the factory that affect all workers, such as low pay, unhealthy or unsafe conditions, and forced overtime.

Make time to talk with other workers about the problems they face. A problem that affects one person can easily become a problem that affects many.

Developing relationships with other workers in your factory can also help you feel less lonely and stressed. You can develop a resource guide from the information that each of you knows or a map that shows the dangerous areas of the city, stores to buy less costly goods, health centers, and police stations.

Empty Night, Not Alone

My name is Xiaomei and I moved to Shenzhen to work in a factory. I was very sad when I moved here. I didn't have any friends and I didn't want to tell my family about my problems because they would worry. I actually didn't want to work in the factory at all. When I was growing up, I dreamed of working in a radio station. So when I moved here, I would go to the local radio station whenever I had free time and offer to help. One day, the radio host was sick so they asked me to host the show. I didn't know what to talk about, so I started talking about my life in the factory. I talked about feeling lonely and the conditions in my factory, which were not good. The owners of the factory heard the show and fired me the very next day. I was really upset! But then the radio station owner told me that many people liked the show. When I told them I had been fired, they offered me a job.

My show is called "Empty Night, Not Alone" and it is a space for young migrant women workers to share their experiences and feel like they are "not alone," that someone understands the challenges of their lives, their joys and sorrows. We talk about worker rights and some of the resources available in Shenzhen, where to find internet cafés to connect with our families, where to learn the language, how to protect ourselves, and many other things.

Build a social organization

Many migrants move to a new place because they have family or friends who have already moved there. You can begin to get together on days off to share traditional foods from your region and discuss problems faced in the workplace, news from home, and how you might help family and friends left behind. Migrant associations provide a supportive place to socialize and often raise funds for projects back home, such as buying a community ambulance or helping a school. Working with your new community, you can organize for better conditions for yourself and other migrant workers while you nurture your connections to your culture and home.

Social centers for migrant workers

The National Workers' Congress (NWC) in Sri Lanka opened union membership to migrant workers in 1995. But organizing migrant workers inside the export factories was no easy task because many were scared of organizing. The boss controlled their free time and since they lived and worked inside the factory compounds, they ended up working a lot. The boss had also threatened that if they joined the union they would be fired and sent back to their countries.

To give migrant workers a safe space to explore organizing, NWC created "Friendship Houses." These spaces are located outside the factory compounds. Workers can go there to borrow books or magazines, talk to other workers, watch television, and find information about labor rights. The staff also organizes health trainings and invites workers to attend conversations about union organizing. They want to empower workers to take more control over their work lives and become leaders in their own factories.

It was at the NWC Friendship House that I first heard of trade unions. I had gone there to use the library, and found out that it was possible to take training courses there on workers' rights. After 3 years I became a member of NWC and started organizing other workers.

Make migrants part of worker movements

Migrant workers are often exposed to some of the worst conditions of work, from poverty wages and violence to fear of deportation, especially if they do not have legal documents. When migrant workers are unorganized, employers think they can pay all workers less. However, when unions and other worker organizations fight for the rights of migrant workers they are helping to eliminate these conditions and forcing their governments to enforce labor laws and standards for all workers.

For example, labor rights groups in the United States, where many workers migrate for jobs, campaign for the rights of migrant workers on International Workers Day, May 1 (also known as May Day). On May Day they launch campaigns to bring awareness to the working conditions of migrant workers and to demand that the government of the United States give full rights to these workers, including access to education, medical care, and housing.

Unions are strengthened when they make an effort to include migrant workers in workplace organizing and social activities. When workers of different ethnic or language groups are used to working together, the boss cannot use racism or rivalry between groups to divide and weaken the union. By communicating in the languages of the workers in a factory, the union can make sure that everyone knows what is going on and that workers have a way to pass information back to the union. And when a union stands up for equality and people's rights both inside and outside the workplace, it builds loyalty, respect, and support that can help it win struggles for its members into the future.

Migrant Burmese workers' union in Thailand

Sandar crossed the border from Burma into Thailand to work for the Value Trend Company garment factory in Mae Sot. The workers were paid less than half as much as Thai workers, even though they were doing the same amount of work. And although all the workers had work permits and were fully guaranteed labor rights according to Thai labor law, the employer kept the original copies of the workers' permits. If the Burmese workers demanded their rights, they were fired, deported, or even murdered by police or gangsters. In a nearby factory, a male worker was killed and 3 women workers were raped as a warning to other workers to stop organizing.

Sandar was afraid of being deported or attacked, but she felt it was time to fight for her rights and the rights of her people. She began to talk one on one with other workers to find out what their problems were and if they were interested in fighting for better conditions. At the same time, she learned about worker and human rights through trainings organized by the Yaung Chi Oo Workers Association (YCOWA), a union that supports and organizes Burmese workers in Thailand. She started holding secret meetings with other workers to tell them about the YCOWA union, and soon many workers joined. YCOWA organized workers to leave their jobs to demand better pay and working conditions. When 119 of them left together, the employer was really surprised. He had not thought the migrant workers would organize. The union stepped in to represent the workers in the negotiations with the owner. Through a well-planned campaign that involved the community and support from local and international organizations, the workers were able to win a new union contract with many improvements. The employer promised to pay them minimum wage, which was more than double what they had earned before, and higher overtime pay. He also returned their original work permits, so they could have control of their working lives.

Children who work

Factories today are not safe places for children to work. Conditions in the factory can hurt children's growing bodies and reduce their chances of becoming healthy adults. As the ILO says, "Children belong in schools, not supply chains."

You and your union or community organization can help children stay in school and help end child labor in the factory.

- **Reach out to children who work and their families** to understand their needs and find solutions that help them, not penalize them for being poor.
- **Negotiate** with the boss to pay fair wages to children who work and to help children who work to go to school.
- **Refuse to work alongside child laborers** when the boss hires workers who are too young or gives them dangerous work.
- **Report factories who hire children illegally** to the authorities and to child welfare agencies so they can help child laborers attend school and receive income.
- **Organize to win laws** that protect children and punish those that hire children illegally.
- **Organize for a living wage** that allows families to have a decent life, keep children in school, and have access to childcare. See page 289.

Factory work harms children

Work dangers that affect children are not different from the dangers faced by adults. They include noise, dust, chemicals, fire, and repetitive motion.

Child labor can happen in a factory or at home.

But dangerous working conditions can harm children more because their bodies and minds are still developing and are more vulnerable to injury and disease. An injury or illness due to work can slow a child's development or cause a disability that will prevent the child from learning, working, or getting a better job as an adult.

Young people who work

Child labor is work done by children that harms their health, their development, or their education. Child laborers are usually younger than the age allowed for regular work in their country, and are usually working when they should be in school. Child labor is less common inside factories, but child laborers often do factory work at home or in smaller workshops.

Many countries allow **school-age children to do some work**, usually around the home or in a family business. Laws may limit the type of work school-age children can do and the hours they can work. When children are not exposed to chemicals or dangerous conditions, and have enough time to go to school, study, play and rest, the work they do usually does not harm them.

Young workers are between 15 and 18 years old, and have regular jobs in a country where the legal age for work is under 18. Young workers may no longer be "children" in the eyes of the law, but they do not yet have the skills and judgment of older workers. Their bodies and minds are continuing to grow, and exposure to chemicals and repetitive work affects them more than it does older workers. Often the need to earn money effectively ends the possibility for further education. For these reasons, factory work is more harmful for them than adults.

Children are injured more often than adults

Some factory owners hire children for certain jobs because they think they have nimble fingers. However, children are at greater risk of becoming injured because they are smaller and do not have as much control as adults over their bodies and movements. Machines, tools, and workstations are designed for adults, not children's smaller bodies.

Dangers that affect children more than adults

Noise: Young workers are more at risk of hearing loss than adults. Noise exposure limits set for adults are not safe for children. See chapter 13: Noise.

Heat: Young workers also have a lower heat tolerance than adults. A safe environment for an adult might not be safe for a child. See chapter 15: Heat and cold.

Heavy work: Heavy work may place excessive stress on growing bones and might cause bone damage or impaired growth.

Chemicals: Children are more easily and seriously harmed by chemicals because:

- Their bodies are smaller so they receive a proportionally higher dose of toxics than adults when exposed to the same amount.
- Their bodies are growing and are more vulnerable to damage caused by toxic chemicals. Toxic exposure at work can harm children's growing organs, hormonal balances, and skin, and increase their risk of cancers.
- Their bones and bodies absorb lead, other metals, and fumes faster than adult bodies do, which can cause learning and developmental problems.
- They breathe faster than adults, which makes it more likely that they will get sick from indoor and outdoor air pollution.
- They are closer to the ground and are more likely to eat, breathe, or touch chemicals that drift to the ground.

Physical development harmed

Working children suffer growth problems and slowed physical development because of:

Lack of activity: Child workers often cannot play, explore their neighborhood, or interact with other children. Neither do they rest as much as they need to for healthy physical development.

Children exposed to toxics may learn slowly, be irritable and restless, or show other signs of slow development.

Exposure to toxics: Working children exposed to toxics can have health problems such as headaches, difficulty breathing, long-term reproductive problems, cancers, or even death. Toxics can also harm a young person's ability to learn.

Lack of food: Some children work so the family can eat. Yet children working in factories often put off meals while working or to meet production targets. Malnourished children can have poorer health, loss of vision, stunted growth, learning disabilities, and less energy compared to other children.

Learning denied

Boring work: Children doing simple, boring work instead of going to school, studying, and playing will not gain the mental, social, and learning skills important to do well in their community and society.

Missed school: Child laborers usually cannot complete school and may not learn to read, write, or do math. Children who do not get an education have fewer work opportunities as adults.

Noor's story

Noor lives in Serdang Lama, a small village in Selangor state in the country of Malaysia. She has been working since the age of 7 in a small T-shirt factory.

She folds printed T-shirts to be packaged. She works 6 days a week from 8:30 in the morning until 5:30 in the evening. She does not have time to play with other children.

"I would like to go to school. But we don't have money. So I'll continue to work here."

Signs a child's work is appropriate

- The child is the legal age to do legally regulated work or is working in a family business.
- The child attends school and has time to study, play, and rest.
- The child looks cared for, healthy, and happy.
- The work is appropriate to child's age and physical and mental capabilities.
- The girls and boys have equal opportunities to work.
- The child is supervised by responsible and caring adults.
- The workplace is safe, not dangerous to the health or life of the child.
- The work pays a decent wage and provides job skills so the child can get better work in the future.
- The child is not working to pay a family debt.

Signs of harmful child labor

- The child is school age but is not going to school.
- The child's age and the type of work violate national or international laws.
- The child looks tired, dirty, underfed, ill, or unhappy.
- The child is forced to work because of family poverty, abandonment, or the illness or death of parents.
- The girls have to work because they are denied schooling.
- The child is not paid a decent wage.
- The child is forced to work for little or no pay.
- The child works unsupervised or is supervised by abusive adults.
- The child works during school hours, when she should be studying, or very late or early in the day, when she should be resting.
- The work is dangerous, unhealthy, or too difficult for the child's age and physical or mental abilities.
- The child faces emotional, verbal, physical, or sexual abuse.

Causes of child labor

Family poverty, debt, or being orphaned often force children to work instead of going to school.

Unemployment and no living wage

Working adults should be paid enough in a regular work week to support their family. However, low pay, unstable employment, and unemployment among adults keep many families in poverty. Export factory jobs usually do not pay enough for families to survive, so even children have to work.

Employers often recruit child workers because they can pay them less than adults. Yet they expect the children to work the same as adults.

The false promise of job training

Children and young people sometimes work for little or no pay because the job promises to teach them skills for a job in the future. In many countries it is legal for the factory to offer internship wages. But then they try to get away with paying young people these lower wages for longer periods.

Illness and lack of health care

HIV, TB, malaria, and lack of health care weaken people's ability to care for their children, who are often forced to work to make up for a missing or ill provider. These diseases can be prevented and treated when people have access to medicines and health care, and jobs that pay enough for them to eat a healthy diet and live in healthy conditions.

School is not possible

Although many countries have laws that say all children can go to school, many children are still denied education. Schools might not be affordable, or may be far away and there is no transportation. Girls often leave school to work to pay for their brothers' school fees or are pressured to marry young.

I may not have enough money to pay their school fees next session.

If I can't go to school then I want to work so I can help my family.

Protect children and end child labor

National governments set the minimum age when a young person can begin regular paid work. This is often the same age when children finish the years of schooling required by law, and is usually between 12-15 years old, depending on the type of work. Wealthy industrialized countries usually require more years of school, and young people may start regular work when they are 17 or 18 years old. The International Labour Organization (ILO) and the United Nations (UN) established a general minimum age of 15.

 ## The UN & ILO on children and work

The **UN Convention on the Rights of the Child** says a child is any person under 18 years old and that children should be protected by their governments.

- Children have a right to an education.
- Children have the right to rest and leisure, and to play.
- Children cannot do work that may be dangerous, work that interferes with the child's education, or work that is harmful to the child's health or physical, mental, spiritual, moral, or social development.
- Governments must set a minimum age for beginning regular work, regulate the hours and conditions of work, and promote the physical and psychological recovery and social integration of child laborers.

The **ILO Minimum Age Convention (No. 138)** and **Worst Forms of Child Labor Convention (No. 182)** say:

- Children may do light work beginning at 12 to 13 years old, but it may not interfere with school, rest, play, or be harmful to their health.
- Minimum age to work is 15 years.
- Minimum age for dangerous work is 18 years.
- The worst forms of child labor should be banned.

The **ILO Medical Examination of Young Persons Convention (No. 77)** says:

- Medical examinations should be given to children and young persons before they begin work and each year while they are working.

The roles of the UN, ILO, and other international organizations that promote workers' rights are explained in Appendix A.

Focus on the root causes

To eliminate the root causes of child labor, we need an economy that works against poverty and supports education for every child.

- **Organize to create better conditions and pay** for all workers. This reduces the number of children forced to work to help support their families.

- **Provide education and job training** for adults to increase their ability to earn better wages.

- **Enforce laws to** ensure that workers get the pay and benefits they are due, such as a minimum wage, overtime pay, social security, health care, and maternity benefits.

Child workers' associations

When I had been working a few years in a factory in Bangkok, a friend told me about the Child Workers Club. The Club helps child workers get organized so we know our rights. It also campaigns with employers to give child workers educational opportunities to prepare for a better future.

I started going to Club meetings, and the staff of the Club encouraged me to become a full-time, paid organizer for the Club. I visit child workers in their places of work to find out about conditions. Then we talk about child workers' rights and I encourage them to come to the Club's activities to learn more. I write for the newsletter and sometimes help with events.

Prasert is a young boy from Khon Khaen province in northeast Thailand.

In the factory, I worked the whole day without thinking about anything else, just finishing the assigned work. Here I have to think a lot. Organizing is far more difficult than anything else I have done. Sometimes I've been so worried that I've wanted to quit, but staff here have encouraged me to continue and I have gotten pretty good at this work!

Education for all children

Education needs to be available nearby, relevant to the child's needs and interests, good quality, and free (or at least affordable). If workers pressure an employer to fire child laborers, the children are often forced into other, even worse jobs to earn a living. For the child to have a real alternative to working, the family's poverty must be lessened, and there must be a school the child can attend. Your organization can:

- help child laborers find and get into free schools, sometimes offering vocational training, and make sure these school also offer free, nutritious food.
- provide economic support to the family, to replace the income the child earned.
- give orphan child workers food and shelter, so they can attend school and vocational training instead of work.
- reconnect children with their families if they are separated.

Money-for-school program helps prevent child labor

To help stop child labor, the government of Brasilia, a state in Brazil, launched a grant project to support poor families. Most children who work do so because their families depend on the money they make working. The program, called Bolsa Escola (school grant), pays poor families a monthly stipend for each child in the family (from 5 to 17 years of age) who goes to school regularly. This money replaces the children's contribution to the family income and it allows their families to afford basic needs.

The Bolsa Escola has been successful at giving children the opportunity to go to school instead of work: school attendance has doubled in some communities and children miss fewer days of school. Bolsa Escola is now a national program. It was integrated into Bolsa Familia (family grant), a program that also offers money to families for vaccinating their children. The program has also spread to other countries in Latin America and Africa.

The government should ensure children's rights

Pressure the government to do its job:

- **Enforce child rights** granted in international conventions and national, state, and local laws.

- **Set legal limits on schoolchildren's work:** Laws protecting child workers usually limit the number of hours and time of day a child can work. This is to keep work from conflicting with school time, studying, playing, and resting. The limits usually forbid children from doing work that is harmful such as using power tools, working near dangerous machines, using chemicals, working in hot areas, and carrying heavy things.

- **Create school permits for children's jobs:** In some countries, an employer must get a permit from the school for each child they hire. The permit shows the child is attending school and that the employer knows the limits on children working.

- **Create orphan programs:** Local youth centers can be established to care for orphaned or homeless children who are forced to work to support themselves.

- **Fund income support for families:** Create community-based programs, such as basic income grants, childcare, common kitchens and meals, adult literacy, education, and job training to help families keep children in school and adults earning a living.

Unions take action in Brazil

The United Workers' Confederation (CUT) organized a national campaign to stop child labor in Brazil. First they partnered with research centers and universities to study child labor and people's ideas about child labor in each area. People felt it was better for children to work in urban areas than in rural ones. They said, "At least they are working and not just living on the streets."

Then they tried to build support in communities for the struggle to end child labor. They used radio and TV programs, newspapers, booklets, posters, videos, and a photograph exhibit to raise awareness about the conditions of child workers.

They also encouraged employers to talk about child labor with the unions. The unions stopped children from working in the most dangerous jobs, and helped provide assistance to them and their families. The campaign also built support for better education, income supports, and recreational programs, all of which are a step toward preventing child labor in the future.

Access to health care

The machines get better care than we do!

In most factories, workers do not have access to appropriate health care. Many factory owners see access to health as an extra, costly burden instead of an investment that will pay for itself in healthier workers, resulting in fewer missed working days, less turnover, and increased efficiency. Even when national laws guarantee access to care either in the factory or in the greater community, there is often no way to enforce these laws and get access to care.

In order to change the promise of health care from a goal to a reality, workers need:

- access to care for accidents or emergencies in the factory.
- access to a quality, appropriate, and affordable local clinic open during hours that make it easy for workers to get care.
- access to care for workers' families.
- national policies that recognize and support health and access to care as a human right.
- support for training of health and safety promoters to monitor and advocate for the health of factory workers.

Health care in the factory

Many factory owners do not offer on-site medical services. When they do, services may be limited, and sometimes not very good. Factory-paid doctors and nurses, although not part of management, may be pressured to prioritize production over improving workers' health. But conscientious health workers can be important sources of information and valuable allies for workers.

Without adequate care, minor illnesses or injuries can become major problems. Factory policies around health care can make problems worse. These include rules that make it difficult for workers to get time off or that dock their pay when they go to a doctor, when they need time to recover from an illness or injury, or to care for illness in their families. Expensive health services also prevent workers from getting the care they need.

Care and support for injured workers

The factory should pay medical costs for workers injured on the job. This includes emergency transport and care for injuries, chronic strain and overuse problems, and problems from chemicals, noise, and heat or cold.

Health education classes

Some unions and employers arrange for worker education during the workday on HIV and AIDS, tuberculosis, reproductive health, nutrition, and other health issues. Factory owners support this because it reduces worker illness, absence, and turnover, and so increases worker productivity.

Health promotion in factories

The HERproject of Business for Social Responsibility has been trying to improve health by training workers and supervisors as "peer health educators." They developed a 12-part curriculum to train workers on many health topics, including women's health. Workers then share it further with their co-workers.

In Ciudad Juárez, Mexico, where hypertension and diabetes is common, 50 peer educators were trained to share knowledge with 1,000 co-workers in an electronics factory during breaks, meals, and on commuter buses. The factory clinic then provided checkups to support the health education, including screenings for diabetes, breast and uterine cancer, and high blood pressure, as well as vaccinations, a health fair, and pregnancy and childcare counseling. One of the participants said, "the program provided a way for women to become spokespersons to workers with factory management about important health issues."

First aid and emergency care

Even if there is no clinic in the factory, it is important that every workplace has first aid supplies and provides training to help you and your co-workers respond to emergencies. Training should happen regularly so that if a trained worker leaves, there will be others ready to take her place.

First aid supplies should be kept in safe, clean places throughout the factory. Workers should be able to access them easily. The contents of your first aid supply kit will depend on the kinds of work you do, but all kits should include materials to treat common injuries such as burns, cuts, falls, etc. The materials themselves will not be useful if the factory does not ensure that workers and supervisors have been trained in how to do first aid and stabilize an injured person until they can get to help. Each set of first aid supplies should also include the telephone numbers for local ambulance companies as well as hospitals and clinics.

Activity	An emergency plan for your factory

Use the activity Draw a map of your factory, on page 43 to identify some of the dangers workers face.

Then organize a discussion to find answers:

- where on their bodies are workers getting hurt most often?
- what machines are the most dangerous?
- what kind of attention and help do injured workers receive?
- what actions do the factory owners take to resolve problems?

Use this information along with known risks such as fire, electrical failures, earthquakes, and so forth, in your campaign to create with your employer an emergency plan for your factory.

An emergency plan not only includes first aid kits and immediate treatments, such as eye washes or showers, but also a detailed response system that answers:

- who is responsible for responding first to an emergency?
- what should the person do? For example: Should they cut power to machinery? or How should they deal with blood if a worker is bleeding?
- where can they get additional help from a health worker?
- when and how should they transport an injured worker to the clinic or hospital?

Getting good care at a clinic or hospital

Workers often have a hard time getting good health care. Hospitals and clinics may charge a lot for services or medicines, be difficult to get to, be crowded or not open when you can go, or be unfriendly to migrant workers or women.

Illness due to work creates additional problems, since many health problems are not easy to see or to prove were caused by work. For instance, strain and overuse injuries from repeating the same movement too many times without rest, and short- and long-term effects from chemicals are caused by work and can be lessened or stopped when work conditions are improved. But most employers refuse to accept that workers' back pain, headaches, skin rashes, breathing problems, and cancers are caused by their jobs. Most doctors and nurses do not learn about occupational health or know about conditions in export factories, so workers do not get good treatment.

Often workers who are disabled or injured from work receive no support from their bosses. They might be fired and if their sickness is chronic and they need medicine or special equipment, they often are forced to pay for it themselves. Many cannot afford to do this.

Recognition of work-related injuries and illnesses

Some doctors tell workers that their health problems are not related to the work they do. They blame the worker by saying she had a previous condition that caused the problem, or the problem is due to her bad habits or home life, or is a result of unhealthy conditions in her community.

But work injuries and illnesses are caused by poor working conditions, exposure to dangerous chemicals and machines, lack of training, and no access to emergency care.

> *We made big posters about our co-workers who were killed in the factory. We talked about who they were, how they died, how their families are suffering now. We take the posters to city events, parades, company picnics, and to churches on Sundays.*

Find out how occupational diseases and injuries are defined in your country. This may be useful to you and your group in convincing health, employer, and government authorities that they must recognize injuries and illnesses as work-related, cover the costs of treatment, and include them in workers' compensation systems.

The right to be compensated for injuries caused by work

The **ILO Employment Injury Benefits Convention (No. 121)** says governments should provide care, rehabilitation, and compensation to workers who suffer from occupational diseases, including:

- diseases caused by dusts
- diseases caused by exposure to particles in the air
- diseases caused by exposure to chemicals
- problems and injuries caused by noise, vibration, and other dangers

Also see the **ILO List of Occupational Diseases Recommendation (No. 194).**

The **Employment Injury Benefit Convention** also says that governments should offer compensation for:

- workers who can no longer work because of their disease or injury
- families of workers who lose their life at work or because of work

The benefits provided must cover the medical care and rehabilitation of the worker, but should also include cash benefits, depending on the injury or disease.

The roles of the UN, ILO, and other international organizations that promote workers' rights are explained in Appendix A.

Our clinics are funded — not owned — by the employer

Many organizations in Bangladesh offer affordable and accessible health services. But many people who work in factories cannot use these services because they do not have time or permission to leave the factory. To reach them, the Marie Stopes International organization established "factory health services." These clinics operate within the factory and are funded by the factory owners, though they remain independent. Workers can seek medical help as they need it but the clinic also offers regular checkups and monitors workers' health while they work at the factory. The clinics are open long after the workers finish their workday and the boss pays for every worker to have free service at the clinic. Many more people now have access to health services.

> We worked with many workers and organizers to address the distrust that they had of company-paid clinics like ours. We showed them how the doctors and nurses work for us, not the boss. Even if the boss pays us to let workers use the clinic, the doctors and nurses are independent.

Workers with special needs

All workers are different and we bring these differences to work with us. Usually the workplace is made more productive by our differences. When our health needs differ, we have to make sure everyone gets the attention they need. Workers with HIV can continue to live healthy, productive lives when they have access to the medicines, nutrition, rest and respect they need (see chapter 30: HIV). With medical support and job flexibility, workers with disabilities also can continue to work productively for many years.

Women workers and women's health

Even though women are half the population, and often most of the workers in a factory, women's health needs often are not considered part of basic care nor occupational health. Since many chemicals affect women's reproductive systems, pregnant workers need to have checkups (prenatal care) to find and care for problems with the mother's health and with the baby. If work cannot be made safe, many countries give pregnant women the right to transfer to jobs that are safe for them or grant them paid leave if no safe job can be found.

Women's Health Express

The Chinese Working Women's Network (CWWN) has created new ways for women factory workers in China to meet and talk about health issues. They started the Women's Health Express, a mobile van that stops outside factories in the Pearl River Delta industrial zone. Women who visit the van are checked for signs of many illnesses and given general health information and treatment, as well as information about health problems caused by dangers at work. Staffed by women health promoters, the Women's Health Express is a place where women workers feel comfortable talking about their concerns and problems.

HEALTH VAN

Free health exams

Chinese Working Women's Network

The right to health care

The **UN Convention on the Elimination of Discrimination against Women** says men and women must have equal access to health care information and services, including family planning. To learn more about the conventions to eliminate discrimination in the workforce, see The right to equality, on page 309.

Several **ILO conventions (Nos. 102, 121, 130, 183)** say governments must provide for the health, health care, and social security of workers and their families, including:

- medical care for workers, their partners, and their children.
- paid time off for illness.
- medical care in case of injury at work.
- rehabilitation services to help a disabled worker return to her previous work, or a suitable job for her ability.
- injury benefits paid to workers who are hurt or made ill by work.
- disability benefits paid to workers who are injured and cannot work, or who earn less money than they did before the injury.
- survivor's benefits paid to the family of a worker who dies.
- recognition of work-related illnesses and injuries, including diseases caused by chemicals, dust, noise, vibration, and other dangers.

The roles of the UN, ILO, and other international organizations that promote workers' rights are explained in Appendix A.

How to	Get better care

Health workers are trained to recognize signs of illness, identify problems, and treat them. But many health workers have never been inside a factory. Health workers may know very little about factory work and the conditions that affect workers' health. If possible:

- arrange for them to visit factories and see conditions for themselves.
- take health workers to visit people's homes and community activities.
- organize a meeting or workshop where factory workers tell or act out their stories to help educate health workers.

At the clinic

The doctor, nurse, or health worker who sees you should ask about the problem you are having now and about your past health. Try to give complete information, even if you feel uncomfortable, so the health worker can learn as much as possible about your health. Always tell the health worker about any medications you are taking, including aspirin or family planning methods, because some medications affect how other medicines work.

Most health workers are not trained to treat illnesses and injuries caused by factory work. Show the health worker exactly what you do at work.

These questions can help you prepare to explain your problem:

- When did you first notice the problem?
- What signs made you think something was wrong?
- How often do you have these signs?
- Have you ever had these signs before, or has anyone in your family or community had them before?
- What makes the signs better or worse?

If you suspect that your problem is related to chemicals at work, bring as much information as you can: the chemical name or brand name; what it is used for; its color, smell, or texture; and anything else that might help the health worker find out what it is. See pages 157 to 163.

(continued)

Get better care *(continued)*

You should also ask as many questions as you need to make a good decision about how to solve your health problem. Make sure the health worker explains so you understand:

- What are the different ways this problem can be treated? Are there home remedies?
- What will the treatment do? Are there any dangers?
- When will I get better?
- Will I be cured? Or will the problem come back?
- How much will the tests and treatments cost?
- Are there home remedies?
- Why did the problem happen? Can I prevent it from happening again?

Many doctors and nurses are not good at giving information. Or they may be busy and not want to take time to answer your questions. Be respectful, but firm. Do not feel intimidated by them — your health depends on the services they provide, and you should be satisfied with the services you receive. They should explain until you understand. If you do not understand, it is not because you are not smart enough, but because they are not explaining well.

The health examination

In order to know what is wrong with you and how serious your problem is, you may need an examination. The exam may include looking at, listening to, and feeling the part of your body where the problem is. For most examinations, you need to uncover only the part of your body where the problem is.

- If you would feel more comfortable, ask a friend or family member to stay in the room with you during the exam.

Tests

Tests can give more information about a health problem. Many tests are done by taking a small amount of urine, stool, or coughed-up mucus and sending it to a laboratory. Or, a needle is used to take a small amount of blood from your finger or arm.

- Ask the health worker to show you and explain how he will take the test.
- Ask about cost before you have any test.
- Ask what the health worker will learn from the test and what would happen if the test is not done.

Health care with respect

All people who give health care should do their best to provide you with:

1. **Access:** If you need medical care you should be able to get it, no matter where you live or where you come from, how much money you have, your religion, your language, your age, your skin color, your political beliefs, or what health problem you have.

2. **Information:** Your health problem and the possible treatments for it should be explained to you. Your health workers should help you understand what you need to do to get better, and how to prevent the problem from happening again.

3. **Choice:** You should be able to choose whether or not you are treated, and how. Also, if there are different choices, you should be able to choose where to go for treatment.

4. **Safety:** You should be given information to avoid harmful side effects or new problems that result from treatment.

5. **Respect:** You should always be treated with respect and courtesy.

6. **Privacy:** Things you say to a doctor, nurse, or other health care worker should not be overheard by others or repeated to anyone else. Exams should be done in privacy, where others cannot see your body. If there are other people in the room, you should be told who they are and why they are there. You have the right to tell them to leave if you do not want them there.

7. **Comfort:** You should be made as comfortable as possible during an exam. You should have a good place to wait and not have to wait too long.

8. **Follow-up care:** If you need more care, you should be able to go back to the same person, or be given a written record of the care you have received to take to a new doctor, nurse, or health worker.

Workers' compensation and social services

Too often, companies do not want to take responsibility for the injuries they cause, and refuse to support disabled workers. While many countries have workers' compensation, rehabilitation, and disability benefit programs to support workers who have been injured at work, the forms and processes for filing a claim can be difficult to complete. Many worker organizations offer support for workers filing their claims. People working in the claims office can be very helpful too.

FILING A CLAIM

What happened?

When did it happen?

Do you have names of any witnesses?

Did you receive treatment? Where and from whom?

When you file a claim for compensation, you will need to provide a lot of information about what happened.

COMPENSATION CLAIMS

If this is an injury or health problem that has become worse over several years, such as asthma, they might ask: When did you first realize it was a problem? What things made it worse? Have you had any treatment?

Besides keeping your own information, it is helpful to keep records of injuries, illnesses, and compensation paid to other workers, especially if more than one person was affected. Make this information known to your union, the health and safety committee, the boss, and interested community organizations. Being able to show that work dangers were so serious that they resulted in compensation being paid to workers can help you motivate people to get involved and take action to improve conditions.

The factory might be unwilling to recognize that harm was committed and refuse to pay compensation. You may need to involve lawyers, government officials, environmental, worker, and women's organizations, reporters, and even the large companies whose products are being made in your factory.

Support groups for injured workers

Injured workers benefit from meeting and sharing their experiences about health care providers, treatments, recovery, social services, and returning to work. Workers with experience can help newly injured workers apply for benefits and give emotional support to workers with a difficult recovery or a permanent injury. When employers and co-workers only see the injury but not the person with it, a support group can help you recover your sense of self-worth and belief in your own abilities.

Social insurance and services for injured workers

Ill or injured workers recover more quickly and completely when the health system trains doctors to listen to workers and to identify work-related injuries. Services should include physical and occupational rehabilitation and back-to-work programs if the job no longer poses a danger to the worker. For a worker who can no longer do his job, programs should give job training appropriate to the worker's disability. The employers and government should also provide a social insurance program for permanently disabled workers, including compensation and accommodation at work and in the community.

Each country has different laws regarding health care, from universal health care to private hospitals. Learn what the health care laws are in your country, then help workers decide which issues are most important to them, such as the cost of health insurance, time off to see a health worker, the cost of medicines, or specific health coverage for work-related health problems.

Health care is a union priority

The SITRACOR garment workers' union in Honduras started a campaign for better access to health. They fought for workers' right to time off for medical appointments, and to make sure that every worker was registered in the national health insurance system. They got a lot of support from the government and NGOs after one worker had a miscarriage on the job after she was denied permission to go to her pre-natal appointments.

SITRACOR has also worked on expanding other medical benefits for workers. For example, they found that many garment factory workers needed eye care for irritation, injuries, and eye strain, but the full cost of eye exams and glasses was not covered by the national health insurance. SITRACOR campaigned to get the factory owner to pay for workers' eye care. They also won similar battles to make sure the factory pays for tests for lung problems, HIV, and cancer.

Workers as health promoters

Factory workers can become health promoters in the factory. Forming or joining a safety committee can be a good place to start, since they often help prevent injuries at work. But worker health promoters can do even more by educating others about health dangers, and helping people find solutions and get care when they have a health problem. Worker health promoters develop a better understanding of the problems in the factory and can help others learn to treat the problems, to think about how to prevent them from happening again, and to organize for better and healthier work conditions. Workers often feel more comfortable getting advice from people who share their experiences than from "outsiders." See chapters 2 and 3 for more on becoming a worker health promoter.

By finding out what workers believe are their most important health problems, you can create trainings and materials that they will be interested in and pay attention to. Use the information in this book to create health education materials that explain:

- how conditions in the factory threaten health.

- how to prevent health problems.

- how to recognize signs of problems caused by dangers at work.

- how to fight for workers' right to health care.

Friendly health workers or community groups may be able to help produce booklets or posters, or organize discussion groups or workshops on different health problems. Make sure that talks and materials are in the languages that workers speak and reflect the conditions of their jobs and lives.

Workers' health and safety trainings

The Asia Monitor Resource Center (AMRC) holds occupational health and safety workshops with organizers in Asia. Through training and activities such as mapping dangers, these organizers become health and safety promoters, sometimes even forming national occupational health and safety organizations. Although they do not have all the training or equipment a professional might have, they often have better local knowledge and practical workplace experience. This lets them have a real impact on workers' lives. In Cambodia, Indonesia, and China they organize to remove dangers from the factory, train workers and employers on basic safety, and lobby for personal protective equipment.

Common health problems

Many of the health problems workers have are common in their communities. They may not be caused by factory work, but conditions in the factory make them worse by affecting:

- How they get sick and how often. Dangers at work, including bad ventilation, breathing in chemicals, bad food, and unhygienic toilets can weaken the body's ability to fight illness and infection.
- How sick they get: Chemicals and dusts in the air can make respiratory problems worse. Bad food and unclean toilets spread germs.
- How quickly they get healthier: Not having time to rest or go to the doctor will prevent them from getting better quickly.
- How easily they spread contagious illnesses to others: Not having time or clean water to wash hands regularly, and ventilation that just moves dirty air around the workplace instead of replacing it with clean air contributes to the spread of germs in the factory.

Because workers spend most of their time at work, the factory is a good place to do health promotion. Improving workers' health inside and outside the factory may be something the boss is willing to support. Healthy workers miss less work and are more efficient at work. Healthy workers are able to take better care of themselves and their families, and they participate more actively in the community. Involve workers from the start in the design and implementation of any health promotion program.

Health and hygiene trainings and workshops: Talk with workers or do a survey to find out which health problems are the most common. Bosses might make time for health trainings if they do not focus on how work affects health. Be creative in finding ways to incorporate work-related problems into your sessions. Hold separate trainings for women where women's health can be discussed more openly.

Supply drives: Basic supplies can help prevent common health problems. Find sponsors and donors, such as a health post or a local store, and ask the boss to contribute towards soap, sanitary napkins, pain medications, and rehydration drinks, among other useful supplies.

Free cancer, HIV, and STI screenings: Health clinics or local non-profits often organize early cancer detection screenings, such as pap smears to check for cervical cancer. STI screenings are helpful when workers are guaranteed privacy, confidentiality, and free treatment.

Vaccination campaigns: Invite the health department to provide free vaccinations in the factory, before and after work, or during lunch.

Treat common health problems

Health Info

Treat most illnesses with rest, nutritious food, and drinking lots of liquids. You can learn to recognize when you need to see a doctor.

Common colds are caused by a virus and cannot be cured by antibiotics, which work against infections caused by bacteria. Drink plenty of water, soups, and juices, and rest. Some companies sell expensive tablets for colds but you get the same relief from plain aspirin or acetaminophen tablets, and they are less expensive. Colds are easily passed from one person to another. Wash your hands often, cover your mouth when you sneeze or cough, and tell others to do the same.

Urinary tract infections (UTIs) and **bladder infections** affect women more than men because their urine tube is short and more germs can get into it. Germs can get into the urinary system when a woman has sex, does not drink enough water, or goes a long time without urinating. Drink a lot of water, or teas known in your area to treat them. Do not drink sweet drinks. If you do not feel better in 2 days just by drinking liquids, you may need to take an antibiotic (cotrimoxazole or others). See a health worker or *Where Women Have no Doctor*, page 368.

Diarrhea can be caused by many things, and usually no medicine is needed. However, if a person loses so much water as to become dehydrated, it is more important than ever that the person drink lots of water and eat nutritious foods. If you have trouble keeping anything in you, make and slowly drink at least 3 liters of a home-made rehydration drink. Mix 1 liter of water with half a teaspoon of salt and 8 level teaspoons of sugar. Make sure you do not add more salt, because it could dehydrate you more.

Conjunctivitis, also called "pink eye" is an infection caused by bacteria. Treat it right away with an antibiotic eye ointment (usually tetracycline). See *Where There is No Doctor*, page 378.

TB (tuberculosis) can spread to co-workers and family if you don't get medical treatment. For information about TB , see chapter 31.

Read *Where There Is No Doctor, Where Women Have No Doctor,* and other Hesperian books to learn more about health problems and how to treat them. But remember: Medicines are not a substitute for good health care. Good health care involves explaining why someone has a health problem, what she can do to get better, and how she can prevent that problem in the future.

Women workers organize through health promotion

Our organization, the Self-Employed Women's Association (SEWA), is a trade union of 1.3 million women workers in India. We fight for better working conditions for women workers.

One of the biggest problems women workers were facing was that they did not have access to health care. So we organized many meetings with women where they talked about how expensive doctors were, how they didn't have enough time or money to see a doctor, and what kind of health service they really wanted. We decided that we needed to bring health services closer to women for easy access. We first worked in a small, rural community to help build a community primary health care program.

At first the women saw us as just another organization that did family planning, because many organizations in the past were only interested in family planning. As we gained people's trust and learned about some of the issues women were facing, we soon realized that the people who knew the issues the best were the women themselves. So we started training local women as health workers to respond to the community's needs. We got help from the Center for Health Education, Training, and Nutrition Awareness (CHETNA), and they helped us begin training the first group of 10 women.

At the beginning, the women felt discouraged. They said, "But we have never been to school! How do you expect us to become health workers for the community? People will laugh at us." But then the women realized that they already knew some traditional medicine, they knew the culture, and they knew what the problems were. We always started with what the women already knew and then we asked them what they wanted to learn and what was important to them and their communities. They have now formed a cooperative that helps other women become health promoters, provides low cost medicines, runs TB centers, and offers health insurance and other services.

If you think about it, among us all we know a lot. Working together, we can change things!

Reproductive and sexual health

The majority of workers in export factories, both women and men, are of the age when they are sexually active and raising a family. But instead of taking into account these central activities of people's lives, the conditions in many factories can make pregnancy difficult, cause birth defects, and lead to reproductive cancers and illnesses for young workers. Even though it is against national and international labor and health standards, factories are dangerous to workers' reproductive and sexual health.

Workers need factories that:

- do not discriminate against, penalize, or fire women who get pregnant or have children
- provide maternity and paternity leave, and time off for parents to care for children when necessary
- improve working conditions and replace chemicals that harm men's and women's reproductive health
- make access easy to on-site or nearby quality health clinics and childcare centers

Working affects reproductive health

Reproductive and sexual health can be affected by working conditions and exposure to chemicals that affect reproductive organs. Policies and practices in the factory that control or limit our reproductive choices also harm our reproductive and sexual health.

Women face many challenges from factory work. Some bosses refuse to hire married women, pregnant women, or women with children. Some factories even have policies to prevent women from getting pregnant.

They sent me to a laboratory to do a blood test. They said, "It's the law to check workers to see if they are healthy." But I knew that it was to see if I was pregnant. They send the results directly to the boss. If you're pregnant, they will just tell you there is no work.

Chemicals and bad working conditions hurt women by causing problems with monthly bleeding, complications of pregnancy, miscarriage, or the health of the baby. Chemicals are also linked with cancers in the breasts, womb, and ovaries. Chemicals that hurt people's reproductive health affect women more than men because women's bodies do more of the work of reproduction.

Men are also hurt by factory conditions. Chemicals, heat, stress, and overwork can harm a man's desire for sex and his ability to have sex (impotence) or to have children (infertility). Some chemicals can damage a man's sperm in ways that cause miscarriage or cause a baby to be born with health problems. Other chemicals can cause cancer of the testicles.

Women also face reproductive and sexual harm in communities where their reproductive and sexual health is controlled by men. They are harmed by lack of information and access to services for sexual health, family planning, domestic violence, STIs, and cancer.

Control over women's fertility and family life

For most people, having children is an important part of their sexual health. Reproductive health is especially important for women because they get pregnant, give birth, feed the baby, and are often the primary caregivers of the family.

In many factories, however, women are forced to choose between having children or having a job. Employers attempt to control workers' behavior and their decisions about sex and family planning through factory policies. They try to prevent women from becoming mothers while employed. Some bosses only hire women who are unmarried with no children.

If women do become pregnant, the employers often deny pregnant women safer jobs, paid health care for prenatal visits and delivery, or paid leave before and after giving birth, forcing them to either accept the health risks to themselves and their babies or to quit to take care of their families. When women do not have access to safer jobs and health care, they can suffer miscarriages, have difficult pregnancies and births, deliver babies prematurely, and can even die.

Men rarely are questioned about how having children will affect their work.

We have to get sterilized to get a job

In Brazil, our union receives many complaints from women who are asked to provide proof that they have been sterilized in order to get a job. The employers deny they do this and since the requests are made verbally, there is no evidence. Other companies perform "period inspections" to make sure that female employees are having their periods. Women have to write the date their period is supposed to begin on a giant blackboard in the common room. On that date they have to go see the doctor to prove they are menstruating. This is so humiliating and wrong!

Forced pregnancy tests: Often, a woman applying for work must show proof she is not pregnant. Each woman must bring a note from a doctor or allow the employer's doctor to test her. She is not hired if she is pregnant or refuses the test.

Pressure not to become pregnant: Some women are forced to sign an agreement that states they will not give birth while they have a job at the factory.

Harassment or firing: If a woman worker becomes pregnant, she is fired or harassed into quitting. Harassment includes verbal abuse, higher production quotas, longer work hours, or transfer to a more difficult job, such as from a sitting to a standing job or to a hotter work area.

The clinic at our factory gives out the pill so women won't get pregnant, but not condoms, which would help us prevent HIV and other sexually transmitted infections.

But I am pregnant!

I was transferred to night shift even after I told the employee relations lady I was pregnant. My shift was from 7 pm to 7 am. The worst part was that I had to work standing up. I spent 12 hours on my feet and as my pregnancy progressed, this became really difficult and painful. I asked my leader for a chair and he said no, because my pregnancy didn't show and he didn't believe I was pregnant. But I had a big belly! A few weeks later I was sent to inspect daily quota cards in an area where they use several chemicals that are harmful for pregnant women. I quit because I just couldn't handle it any more, and I lost my maternity leave.

Contract workers and maternity leave

I got a job at the factory through a Manpower (temporary worker) agency in El Salvador. Although I work in the factory the same as other workers, my boss, the one that pays me, is the Manpower agency. When I got pregnant I went to the Manpower agency to ask about my leave and they said it was the responsibility of the factory. And when I went to the factory they said it was the responsibility of the Manpower agency. This went on for a while until I decided to contact the Centro de Estudios y Apoyo Laboral (CEAL). They made a complaint to both the factory and the Manpower agency and got them to agree that it was the Manpower agency's duty to pay for my maternity leave.

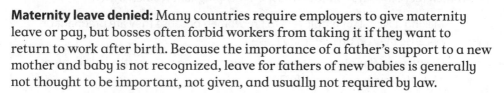

Maternity leave denied: Many countries require employers to give maternity leave or pay, but bosses often forbid workers from taking it if they want to return to work after birth. Because the importance of a father's support to a new mother and baby is not recognized, leave for fathers of new babies is generally not thought to be important, not given, and usually not required by law.

No child care center at the factory: Women must find someone to watch their children during work hours, or leave them unsupervised. If we are forced to do overtime, who feeds and cares for our children?

No place or time to breastfeed infants at the factory: This prevents infants from being fed properly and harms the mother's ability to make milk for breastfeeding. Babies should breastfeed for at least 1 year.

Factories in Bangladesh offer childcare

Phulki is an organization that establishes childcare centers inside factories in Bangladesh. Phulki convinces the factory owners to provide the space, startup costs and caregivers' salaries. The workers who use the childcare facilities pay a small fee for food and other expenses.

The Phulki program has been very successful because it benefits both the workers and the factories. It is a sustainable model that can be adapted to each factory. Workers do not have to worry about their kids being alone at home, or having to find childcare for them, which is often costly. Mothers have access to their children for breastfeeding during breaks. Employers who have an on-site childcare facility find workers miss fewer days of work and are more productive.

The right to work that does not affect reproductive health

The **ILO Chemicals Convention (No. 170)** and **Occupational Safety and Health Convention (No. 155)** says the employer must protect you from chemicals and conditions that affect your health, including reproductive health.

The **ILO Maternity Protection Convention (No. 183)** says:

- Medical benefits, including prenatal, childbirth, and postnatal care, must be provided for women and their children.
- Forced pregnancy tests are prohibited unless the work is proven to be harmful to pregnant women and their babies.

The **UN Convention on the Elimination of All Forms of Discrimination Against Women (CEDAW)** says countries must protect pregnant women by:

- Making it illegal for employers to fire women because they are pregnant or because they go on maternity leave.
- Giving special protection to women during pregnancy, particularly in types of work proven to be harmful.

The roles of the UN, ILO, and other international organizations that promote workers' rights are explained in Appendix A.

Chemicals

Most chemicals in use today have not been tested for how they affect our reproductive and sexual health. The chemical industry often challenges the health research that is carried out, and opposes the regulation or banning of dangerous chemicals, saying it unfairly limits their rights — and their profits. OSH professionals can play an important role by educating themselves, factory management, and workers about chemical research and always looking for ways to use safer chemicals at work.

Can work make you infertile?

I work in the cleanroom of an electronics factory. We dip wafers into chemicals to make computer chips. After a couple of months on the job, I began having problems with my period. Before, I was very regular. But it started coming at odd times or didn't come at all. Once I thought I was pregnant and was scared I would lose my job. At my plant, pregnant women are fired. Then my period finally came. But about a year ago, my period just stopped. After 5 months, I told one of my co-workers. She had the same problem! And so did the other woman we worked with. How could it be we were all having the same thing?

We went together to talk to a doctor. After many tests that found nothing, the doctor asked what chemicals we used at work. We didn't know. We didn't even know how to find out. She told us to look for labels on the containers the chemicals came in. They had such long names we had to learn to memorize them letter by letter so we could write them down at night in our dormitories. We took the list to the doctor. The doctor found studies showing that one of the chemicals, called 2-bromopropane, affected women's reproductive systems. I wondered if the bosses chose this chemical so we wouldn't have children! That way we could work all the time without family responsibilities. We were all very angry.

The doctor told us to talk to the factory's occupational health manager. He said we were not the only ones suffering this way. And it wasn't just women — men were having problems, too. The Department of Labor and the National Institute of Occupational Health were called to investigate. They found a number of workers with reproductive problems caused by 2-bromopropane. The company was forced by the government to stop using 2-bromopropane. They also had to pay us compensation for harming our health.

Reproductive health problems caused by some chemicals

Acetone (page 529) used in manufacture and cleaning of chips and LEDs may cause miscarriages and reduced fertility in men.

Benzene (page 522) used in manufacture and cleaning of chips and PCBs may cause reduced fertility in men, menstrual problems and anemia in pregnant women, and may harm the baby inside the womb.

Cadmium (page 504) used in soldering and plating may damage men and women's reproductive systems. It can cause birth defects. It can cause prostate cancer.

Carbon tetrachloride (page 524) used in manufacture, assembly, and cleaning of chips can affect the testicles and male fertility and may damage the baby inside the womb.

Hexane (page 520) used as a cleaner in garment and electronic factories and in glues in shoe factories may cause reduced fertility in men.

Lead (page 504) used in solder, batteries, colored plastics, glazes and paints may damage men's reproductive system, may cause menstrual problems, and may cause birth defects and learning problems in babies.

Trichloroethylene (TCE) (page 524) used for spot cleaning in garment factories and cleaning, assembly, soldering, encapsulating, and bonding in electronics factories can cause birth defects.

Toluene (page 522) used in glues in shoe factories and in cleaning, assembly, and soldering in electronics factories may cause defects.

Xylene (page 522) used to manufacture, clean and assemble chips, PCBs, LCDs, and LEDs may cause birth defects.

For information on cancer of the reproductive system, see page 384.

For more information about chemicals that harm reproductive health, see Appendix B: Common chemicals and materials.

Organize for safer chemicals

Find out as much as you can about the chemicals you work with. If your employer divides or mixes the chemicals before bringing them to your workstations, get labels from the original containers.

Find out if women and men have signs of sexual or reproductive health problems. Talking about this may be uncomfortable, but knowing how many people in the factory have these problems is just as important as knowing how many people have breathing problems or have been injured by a machine.

Join or form groups to protect workers from reproductive dangers and get OSH professionals to help you understand the technical information and alternatives. Unions and consumer groups can help pressure employers and governments for safer chemicals to be used.

Chemical that causes infertility is banned in the USA

My wife and I were trying to have a baby, but she couldn't get pregnant. We both went to our doctors. Her examination was normal but mine showed I had no sperm in my semen. I knew that some chemicals cause reproductive problems, and I worked with almost 100 different chemicals. It was hard to figure out which caused the problem.

I talked to my co-workers and they told me about other couples who also had been unable to have children. I convinced 5 to get tested. Tests showed all 6 of us had few or no sperm at all! Our union, the Oil, Chemical, and Atomic Workers (now part of the Steelworkers) sent us to a doctor for help. He confirmed the results, did more tests, and agreed our problem was caused by exposure to toxic chemicals.

4 of 100 chemicals in the factory had been shown to have reproductive effects on animals. But one chemical, DBCP, was being produced in very large amounts. The union had workers tested in 2 other factories where DBCP was produced, and got similar results. The connection between DBCP and fertility problems became clear when we found out that DBCP was the only chemical that workers in all 3 plants had in common.

We fought to get DBCP banned, while the industry argued we just needed better safety measures. But too many people had already become sterile, and we could not let that continue. Then our union's media campaign got the attention of the Environmental Protection Agency (EPA) and we finally convinced them to ban DBCP use in California, and then in the entire country. Unfortunately, the EPA did not ban production of DBCP, so companies in other countries continue to buy and use it, denying workers around the world the joy of having children.

Health Info

Finding reproductive system cancers early

Cancer can happen to anyone. But cancers found early may be curable. One way of finding cancer is by having regular checkups and tests. Some you can do at home and some you need to do in a clinic.

Breast exams

Every woman can learn how to examine her own breasts. Do it every month, a few days after your period.

Look at your breast in the mirror for any changes, lumps, or dimples. Stretch your arms above your head and feel your breasts with the flat of your fingers, pressing your breasts in a circle to find any lumps. Squeeze your nipples. If you see blood or discharge, get medical help.

If you find a hard lump that has an uneven shape, is painless, or does not move when you push it, see a health worker.

The only way to know if a lump is cancer is by removing all or part of it, a process called a "biopsy," and testing it in a laboratory.

Cervical exams

A woman can have cancer of the cervix (the opening of the womb) for a long time and have no signs. Detect early signs of cancer with either of these 2 tests:

For the **Pap test**, the health worker gently scrapes a bit of tissue from the cervix and sends it to a laboratory. Positive results mean you need treatment. Get a Pap test every 3 years. It is not painful and only takes a few minutes.

For the **vinegar test**, also called visual inspection, the health worker paints a little white vinegar on the opening of the cervix (it does not hurt) to see if any tissue turns white. If it does, you will need a Pap test to confirm it is cancer or to treat it by freezing, called cryotherapy.

To learn more about the vinegar and Pap tests, see *Where Women Have No Doctor*, pages 377-379, or ask a health worker for information.

Testicular exams

Men should do a testicular self-exam monthly. Gently roll each testicle between your fingers. Feel for lumps, swelling, pain, or changes in size, shape, or texture. If you find any, see a doctor. An ultrasound can confirm if it is cancer. This cancer grows quickly, so get treatment as soon as possible.

Educate on family planning and STIs

Many people work in a factory during the period in their lives where they are likely to be most sexually active. It is important that they have information about and access to resources on family planning, sexual health, and how to prevent and treat sexually transmitted infections (STIs).

Workers and worker organizations can collaborate with women's organizations, health workers, nonprofit organizations, and even government health officials to design workshops on:

> *I had never heard of the Pap test until the Chinese Working Women's Network health van came to our factory zone and offered free exams.*

- early detection of cancer
- family planning
- STI tests and treatments, and prevention

Workshops are most effective when they include discussions and activities that encourage people to explore how work, culture, society, family, and personal preferences affect their reproductive and sexual health. They should also include information on community resources, such as free or low-cost clinics and government programs, and on the best ways to educate and provide services within the factory.

A workers' health committee can invite organizations that offer free or low-cost STI exams and treatment, maternity care, breast exams, Pap and vinegar tests, and family planning services to your community.

The rest of this chapter provides information on these topics that you can use in workshops. Make sure to talk with women and men at the factory to find out the issues they think are most important for workshops.

Information about family planning

Family planning is having the number of children you want, when you want them. If you want to wait to have children, you can choose one of several methods to prevent pregnancy. These methods are called family planning, child spacing, or contraception. Condoms for men and condoms for women are the only methods that also prevent sexually transmitted infections. Each method works better for some people than for others, and women with certain health problems should avoid certain methods. The chart on the next page shows advantages and disadvantages of each method. Talk to a health worker to decide which might be best for you.

Health Info

(continued)

Health Info

Information about family planning (continued)

Type of family planning	Preventing pregnancy	Protection from STIs and HIV	How often	Other important information
Condoms	GOOD	BEST	Every time	Most effective when used with a spermicide and a water-based lubricant. A condom needs to be used every time you have sex.
Birth control pills	VERY GOOD	NONE	Every day	Important to take at the same time every day. Talk to a health worker if you have had breast cancer, have high blood pressure or liver disease, or if you are pregnant or nursing.
Implants	BEST	NONE	Every 3 or 5 years	Must be inserted and removed by a specially trained health worker and replaced every 3 or 5 years depending on the type.
Injections	VERY GOOD	NONE	1, 2, or 3 months	Need to be repeated every 1, 2, or 3 months depending on the type.
IUD	BEST	NONE	5 or 12 years	Effective for 5 or 12 years depending on the type. Must be inserted and removed by a specially trained health worker.
Pulling out (withdrawal)	LEAST	NONE	Every time	The man needs to withdraw every time you have sex. Even if he pulls out, some liquid from the penis may enter the vagina during sex, which can cause pregnancy or pass STIs.
Breastfeeding (during the first 6 months only)	VERY GOOD	NONE	Breastfeeding several times a day and at night	This method is only effective if the woman is feeding her baby only breast milk and if her menstruation has not returned.
Fertility awareness	GOOD	NONE	Every time	This method does not work well for women with irregular menstrual cycles.
Sex without intercourse (penis not inside vagina)	BEST	DEPENDS	Every time	If the penis is not inside or touching the vagina, the woman cannot get pregnant. Anal sex can easily pass STIs, oral sex is less likely to pass STIs, and sexual touch rarely passes any STIs.
Sterilization	BEST	NONE	Once	Once a woman or man is sterilized, they will never become pregnant or get someone pregnant.

For more information about family planning, see *Where There Is No Doctor*, chapter 20, or *Where Women Have No Doctor*, chapter 13.

Unwanted pregnancies

Many women have unwanted pregnancies, especially if their partners, families, communities, or workplaces prevent them from getting family planning information and services or making choices that are best for them.

Prevent pregnancy by using family planning methods described on page 386. Several kinds of emergency family planning or "morning after" pills are available (such as *Plan B, Postinor,* and others) but they must be used within 5 days of unprotected sex. See *Where Women Have No Doctor,* page 524.

If a woman decides not to continue a pregnancy, she may choose among 3 different methods of abortion if they are available.

Abortion by medicine: Also called medical abortion, the pregnancy is expelled by the woman after taking the medicine misoprostol alone, or both misoprostal and mifepristone. Since nothing is put inside the womb, there is less danger of infection, but it is still best to be near a clinic in case heavy bleeding occurs.

Abortion by suction: Also called vacuum aspiration or MVA, the pregnancy is removed by putting a special tube (cannula) through the vagina into the cervix and sucking the pregnancy into a type of syringe. It can be done in a clinic or doctor's office in about 10 minutes.

Abortion by scraping: Also called a D and C, the pregnancy is removed by scraping with a small, sharp, spoon-shaped instrument. It is usually done in an operating room in about 20 minutes, and the woman may be given a medicine to make her sleep.

Unsafe abortions can result in infections, pain, infertility, and sometimes even death. But a safe abortion is less likely to cause harm than having a baby. Safe abortions are done:

- by a trained and experienced health worker.
- with proper instruments or medicines.
- under clean conditions. Anything that goes into the vagina and womb must be sterile (without germs).
- no more than 3 months after the last monthly bleeding, unless it is done in a hospital with special equipment.

It is often hard for a woman to decide to have an abortion. Women who want or need an abortion should be treated with respect and dignity. Having a list of safe abortion services in your community can help save women's lives. You can also help reduce the need for abortion services by increasing information about and access to family planning.

Health Info

Information about sexually transmitted infections (STIs) and other infections of the genitals

Sexually transmitted infections (STIs) are infections passed from one person to another during sex. They affect men, women, and sometimes even their children. Although you can only get pregnant from having sex in the vagina, STIs can be transmitted by many kinds of sex, including oral sex and anal sex. Sometimes you can even get an STI from rubbing your genitals against an infected person's genitals.

Some infections of the genitals are not STIs and you can learn to recognize the symptoms. If you are in doubt, get tested right away. A change in the smell, color, or texture of vaginal discharge and itching in or on the vagina can also be signs of a yeast infection or a bacterial infection in the vagina, which may not be sexually transmitted. A yeast infection may go away by itself or by using an antifungal medicine (such as miconazole, nystatin, clotrimazole, or others). See *Where Women Have No Doctor*, page 266. But for a bacterial infection you will need to take antibiotics.

If you have pain or a burning feeling when passing urine, and your urine smells bad, looks cloudy, or has blood or pus in it, you might have a urinary tract infection (UTI), which is not an STI. Drinking lots of water may cure the infection, but if you do not feel better in 2 days you will need an antibiotic (such as cotrimoxazole). See a health worker.

Common signs for STIs are:

- bad-smelling discharge from the genitals
- itching genitals
- painful genitals
- sores, blisters, warts, rashes, irritation or itching in, on, or near the genitals or anus

- pain or swelling of the testicles
- pain during sex
- pain when peeing
- pain in the lower abdomen
- bloody discharge from your genitals

It is also very common to have an STI and have no signs at all. Many women and men have STIs but do not know it. HIV, for example, can be in your body for a long time without causing any symptoms. That is why it is important to be tested regularly, especially if you are having sex without a condom.

(continued)

(continued)

These are the most common STIs:

- **Gonorrhea and chlamydia** are easy to cure if treated early. Since they have the same signs, if you test positive for one, treat for both.
- **Trichomonas** is an itchy STI that often causes no signs in men, even though they can still pass it to others.
- **Syphilis** causes painless sores on the genitals. Since these may go away by themselves, it is easy to think you are cured, but the disease continues to spread throughout the body. If untreated, it can lead to serious problems including death.
- **Chancroid** causes painful sores on the genitals or anus.
- **Genital herpes** causes painful sores on the genitals or in the mouth that come and go. It is a virus that is not curable but there is treatment to feel better. Herpes spreads easily, so do not have sex when you have sores and use a condom every time you have sex.
- **HIV** is a very serious STI that, if not managed, can lead to AIDS. See chapter 30 for HIV symptoms, management, and prevention.

If you have signs of an STI:

- **Treat the infection right away.** See a health worker to get the correct antibiotics. Ask for more information to help you prevent STIs. You can also find more information, including medicines for STIs, in *Where There Is No Doctor*, and *Where Women Have No Doctor.*

If you take a medicine and the signs do not go away, see a health worker. It could be another illness.

- **Do not wait until you are very ill.** Early treatment will prevent serious problems, and prevent the spread of infection to others.
- **Make sure your partner is treated** at the same time. If he or she is not treated, your partner can infect you again during sex.
- **Take all the medicine,** even if your signs go away. You will not be cured until you have taken the full course of medicine.
- **Practice safer sex.** Safer sex means lessening direct contact with your partner's genitals and body fluids. Use a condom each time you have sex to protect you and your partner from STIs.
- **Get tested for HIV.** HIV infection often occurs with other STIs.

Health Info

27 Stress and mental health

When our minds and spirits are healthy, we have the emotional strength to meet our needs and those of our families, to look for ways to solve problems, and to plan for the future. But when we are made unhealthy by too much stress, we are less able to cope with the challenges presented by life.

When work is dangerous, lasts too long, is too intense, and feels out of control, it can damage workers' mental health. To make factories healthier:

- Bosses must find respectful ways to involve workers in decision-making instead of imposing their decisions through force or fear.

- Workers' pay and benefits must allow for a decent standard of living and stability for workers' families.

- Toxic chemicals that affect the way workers think and feel must be banned from the workplace.

- Workers must have the time and materials to make quality products and take pride in their work.

- Work rules that prohibit talking and social interaction must be dropped.

- Health problems, including mental health problems, must not be stigmatized, and access to care for these problems must be encouraged.

Common causes of mental health problems

Not everyone who has the problems described in this chapter will develop a mental health problem. A person usually is more likely to develop a mental health problem when the pressures he faces are bigger than his ability to cope (manage the problems). Sometimes, mental health problems do not have a cause that can be identified, and we do not know why someone develops them. Regardless of the reason, people who suffer from mental and emotional health problems need support and help in talking about their problems and seeking help from a health worker. Employers must be pressured to change conditions in the factory that create problems for workers.

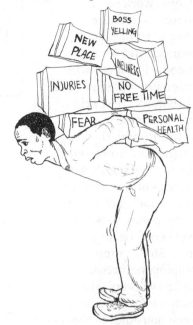

Fear

Fear is a particular kind of stress. Fear is often created on purpose by the boss and supervisors to control workers and keep them from organizing. When management threatens workers with firings, blacklists, violence, and other kinds of retaliation, they may be breaking the law and violating workers' human rights. Even if they do not hurt you in a visible way, they can harm your mental health. See the activity Facing fear together, on page 321.

Overcoming fear

We were very scared of what the boss and his thugs could do to us. Nobody wants to get hurt or lose their jobs. But we knew that this fear, the threat of violence, was their most powerful tool and we had to overcome it, stand together, and fight for our rights as workers, as women, and as human beings.

Economic insecurity

People work in factories because they need to earn money. And when income is not certain, when unemployment threatens the survival or well-being of your whole family, this can create fear and stress for the worker. Factory owners often threaten to cut back jobs or to move away, making workers fear for their jobs. Since many employers threaten to fire workers who complain, fear can keep you quiet in the face of injustice.

I don't want the plant to close! How am I going to send money to my family? They are going to think I am a bad daughter if I lose my job!

Fear of losing your job is used by employers to get away with not fixing conditions that harm workers.

Workload

Our bodies need rest to be healthy and so do our minds. Working long hours and on weekends stresses our bodies and minds. Overtime also limits the time we spend with family and friends, an important part of having healthy relationships. Too many hours can make us feel isolated, lonely, and exhausted.

The pressure to produce more in less time can also be harmful to workers, especially if the speed-up makes production lines move too fast to let workers complete each task well. Your body and your mind need lots of little breaks during the day to stretch, relax, and stay healthy. Some factories increase production line quotas in ways that make you feel like you cannot ever succeed. Every time you reach your production target, it gets raised again!

Work relationships

Relationships with your boss, supervisor, guards, and other workers can be stressful. Other people can make life easier or more difficult at work and outside the factory. It can be very hard to change these relationships, especially with people who have control over your job or salary.

Having a strong sense of unity with other workers can be a way of fighting for more equal relationships with the boss and union. But bosses often give workers isolated or solitary work or prohibit them from speaking or relating to their co-workers, making it hard to feel like you are all part of a community.

The workplace can be very unfair. Sometimes there's discrimination against workers, sometimes bosses favor some workers. This is especially true for women who see they are being paid less for the same work or effort that a man does for more pay. It is hard to feel like a community when workers are pushed and oppressed and made to feel like they don't deserve better. The bosses make workers compete against each other to get more power or money. Then they offer one worker more money or a better position and try to break apart all the trust we have built. How can we overcome all this oppression and rebuild relations of solidarity?

Self-esteem

Our self-esteem and self-value come from the beliefs that we grew up with, and our relationships in our work, our community, and our families. Good self-esteem is an important part of mental and emotional health. When we see ourselves in a positive light, we are better able to manage daily problems.

For many workers who spend most of their time working and living inside the factory walls and away from family and friends, self-esteem is heavily determined by work. Facing repetitive and monotonous work, having few breaks or holidays, bosses that yell insults to hurt workers, and having no time to make friends and build relationships, can create mental health problems for workers.

You've made a mess again, you stupid girl!

Work environment

Many bad conditions in the workplace can create anxiety and stress for workers, such as too much noise, too much or not enough light, temperatures being too hot or too cold, doing repetitive work, and working with chemicals that may harm you. Also when there are not enough washroom facilities, a lack of privacy, or facilities that are always dirty, this too can have an effect on mental health. Unsanitary or overcrowded eating facilities can also create stress for workers.

Injuries in the workplace

Injuries in the workplace obviously harm the physical health of the worker. But they can also harm that worker's mental health and the mental health of other workers who are witnesses to injuries. Experiencing injuries, either your own or seeing them happen to others, can make a worker feel unvalued, unsafe, fearful, helpless, and unable to trust the world or the people around her. Without even being aware of how much it weighs on your mind, you can be affected by trauma from an accident for many years.

Often when injuries or even death occurs in a factory there are no opportunities created for people to work through their feelings. In the worst cases, management refuses to stop production to acknowledge that a problem occurred. Entire factories of workers have suffered mental health problems after a serious accident.

Exposure to toxic chemicals can also cause mental health problems. In cases like this, it is very difficult to separate the physical health problem from the mental health problem. Physical injuries or chronic conditions can also result in mental health problems, including chronic pain, side effects from medicines, and head injuries. These problems are often made worse when workers hide injuries for fear of reprisals or losing their jobs.

Moving to a new place

Export factories attract people across long distances with the promise of jobs and income. Young women in particular often move away from their families and communities in order to find work in factories. Sometimes factories plan on drawing workers from far away and build dormitories (shared living quarters) for workers near, or even on top of, the factories. Whether or not the factory provides housing, living away from your family, community, culture and your accustomed rhythms of life can make you feel lonely and homesick.

Loneliness

It is often difficult to be away from the people you love and who care about you. It can be hard to meet other people and make new friends, especially if you come from different places and cultures than they do, and if you are tired from working long hours.

Group living situations

Conditions in many factory dormitories are often difficult. Whether in factory-provided dormitories or in shared rooms in crowded neighborhoods near factories, workers are often forced to live with people they may not know very well, with limited privacy. For people who before had only lived with their families, or come from rural areas where it was always possible to find a little space to be alone, this can be very stressful. This mental stress is often made worse when conditions are physically dangerous as well, such as through overcrowding, not enough exits, fire dangers, not enough washing or sanitary facilities, and unclean cafeterias and cooking or eating areas.

The owner does not allow air conditioning in our dormitories so we want to stay longer at the factory, where it is cooler.

Our communities and families

When young people, especially young women, begin to work in factories, their lives and the traditional ways of their communities begin to change in ways that may be both good and bad. People begin to have a different relationship to the land and young people may "forget" how to farm.

New businesses may bring strangers, increased noise, traffic, crime, and pollution to a formerly rural area. Relationships within the family and respect for older community members may change, leading to stresses for workers as well as people who do not even work in the factories. When life changes so much that the old ways of coping do not work any more, people may begin to have mental health problems.

Other sets of changes may take place in families when suddenly the woman is working outside the home and the man may be earning less or staying closer to home and doing more of the family care. Sometimes these changes in gender roles can be good: women may gain more independence and men may learn to value the work of raising children and maintaining the family. But changes like that, especially when they are forced on people and not the result of their own choices and decisions, can also be harmful. And whether change is wanted or unwanted, change often brings added stress and pressure to family relationships.

Problems outside work

It is stressful when a family member is sick, a marriage is having difficulties or a friend moves to a distant city. Employers make it even more stressful when they do not give workers enough time or energy to attend to problems outside the factory without fear of losing their jobs.

Common mental health problems

Although there are many kinds of mental health problems, the most common ones are anxiety, depression, and misuse of alcohol or drugs. Stress is not a mental health problem in itself. However, when we are not able to recover from stressful situations, stress builds up in our bodies and minds. When someone can no longer cope with the challenges they face because of the stress they are suffering, then stress has become a problem.

Most people have some signs of stress at different times in their lives, because everyone faces problems at one time or another. Signs of mental health problems can vary from community to community. Some behavior that looks strange to an outsider may be a normal part of a community's traditions or values. At the same time, behavior that seems normal to an outsider may be considered strange or abnormal in a community. Since many factories include management and workers from foreign countries and cultures, this is important to remember.

I am so lonely, and everybody else seems to be happy. What's wrong with me?

Stress

When a person experiences stress, the body gets ready to react quickly and fight off or run away from what is causing the stress. These are the same effects caused by fear. Some of the physical changes that occur are:

- the heart starts beating faster
- blood pressure goes up
- breathing speeds up
- the digestion slows down

If the stress or fear is sudden and severe, you may feel these changes in your body. Then, once the fears or stresses are gone, you will feel your body slowly return to normal. But when fear or stress is less strong, builds up slowly, or continues for a long time, you may not notice the changes that happen in your body because you have grown so accustomed to them.

Anxiety (feeling nervous or worried)

Everyone feels afraid, nervous, or worried from time to time. Usually you know what is causing the feelings and usually they go away soon. But if anxiety continues or becomes more severe, or if it comes without any reason, then it may be a mental health problem. Signs of anxiety include:

- feeling tense and nervous
- hands shaking
- constant sweating
- heart pounding
- difficulty thinking clearly
- frequent physical complaints that are not caused by physical illness and that increase when you are upset

A panic attack is a severe kind of anxiety. In addition to the signs above, you will begin taking quick and shallow breaths even without noticing, and feel terror or dread, a strong feeling that something terrible is about to happen, and maybe that you or a co-worker might get sick, have an accident, or die. A panic attack can happen suddenly and can last from several minutes to several hours.

To handle a panic attack, you must make a strong effort to regain control of your breath. Force yourself to take deep breaths. Breathe in as deeply as you can through your nose and exhale through your mouth. Do this for as long as it takes for you to feel like you have control over your breathing. If your friends and family are prepared and know what to do, they can support you.

Burnout

Stress or anxiety that continues for a long time and finally overwhelms a worker's ability to cope can lead to "burnout." Burnout combines feelings of mental and physical exhaustion with a sense of personal isolation. Some physical signs of burnout can be:

- headaches
- intestinal problems
- lack of energy
- high blood pressure
- difficulty sleeping
- low sexual desire, inability to enjoy sex
- difficulty remembering things
- various muscle and joint pains

Depression (extreme sadness or feeling nothing at all)

It is natural to feel sad at different times in our lives: when a friend or family member is very ill or dies, when you lose a job, or when a marriage or relationship ends. But depression becomes a mental health problem when any of these signs last for a long time:

- feeling sad most of the time
- sleeping too much or too little
- difficulty thinking clearly
- feeling like crying, or crying for no apparent reason
- loss of interest in pleasurable activities, eating, or sex

- physical problems such as headaches or intestinal problems that are not caused by illness
- slow speech and movement
- lack of energy for daily activities
- thinking about death or suicide

Some people can cope and heal from depression by talking about their problems with another person or support group. Some people also need medicine, called anti-depressants, to get better. Ask at your community health clinic for information, as these medicines may have side effects.

Sometimes depression can lead to other problems, including suicide (killing oneself). Many people might consider suicide when their problems seem bigger than any solution. However, if a person has a plan about how to kill herself, has lost the desire to live, or has tried suicide before, she is more at risk for suicide. She needs help immediately. To help, first try to talk with her. If talking about her problems does not help, or if you are afraid she might hurt herself, then she needs to be watched closely. Talk to her family and friends, but tell her you will do that before you do, encouraging someone to be with her at all times. Ask them to remove dangerous objects from her surroundings. If there is a trained mental health worker, find out how she can receive care.

Mental illness

Health Info

People with mental illness need help from trained mental health workers. A few signs of mental illness are:

- hearing voices or seeing things that others do not
- not taking care of oneself
- behaving in strange ways that are not consistent with a person's cultural, social, or family beliefs or traditions

Illnesses, toxic chemicals, drugs, or injuries to the head and brain can cause similar signs, so it is important that someone who has these signs gets help as soon as possible. People who suffer from mental illness deserve to be treated with love, dignity, respect, and kindness.

Alcohol and other drugs

Many kinds of drugs are used in religious rituals or social events, as medicines, or along with a meal. But when a person's life begins to revolve around consuming drugs, especially alcohol, those drugs can create physical and mental health problems, and make existing problems worse.

People misuse alcohol and other drugs to escape from problems, to reduce stress, or to not feel fear. In societies where workers have little ability to change the conditions of their lives, alcohol and other drugs seem to offer a way to feel better, at least temporarily. In some factories, workers are encouraged or even forced to take drugs that keep them awake. These drugs may be addictive, and it can be hard to stop taking them, even when you are not at work.

Unfortunately, drugs and alcohol usually make problems worse and leave us less able to improve our lives. Instead of working to improve bad situations, people who misuse drugs or alcohol spend their time, money, and health trying to avoid and forget their problems.

When does use become misuse?

People who are misusing drugs or alcohol often:

- feel they need a drink or a pill to get through the day or night.
- use it at unusual times, like the morning, or when they are alone.
- lie about or hide how much they use.
- have money problems because they spend so much on drugs or alcohol.
- become violent against their friends and families.
- endanger themselves or others by using drugs or alcohol at work.

Alcoholics Anonymous (AA)

Alcoholics Anonymous (AA) is an organization that helps people stop drinking or taking drugs. There are AA groups in every country. To become a member of AA is free. A person needs only one thing: a desire to stop drinking or taking drugs.

Members meet regularly to share their experience with alcohol. Every member has a sponsor — a person who has stopped drinking for a period of time and who can give support and guidance.

There is also a group that supports the family and friends of alcoholics and drug addicts, called Al-Anon. These groups can give you the tools and support that you need to help family members who abuse alcohol.

Organizing to reduce stress in the factory

When you organize for higher pay, health benefits, or access to toilets or clean water, you are organizing to reduce the problems that cause stress. You can do a lot to reduce your feelings of stress, but it usually it takes a lot of workers together to pressure the management or the government to make the changes that eliminate the causes of stress. As a group, you can work to remove or reduce many of the causes of stress at work.

Reducing stress and improving conditions that affect workers' mental health will benefit everyone in the factory, including the boss. Workplaces where workers are respected, paid fairly, and treated well have fewer people missing work, a more committed workforce, and fewer conflicts that can interfere with work.

Unfortunately, many factory owners refuse to see that being organized and respected reduces workers' stress and improves conditions for work. They see any organizing as a threat to their power and profits. Management often responds to worker organizing with penalties, firings, and violence. This creates enormous amounts of stress for organizers, and fear for workers.

Only you and your co-workers can decide whether organizing around an issue would improve conditions in your workplace. The activities and ideas in chapter 3 can help you think about what might work best for you.

By organizing for:		You can:
Better wages and benefits	→	reduce stress.
Achievable production goals	→	improve self esteem.
Safe working conditions	→	reduce accidents and injuries.
Labor and human rights	→	end abuse and fear.
A voice in your job and workplace	→	end powerlessness.

By promoting equality and community in the workplace, you help create a more positive situation for the mental health of all.

Reduce the stress of organizing

Organizing for change in a factory, whether it is forming a safety committee or building a union, takes time that workers usually use for rest and relaxation. Because of fear of reprisals from management, not all workers or community members will be in support of these efforts. But for many workers, being part of a struggle to improve things is less stressful than doing nothing.

- **Participate in committees:** One of the worst causes of stress is feeling that you have no input into or control over your work. As your committee discusses ways to improve working conditions, also introduce ideas for reducing stress.

- **Set up a personal support networks:** Get families, friends, and neighbors to share responsibilities for meals, childcare and transportation. Knowing you can depend on others can keep you from feeling too stressed.

- **Work with people and groups in the community:** Approach churches, local organizations, and other unions and worker associations for moral support and solidarity. Knowing that others in your community support your efforts can keep you from feeling isolated.

- **Keep information flowing:** Make sure the people you are working with know what is happening and that their views are being heard. Valuing communication promotes participation and feelings of community.

- **Reduce tension at meetings:** People may be tired, worried or upset. Making meetings participatory and productive can help people see that organizing will improve their lives and spirits.

- **Celebrate the small victories:** Don't forget to recognize peoples' work and successes along the way. Knowing that progress is being made can help keep people hopeful through a long process.

- **Have fun:** Laughing, singing, sports, and other ways of having a good time can reduce feelings of stress. Knowing that organizing can include enjoyable activities can both attract more people to the work and build closer and healthier ties among them.

Helping yourself and helping others

A person suffering from mental health problems can begin to feel better with treatment, support, and understanding. There are many things a worker can do on her own and with others.

- **Learn what causes stress for you and others:** It helps to talk to someone about our problems. Sometimes all we need is someone to listen to us compassionately, and maybe they also have ideas about what to do to resolve the problems. You can help others by listening to them, too.

- **Stretch during your breaks, and invite others to join you:** It is not always easy to find the time to breathe deeply or move around, but even a few minutes of stretching and deep breathing can help calm you and put you in a better position to deal with stress at work. In your free time, make an effort to do things you enjoy. Sing, play music, dance, or play sports during time off and during breaks at work. Exercise and moving your body are great ways to reduce stress. Involve other people.

- **Eat foods and use traditional medicines that help:** In many communities around the world, people use foods and traditional medicines to heal from mental health problems. Eating enough food and a variety of foods, particularly fruits and vegetables, provides nutrition needed to keep the body and mind healthy.

  Although there are many remedies that can help us soothe and balance our bodies and minds, there are some that might do more harm than good. Be careful with remedies that are expensive or are sold as a miracle solution — these are often useless.

  Tea from the tila plant is a natural way to calm anxiety.

- **Help each other make time:** Ask friends or family members to help with your chores or childcare so you can have a few moments to yourself, and offer to help with theirs in exchange. When you share chores with someone else, you can also take turns resting.

- **Talk and listen to each other:** Most factory work is planned so that each worker, although surrounded by people, is alone with her task.

- **Form a support group:** Bring people together to talk about problems and connect with others who might be experiencing similar things. Although it is easier for one person to lead the meetings, a good leader will give everybody a chance to talk about their situation and will also help keep the group on track (with time and topic). Before the group starts, talk about the rules of the group, what you hope to accomplish during the meeting, and how each person can participate and be a better listener.

Activity	**Make time to relax**

Spiritual practices such as yoga, meditation, or prayer can help to calm your mind and body as well as build inner strength.

This is an example of a relaxation exercise. You can do this alone or with a group. If you are in a group, ask someone to lead this session (make sure there's time for the leader to relax, too).

1. Find a place where you can sit or lie undisturbed for a few minutes. It is best if it is also a quiet place, but you can do this anywhere and at any time.

There are lots of different ways to relax and to quiet the mind. Some people sing, some sit quietly, some exercise. You can do all of these things, too!

2. Close your eyes.

3. Take slow, deep breaths in through the nose and out through the mouth. Feel your heartbeat slow.

4. You can pray, or repeat a positive word or phrase, or simply try to keep your mind blank.

5. Do this for a few minutes as often as you can.

Close your eyes and imagine a safe, peaceful place where you would like to be at this moment or think about a word or phrase that makes you feel good about yourself.

Keep thinking about this place as you breathe deeply in through your nose and then out through your mouth.

Keep breathing, thinking about the safe place or a positive thought.

Eating well for health **28**

Low wages, tight production deadlines, overtime, and being too tired can prevent workers from buying, cooking, and eating enough nutritious food to be healthy. Some factories have cafeterias that make meals for workers. Other factories provide a space for workers to eat food they bring from home or buy outside the factory. But many factories do neither.

Every workplace must provide:

- a clean, safe place to eat food either made in the factory, brought from home, or purchased outside.
- enough time to purchase, prepare, and eat a healthy meal.
- washing facilities so workers can clean up before and after they eat.
- wages that allow workers and their families to have good nutrition.

Food in the factory

Many factories provide cafeterias or canteens where workers can go buy food and eat. The food might be inexpensive or free, but workers often complain that it is not very good, clean, or healthy. The factory health and safety committee should pay attention to food safety.

Having healthy and safe food in the factory benefits workers and management. Free or low cost meals nourish workers' bodies and minds, increasing worker contentment and productivity.

A clean place to eat and store food

Whether the company provides food for workers or not, they must reserve a clean place for workers to store food they bring to work and an area where they can sit comfortably while eating. The area should be away from work tables, machines, chemicals, dust, and factory noise. The factory must also have wash facilities with soap and clean water near toilets and eating areas, so workers can always wash their hands before and after eating. Workers may also need a place to remove and store dirty work clothes while eating.

Eating outdoors in the shade gives workers a chance to rest, relax, and breathe fresh air.

Healthier workers are good for the company, too

The managers of the San Pedro Diseños textile factory in Guatemala City decided to create a meal program in their factory to respond to workers' demands and comply with new labor laws. The program included nutritious and varied subsidized meals, a clean dining area, an hour-long meal break, and cooking facilities for workers who bring their own foods. The factory subsidized breakfast and lunch and offered free snacks and coffee during breaks.

With workers happier and healthier, production has increased, medical costs and absences have been reduced, and staff morale is high.

Workers demand better food and win a new union

A Korean company opened a garment factory in central Mexico, promising workers pay above the minimum wage, meals, transportation, and a union. But the company did not keep its promises. The pay was low, the hours long, and the bosses harassed and threatened workers who were slow to meet production quotas. And all the food in the factory dining hall was often spoiled or improperly cooked, and served on dirty plates. Many workers got sick. Some were hospitalized for food poisoning.

Workers asked the company-sponsored union representative to do something about the food. When he did not, they called a meeting. The union representative also came to that meeting. The workers decided to boycott the dining hall for one day to demand better food.

That day, no workers went to the dining hall. When the boss asked the union representative why nobody was eating, he blamed the workers who had complained. The company fired 5 workers, refusing to give any reason. The union did nothing. More than 600 of the 850 workers in the factory went on strike and occupied the factory, demanding:

- fresh, safe, well-cooked food in the factory dining hall.
- a new union chosen by the workers.
- reinstatement of the fired workers.

The striking workers were violently evicted by the police, but they continued to fight for a worker-led union for 9 months. They got support from unions in the United States to pressure the Korean company, the Mexican government, and the brand-name buyers of the clothes — including Nike and Reebok — to accept a new union as required by Mexican law and ILO conventions. The workers finally won, and their union became the first independent union in a garment factory in the state of Puebla, Mexico. With this union, they also won better conditions, including safe, clean food.

Food vendors outside the factory

Food vendors offer cheap and fast food, and are a very popular meal source for factory workers. Some factories that do not have a meal plan contract vendors to come and offer food inside the factory. Most vendors sell food outside the factory during meal breaks.

Street food is tasty and often fresh, but when vendors do not wash their hands with soap and clean water when preparing, serving, or selling the food, or they do not keep the food at the right temperature and covered, then the food can become contaminated and make you sick. Dishes and utensils that are not washed properly can also spread diseases. When there are no tables or benches, workers have to sit on the ground or curb around the factory entrance.

Vendors are part of the community and supporting their businesses is also a good thing for the community as a whole. If you feel that the vendors are not offering you clean, healthy food, you might organize a meeting with workers and vendors, as well as the factory managers, to find solutions to the problem. For example, the factory owners could allow vendors to use the factory facilities to wash their hands and dishes. You can also suggest that vendors offer healthier food choices.

Eat a variety of food

When your body is weak from lack of food, you feel tired all the time and you can get sick more often. When you are hungry and tired, you are also more likely to get injured.

Eat local, fresh foods that have a lot of nutrients. Eating enough food is especially important for pregnant women, women who are breastfeeding, and anyone with a health problem.

Everything is so expensive.

I can only afford a few fruits and vegetables. But it is cheaper than buying already-made food.

Carbohydrates are the main food that most people eat with each meal, such as rice, maize, wheat, millet, cassava, taro, plantain, breadfruit, bread, or pasta. They give the body energy but need to be combined with other foods to be nutritious. Whole grains and brown rice are more nutritious than processed grains and white rice, and will make you feel fuller for longer.

Proteins are needed for strong muscles, bones, and blood. Protein foods include legumes (beans, peas, and lentils), nuts, seeds, meat, fish, and dairy products. Blood and organ meats like liver, heart, and kidney are nutritious and cost less than other meats, as are eggs, fish, and chicken. Fish is a healthy protein, but if it comes from polluted water, it may contain mercury and other poisons. To be safe, children and pregnant women should avoid eating fatty fish more than once a week.

Vegetables and fruits contain vitamins and minerals to help the body fight infection and keep the eyes, skin, and bones healthy. Fruits and vegetables of different colors have different nutrients, so try to eat different kinds and colors. You can get some nutrients from canned or processed fruit, but processed fruit juices have a lot of sugar and are as bad for you as a soda or cola drink.

Sugars and fats also give the body energy, but you only need a little. Too much sugar or fat causes serious health problems, such as obesity, diabetes, and heart problems. Choose natural sugar and fats: fresh fruit, honey, whole sugar cane, and molasses are all healthy foods that contain sugar. Nuts, seeds, avocados, vegetable oil, butter, ghee, lard, and fatty meat are foods that contain fats.

Avoid unhealthy foods

Too many foods are available that are unhealthy. Many of them are sold under the pretense that they are actually better for us than natural, local food but that is rarely the case. Local, natural food, the food that our grandparents ate, is better for us than any processed, or junk, food. To be healthy and strong, we not only have to eat healthy, nutritious food, but we must also avoid the unhealthy ones. Unhealthy foods may seem cheaper, but often they cost a lot if you buy enough to fill you up.

Fruits and vegetables cost about the same as junk food, but junk food harms your health.

Around factories you often find fast-food restaurants selling hamburgers or other processed meats, or stores selling soda pop, packaged candy, or salty snacks. These foods do not contain the vitamins and minerals you can get from eating beans, vegetables, fruits, grains, and unprocessed meats. Processed foods usually contain a lot of chemicals, salt, and sugar to make them taste good and to addict you to them. They cause health problems such as diabetes, hypertension, heart disease, obesity, headaches, and digestive problems. Sugary foods also damage the teeth.

You know that this food is not very good for you or your family.

But my wife and I both get home so late that we don't have time to cook. Besides, my kids really love these donuts.

Eat well with little money or time

Workers who have little time can look for foods that do not take much preparation, but that taste good and have a lot of nutrition.

- **Buy inexpensive, local foods,** such as beans and grains. Sometimes we think that as we earn more money we should stop eating what some see as poor people's foods. But often, these are the most nutritious.

- **Don't throw away the greens of vegetables** that grow under the ground, such as beets or radishes. Add them to dishes you are cooking — they are full of vitamins and minerals.

- **Keep the water** that you used to boil beans, meat, or vegetables. You can drink it or use it to cook grains because some vitamins stay in the water.

- **Fruits, nuts, seeds, cheese, and cooked or raw vegetables** are all fairly quick to prepare and eat.

- **Spend your money on fresh, whole foods** that you can cook, instead of spending your money on packaged or canned food.

Bringing home-cooked food to work is the cheapest and safest way of eating healthy foods. Save some of your meal from the previous day to bring for breakfast, lunch, or dinner the next day. This way you will not have to buy food from the cafeteria or the vendors.

- **You can grow some foods,** even if you live in the city and have no land. You can grow food in containers, for example. Many vegetables will grow in a small patch of dirt that gets sun and regular watering. A community garden can provide fresh, healthy food at a very low price. Neighbors can raise chickens together and share the eggs and meat. (For more ideas on improving urban diets, see chapters 12 and 15 of *A Community Guide to Environmental Health.*)

Share the work of buying and cooking food

Co-workers or several families can often save money by buying food in larger amounts to share. Buying more food in one trip can save money on transportation. When people take turns doing the shopping, each person saves time and money.

When all the adults in a household work for pay, it is not fair for some — usually the women — to do all the cooking and cleaning. When the work of planning and preparing meals is equally shared, it is easier for everyone to eat healthier, get more rest, and feel less stress. Even if you eat together only one night a week, it can be a good break. It is also an excellent way to talk about common concerns in a relaxed situation. Plan ahead and decide:

- how much each person or family will spend on food.
- how and when to collect the money to buy food.
- how to prepare the menus ahead of time.
- how to assign each person or family's task for each meal.
- how to take turns shopping, preparing the food, cooking, and cleaning up.
- how to help everyone learn to cook tasty, nutritious meals.

When we cook together, we save money on food and fuel and we get to talk about what is on our minds.

Access to safe water and toilets

To stay healthy, you need to drink plenty of clean water and use the toilet when necessary. You need to be able to wash your hands with clean water and soap. Clean, safe water is necessary for emergency showers and eye washes.

Bosses often deny workers these basic necessities as they pressure employees to work faster and take fewer breaks. Limiting access to water and toilets is one way bosses make workers sick. A factory must:

- provide safe drinking water for all workers near their work areas. Allow workers to drink as much and as often as needed.
- allow all workers to use the toilet as needed. You should not have to ask permission, get a pass, or explain why you are going to the toilet. Like breathing, it is a necessary human function.
- add more toilets and urinals so workers do not have to wait in line. It is also easier to keep toilets clean when fewer people use each one.
- make sure each toilet room and stall has a door for privacy.
- place sinks or wash basins with soap and towels around the factory near toilets, drinking water, and eating areas.
- keep toilet rooms supplied with toilet paper, soap, and clean towels.
- keep a supply of pads for monthly bleeding in the women's toilet rooms. Women workers can also make a shared space for sanitary supplies where they can contribute supplies and replace what they use.
- hire workers to maintain and clean toilets.

Safe water

If you do not have to pass urine during the day, or you pass only a small amount of urine, you need to drink more water. Other signs of not drinking enough water are:

- thirst
- headache
- feeling weak or dizzy
- bladder or kidney infection

- nausea
- muscle cramps
- dark-colored urine
- stomach pain

If you work in a hot climate or near hot machines, or if working makes you sweat, you should drink liquids whenever you are thirsty to prevent heat stress. Pregnant women need to drink even more. For more information about health problems caused by heat, see chapter 15: Heat and cold. For more information about pregnancy, see chapter 26: Reproductive and sexual health.

Drinking water is the best way to give your body the liquid it needs. Less liquid stays in the body if you drink tea, coffee, alcohol, or cola drinks. So drink plenty of plain water.

Safe drinking water and clean cups should be available in every work area. The water container should be clearly labeled. If the factory is very hot, the water must be kept cool.

Because illnesses such as colds and flu can be passed from one person to another if you drink from the same cup, the factory should provide clean cups. Wash used cups after every use with warm water and soap or bleach (1 part bleach to 10 parts water), and rinse with clean water.

Water for first aid

Emergency showers and eye washes are necessary in areas where chemicals are used or stored. These first aid systems must provide clean, running water for at least 15 minutes. Running clean, cool water over a body part that is burned or has come in contact with a chemical is one of the best ways to reduce pain, lessen damage to a person's body, and restore their health (see page 175). If there is too little water, this treatment may not work.

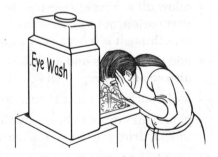

If the water for eye washes comes from a tank, change the water every month and flush the pipes every week.

Water for washing hands

All workplaces should have areas where workers can wash their hands with clean water and soap. Washing hands with clean water and soap prevents illness from spreading, can keep wounds or burns clean, and removes chemicals.

Water for washing hands should be available near the toilets. There should also be clean water for hand washing in the work area for workers to wash their hands before going to eat or after working with any materials or chemicals. Areas for hand washing should be labeled and away from anything that might contaminate the water. All areas for handwashing should have soap.

Hand washing is especially important if you handle lead, dyes, or solvents, even if you wear gloves.

Do not use solvents to clean your hands — use only soap and water.

Toilets and urinals

Workers must be able to use the toilet when they need to. If you cannot pass urine when necessary, you may get a bladder infection. This problem affects women more than men, because women get bladder infections more easily.

Toilet rooms should be close to work areas, and there should be enough toilets so no one has to wait in line. The minimum is 1 toilet for every 20 men and 1 for every 20 women. In large factories, several toilet rooms located around the factory are better than one large toilet room.

It is the boss's responsibility to make sure toilets, wash basins, and water areas are kept clean, in good repair, and supplied with toilet paper and towels. Waste buckets should be emptied and cleaned every day. Tell the supervisor and maintenance staff if a toilet stops working.

Women's needs

When women have their monthly bleeding, they need soap, water, and privacy. If they cannot change pads or wash during monthly bleeding, they are more likely to get infections. The boss should keep a supply of clean cloth, cotton, or sanitary pads in women's toilets for women workers to use as needed. Each toilet for women should also have a waste bucket with a lid.

Women are more likely to get infections of the bladder or kidneys, called urinary tract infections or UTIs, when they do not pass urine regularly. A UTI can be treated easily if it is discovered early. However if it is left untreated or if a woman is not allowed to go to the toilet, a simple bladder infection can develop into a serious kidney infection. See *Where Women Have No Doctor*, pages 364 to 368.

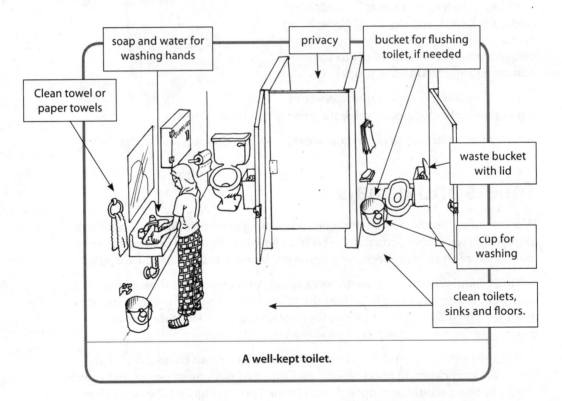

soap and water for washing hands

privacy

bucket for flushing toilet, if needed

Clean towel or paper towels

waste bucket with lid

cup for washing

clean toilets, sinks and floors.

A well-kept toilet.

Workers take over the bosses' toilet

My name is Elena. I work in an electronics factory in Mexico, near the border with the United States. We used to have only 3 toilets for more than 300 workers. We had to wait in lines, and the toilet rooms were always dirty. When we talked about problems in the factory, the toilets were one of the things that bothered us most. One day, when there was a long line, I said to my co-workers, "Let's use the toilet in the bosses' office." Together we walked into the office. The bosses were surprised and asked us what we were doing. We told them our toilets were dirty and there was a long line. That time, the bosses let us use their toilet.

We told the rest of the workers they could use the office toilet when there were long lines in the factory. When we started going to the office to use the toilet all the time, the bosses got upset. They said, "This is our toilet, you have your own in the factory." We told them we did not have enough toilets, and that the toilets were always filthy. Finally, the boss added 10 more toilets for the workers and kept them cleaner than before.

30 HIV (Human Immunodeficiency Virus)

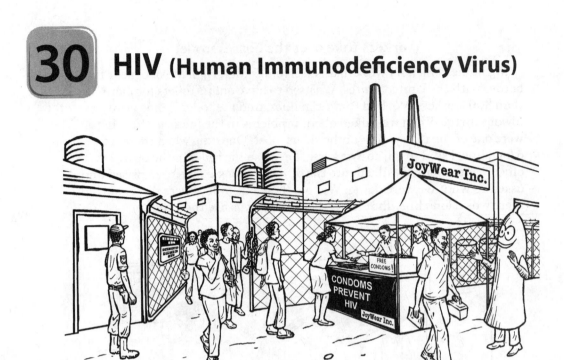

Many people in every country of the world have HIV, the virus that causes AIDS. With the right medicines and good working and living conditions, people with HIV can stay healthy, work, and raise families. Workers can help stop the spread of HIV by only having sex in ways that do not pass the virus, getting tested for HIV regularly, conducting HIV education and prevention programs in the factory, and helping workers with HIV keep their jobs as long as they are able to work.

Since people spend so much time at work, factories should develop comprehensive HIV programs that include:

- free, confidential testing for HIV, or time off to get tested.
- non-discrimination policies against workers who are HIV-positive.
- safety trainings to reduce the risk of infections that might result from accidents or injuries at work.
- time off for workers with HIV to take care of their health and the health of family members.
- information about HIV prevention, transmission, and services — including HIV counseling, testing, and treatment — for all workers and their families.
- support for safer sex, such as free condom distribution.

What you need to know about HIV

HIV (Human Immunodeficiency Virus) is a virus which causes AIDS (Acquired Immune Deficiency Syndrome). There is still no cure for HIV, but people with HIV can now live long and healthy lives by taking ART (Anti-Retroviral Therapy) medicines, getting prompt medical care when needed, eating nutritious food, drinking clean water, having decent housing, and getting emotional and spiritual support.

Without treatment, HIV slowly destroys the body's immune system — the parts of the body that help fight infection and recover from sickness. Overwork, malnutrition, exposure to some chemicals, and illnesses can also weaken the immune system. Without treatment and proper care, people with HIV usually get very sick with health problems and diseases, such as TB (tuberculosis) and pneumonia. When the person's immune system gets so weak that their body can no longer fight illness or heal, they will die. But AIDS is preventable if HIV is diagnosed and treatment is started.

People with HIV can look and feel strong. And a person who does not have HIV can be sick and have some of the same symptoms as someone with HIV. The only way to know for sure if a person has HIV is to get a test.

Work keeps us going and enables us to bring home food and medicine. When we are healthy and when we have access to HIV medicines we can continue to work just as long as workers who do not have HIV.

Signs of HIV

People can have HIV for many years before they have any signs of illness. Often the first signs to appear are:

- swollen lymph glands in the neck, armpits, or groin
- frequent fevers and night sweats
- weight loss
- tiredness
- decreased appetite
- diarrhea
- white spots (thrush) in the mouth
- for women, frequent vaginal yeast infections

These signs can also be caused by other problems. Getting tested for HIV when you first notice these signs will help you begin treatment earlier, when you are still strong.

How HIV is passed from one person to another

HIV lives in body fluids — blood, semen, wetness in the vagina, and breast milk. When any of these fluids from an infected person's body gets inside another person's body, the virus can spread. This can happen when:

a person with HIV has sex with another person and does not use a condom.

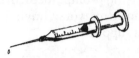

a person's skin is pierced or cut with a needle or other tool that has not been properly cleaned.

A woman who is pregnant with HIV or becomes infected during pregnancy can pass the virus to her baby. HIV can also be spread through breastfeeding.

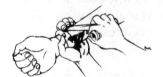

blood from an infected person gets into a cut or open wound on another person's body.

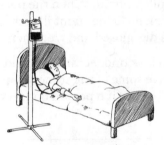

In places where blood is not tested for HIV, people can also get HIV from blood transfusions.

The HIV virus does not live in other body fluids such as sweat, tears, or saliva. It cannot live outside the body, in the air or in the water, for more than a few minutes.

You cannot give or get HIV by:

- sharing cups, dishes, chairs, tools, workstations, or telephones
- sharing food and drinks
- sharing bathrooms
- touching, hugging, or kissing
- sneezing or coughing (HIV is not passed like the flu or TB)
- mosquito bites (HIV is not passed like malaria)

Women are at greater risk than men

It is more difficult for women to protect themselves from HIV and other sexually transmitted infections (STIs) than it is for men. Factory bosses, husbands, and boyfriends expect young women to be obedient. Men are often unwilling to listen to women's concerns about sexual health. When a man refuses to use a condom, many women feel powerless to refuse sex.

Rape and sexual assault harm women more than men. When sex is forced, a woman's genitals are often injured. If her attacker has HIV, the infection can pass more easily to the woman through cuts in her vagina (see First aid after rape on pages 327 to 328).

Not using a condom increases your risk of getting other STIs. Having an STI increases your chances of getting HIV because they often cause open sores on the genitals. See pages 388 to 389 for information about preventing and treating STIs.

Using a condom every time you have sex helps protect you and your partner from HIV and other STIs.

The HIV test

The only way to know for sure if you or someone else has HIV is to get tested. There are 2 types of tests. The viral test looks for the virus in your blood, takes longer to give results, and is more expensive but is also more trustworthy. The antibody test (rapid test) looks for your body's reaction to HIV, gives results in less than 1 hour, and is less expensive.

After the virus has entered the body, it takes 1 to 3 months for it to show on a test. If you think you may have been exposed to HIV but the test does not show any infection, it is a good idea to get tested again after 3 months. Always use a condom. If the virus is in your body, it can pass from one person to another even if it does not yet show up on a test.

Many communities have free rapid testing services. If a person tests positive for HIV on a quick test, the clinic or health worker will usually run a viral test to be certain.

HIV tests should be:

- free or low cost.
- voluntary — no one should be forced to take an HIV test.
- confidential — the results should be shared only with the person being tested, not the boss!

Respect the privacy of others as you would like your own privacy to be respected. Don't spread rumors or "news."

Counseling is part of testing

A counselor will explain how the test works and answer your questions about the test before you take it. When the results are ready, the counselor will meet with you in a private space and explain them. If the results show that you have HIV, she will give you information about clinics, treatment, and other services and support groups in your community. Although HIV cannot be cured, you can manage it and lead a healthy and active life.

Getting support from your community

Any person who is ill can feel better and heal better if she or he has support, love, and understanding from family, co-workers, and community. People with HIV need support: treat them with kindness and respect, fight against discrimination and for free treatment, work for better conditions in the workplace, and do not gossip or spread rumors.

Medicines to manage HIV

As soon as you test positive for HIV, look for an HIV care and treatment program. These programs can provide you with the resources you need to stay healthy. Anti-retroviral therapy (ART) medicines can help your body strengthen its immune system to fight HIV infection, but small amounts of the HIV virus will always remain hidden in the body.

Using ART means taking a combination of at least 3 anti-retroviral medicines every day. The medicines available may differ depending on where you live. They might be combined into one pill, or they might come in 3 separate pills. But what is the same everywhere is that once you begin taking ART, the medicines must be taken every day and at the same time. A person taking ART will gain weight, and look and feel healthier. But if he stops taking ART, or misses doses of the medicine, or takes it at the wrong times, then the HIV can become stronger and make him sick again.

Women with HIV who are pregnant should also take ART. It will help them be healthier and protect their babies from being born with HIV.

Another medicine, cotrimoxazole, can be taken daily to help prevent infections. Cotrimoxazole is often a part of HIV treatment programs.

ART is becoming less costly and more available. Government health clinics as well as factory clinics may offer ART at low or no cost.

HIV in the factory

It is harder for people with HIV to get treatment and live healthy lives when they face stigma in their communities or workplaces. Stigma means the negative beliefs, attitudes, and behaviors people direct at those who have HIV. Stigma includes shaming, insulting, and gossiping about people with HIV, and even acting violently against them. Stigma comes from fears and misinformation about HIV and pushes people to hide their HIV status.

Workers with HIV also face discrimination from bosses. In some places, employers demand an HIV test before hiring. Others fire workers with HIV or thought to have HIV. When workers with HIV cannot get or keep jobs, they are even less likely to get care or stay healthy.

In factories where people with HIV keep their jobs, they may still face discrimination, such as denial of health insurance, pay raises, promotions, and even denial of permission to use the toilet. For more about discrimination, see chapter 21.

Fear of HIV keeps people from taking care of their own health and the health of others.

Activity　　　　**HIV is not transmitted at work**

1. Divide the group into pairs and ask them to discuss how they fear HIV spreads in the factory. Have them call out their fears and write them on the board. Be ready with ideas to help start the discussion if necessary.

Sitting together
Sharing toilets
When someone is injured
Shaking hands
Sweat, saliva, or tears
Sharing soap
Drinking from the same glass
Eating from the same plate
Sharp objects

2. Choose a fear from the list to conduct a role play (for how to do a role play, see page 325). For example, if one fear is "shaking hands," do a role play where a person with HIV greets his or her supervisor by extending their hand in a handshake. What will the person do? Why do people think this contact could lead to HIV infection? Have people explore what is really behind their fear.

3. Review as a group the HIV information on the previous pages, focusing on How HIV is passed from one person to another and How you cannot give or get HIV. Ask people to say if they still think each action on the list could spread HIV.

NOTE: "Sharp objects" is the only item on this list where there could be HIV transmission is when a worker is injured and there is blood. If this comes up in your discussion, talk about how HIV spreads through contact with blood and how using gloves or plastic bags can prevent infection. For ways to safely help injured workers who are bleeding, see page 203. People who are raped or coerced to have sex can also be at risk of HIV infection. See First aid after rape on pages 327 to 328.

| Activity | **HIV is a disability, not an inability** |

Workers living with HIV can continue working without putting other workers at risk. As with with other disabilities, it is possible to make the workplace safe for people with HIV. While dangers such as overwork, unsafe equipment, dirty bathrooms, bad food, lack of ventilation, and others are problems for all workers, these dangers are particularly harmful to workers with HIV. People with HIV can become sick more easily and are more likely to die from common illnesses. Improving conditions for workers with HIV will bring improvements for all workers.

1. Make a list of work dangers that workers face in the factory.

2. Going down the list, ask workers to compare how each danger affects healthy workers versus workers with HIV. You can also use this activity to talk about how some dangers affect pregnant women, people with physical or mental disabilities, and other vulnerable workers.

Machine injury

Chemicals and dust

Overwork

No water

Dirty toilets

TB

Eating well

	Healthy workers	Workers with HIV
Machine injury	Get hurt. Injury. Amputation	Same as healthy. Other workers can get infected. Maybe nobody will want to help
Chemicals and dust	Irritants. Asthma. Coughing	Same as healthy. Immune system. Might get sick more
Overwork	Tired. Exhaustion. Stress	Same. Might get sick more
No Water	Everybody needs water	Get dehydrated more easily
Dirty toilets	Filth makes everyone get sick	They can get very sick and can die from germs in water or toilets
Eating well	Get hungry. Tired. Dizzy	Same as healthy. Can become very ill from not eating enough food
TB	Get very sick. Needs treatment	Gets TB more easily and TB can kill a person with HIV more quickly

The rights of people with HIV in the workplace

Based on the **Discrimination (Employment and Occupation) Convention (No. 111)**, the **Social Security Convention (No. 102)**, and the **Occupational Safety and Health Convention (No. 155)**, the **ILO HIV and AIDS Recommendation (No. 200)** says employers must address HIV and AIDS in the workplace:

- Recognize HIV and AIDS as workplace issues.
- Take steps at work to limit the spread and effects of the HIV epidemic.
- Eliminate discrimination against workers living with HIV. HIV tests must not be required of job seekers, and having HIV should not cause workers to lose their jobs.
- Provide a healthy and safe work environment for all workers and accommodate the needs of workers living with HIV as much as possible.
- Focus on HIV prevention through information and education.
- Offer health care that includes treatment for workers with HIV.
- Facilitate access to HIV treatment, care, and support.

The roles of the UN, ILO, and other international organizations that promote workers' rights are explained in Appendix A.

HIV programs in the factory

Your group or union can educate at work and in the community about how HIV is spread and prevented. Your members can learn how to counter wrong ideas about HIV, distribute free condoms, and publicize organizations that offer HIV tests and medicines. You can help people with HIV get access to treatment and services so they can live long, healthy lives and contribute to the community.

Training peer educators

The Program for Appropriate Technology in Health (PATH) trained us to become HIV peer educators in our factories. We learned about prevention, HIV testing, and condoms. The company gives us a space in front of the factory to distribute condoms, explain how to use them, and hand out pamphlets about HIV programs in our community. Sometimes we also give information to workers' families in town.

Workplace programs

Some campaigns focus on showing employers how they benefit from keeping workers healthy. Others focus on workers' right to health. In places where many people have HIV, it is clear that HIV programs at work prevent turnover and maintain the quality of production.

A comprehensive HIV program in factories should include:

- free and confidential HIV testing, or time off for workers to get tested.
- confidentiality regarding HIV status.
- a policy prohibiting discrimination against workers who have HIV.
- training in safety and health practices that reduce the risk of infection when accidents happen. If accidents lead to blood exposure, the factory should make available PEP (post-exposure prophylaxis) treatment to prevent HIV (see *Where Women Have No Doctor*, page 521).
- time off for workers with HIV to care for their health or the health of family members.
- free workshops about HIV prevention, transmission, and treatment.
- support for safer sex, such as free condoms.
- health care services — including HIV counseling, testing, and treatment — for all workers and their families.
- tuberculosis testing, treatment and prevention, because TB is common in people with HIV (see chapter 31).

Factory pays for ART

The Volkswagen car manufacturing company started an HIV program in their factory in Brazil in 1996 to respond to the growing number of their workers and managers who have HIV. Like most HIV programs, it includes HIV testing. For those who test positive, Volkswagen offers a treatment package that includes care by medical specialists, free medicines, and clinical monitoring of ART treatment, home care, and help returning to work after illness.

The Volkswagen program also includes testing, treatment, and support for workers' families. With this care and support, almost 90% of the workers with HIV are active and without symptoms. Another part of the program is a strong education effort. Workers are invited to trainings about HIV and then supported in sharing information with their co-workers. Many companies are scared of starting an HIV program that includes free or subsidized ART, but this program (and many others around the world) actually saves money by keeping skilled workers with HIV healthy instead of hiring new people all the time.

31 TB (tuberculosis)

Tuberculosis (TB) is a dangerous infection, usually in the lungs, that can be treated with medicine and cured. Without medicine, TB slowly destroys the lungs and causes death. Many countries have public health programs that provide free testing and free medicines for TB.

When someone who has TB coughs or sneezes, they spread TB germs into the air. Other people who breathe in the germs can get infected with TB, especially if they share a closed space with an infected person for weeks or months. Overcrowding and poor ventilation in factories, dormitories, and boarding houses help spread TB. Factories should have a TB policy that:

- recognizes that TB is a workplace issue, educates management and workers about TB, and prohibits discrimination against workers with TB.

- provides free, confidential, on-site TB testing and treatment or has clear guidelines that allow workers paid time off to be tested and treated, and to have time to recover before returning to work.

- changes conditions to stop TB from spreading at work and in dormitories, by improving ventilation and relieving overcrowding.

TB can spread rapidly when people live in crowded dormitories with poor ventilation.

Preventing TB at work

A factory that has good ventilation can help prevent TB from spreading. And if factory workers live in dormitories, it is just as important that those buildings have good ventilation systems too.

Workers who breathe in a lot of dust are more likely to get TB. Dust irritates the lungs and makes them less able to resist TB infection. Smoking tobacco also irritates and weakens the lungs.

People who are sick or do not get enough food or rest are also more likely to get TB because their bodies are already weak. This is especially true for people with HIV, who should be tested for TB even if they have no signs. People with TB should also consider getting an HIV test.

When workers in a factory have TB, other people in the community usually have TB also. If anyone in your factory has signs of TB, or if people in your family and community have TB, unions, local organizations, health promoters, and clinics can work together to create a testing, treatment, and prevention program. Educating everyone in the factory, both workers and management, to know the signs of TB and where to get medicines and support is important for prevention.

Support for people with TB

The factory is healthier for all when every worker with TB gets medicine. In some places, the government health agency will send health workers to a factory to talk with workers, begin testing, and give TB medicine to each worker with TB until she is cured. Social service agencies often help people with TB by offering free transportation to get health care, food support, and compensation for loss of pay due to illness. Make sure the factory TB program is linked to TB programs in the community, and that all workers know about the services that are available.

TB medicines cure and prevent sickness

A person with TB who takes medicine regularly will begin to get better and not pass TB germs to others. This is why it is very important to start taking TB medicines as soon as you know you have TB. In most countries, government health services do not charge for TB testing or medicine. Many other organizations offer free testing and treatment, too.

If you have any of these signs of illness, see a health worker right away to find out if you need medicines for TB.

Signs of TB

- A cough that lasts longer than 3 weeks.
- Coughing up mucus with blood in it.
- Slight fever in the evening and sweating at night.
- Chest pain and shortness of breath.
- Weight loss and weakness.

Always cover your mouth and nose with a cloth when you cough or sneeze to keep germs out of the air.

TB tests

There are 3 types of tests for TB.

- For the **skin test**, a small amount of liquid is injected under the skin on the arm. If the person has TB, a raised patch of skin will appear within 1 to 3 days.
- For the **sputum test**, the health worker will ask you to cough hard so that you cough out some mucus. This mucus, called sputum, is then tested in a laboratory to see if it contains TB germs. Usually you will do 3 sputum tests. If 2 tests show you have TB germs, you will need medicines.
- If it is not clear if you have TB, a health worker might take a chest x-ray to look for TB in your lungs.

If the TB tests are negative but you still have the signs of TB, see a health worker trained in treating lung problems. You might have silicosis, pneumonia, asthma, or another lung disease.

Medicines for TB

The medicines for TB vary from country to country, but treatment everywhere lasts at least 6 months. Usually a person must take 4 medicines (isoniazid, rifampicin, pyrazinamide, and ethambutol) for 2 months, and then just 2 medicines (isoniazid and rifampicin) for 4 more months. It takes that much time and that many medicines to kill the TB germs inside your body.

It is important to take the medicine for the entire time needed, 6 to 12 months or more. You will start feeling better after a few weeks and may think you are cured, but stopping the medicines early is very dangerous. If all the germs have not been killed, you will still be able to infect others and you, your family, and your co-workers can get sick with a kind of TB that is very hard to cure, called MDR (multi-drug resistant) TB.

If you are taking TB medicines but are not feeling better, you may have MDR-TB and need different medicines to be cured. See a health worker.

After a person starts to feel better from taking TB medicines, it is very important for family, friends, and co-workers to support her through all the months of treatment. Help her to remember to take her TB medicines every day.

32 A decent place to live

The government uses public money to make sure export factories have electricity and streetlights, running water and sewer systems, paved roads and parking areas, telephone service, and security guards. And the factories may not even pay taxes! We are organizing to demand better housing and services for workers. The factories owe us not only a fair salary, but also better communities.

WE NEED:	BECAUSE:
Water and sanitation	prevent illness
Electricity	improves the quality of life of the community
Paved streets	help prevent pollution and illness
Trees and green space	help the community breathe
Police, fire, ambulance services	protect workers

When governments allow factories to set up in your community, together they plan the buildings, roads, electricity and other services a factory needs to operate. But they often do not take workers' needs into account. In their plans, only the workers' labor counts — not their well-being.

Because export factories employ so many people, governments and employers need to make sure they have enough public services, such as housing, sanitation, safe water, and transportation. For good health and safety, they must also install sidewalks and streetlights, plant trees, build parks and playgrounds, and, of course, build and staff schools, clinics, hospitals, and cultural centers.

Housing

In China and Indonesia, most export factory workers live in crowded dormitories inside factory zones. In other places, such as Mexico and Kenya, workers must find or build their own houses, often in areas without electricity, running water, safe transportation, or other services. Workers in other countries live in similar conditions and share the same problems: they have jobs but do not have a decent place to live.

Six of us share this room in a boarding house. More than 100 women live here, but there are only 4 toilets, and there is never enough water. We have to carry water from a public well down the street.

Many factory workers can barely afford to pay for a place to sleep. But to stay healthy, you need to live in a place where you can bathe and use the toilet, drink plenty of clean water, store and prepare food safely, keep dishes and utensils clean, wash and dry clothes, and sometimes just relax.

We have been successful at winning more benefits in the dormitories. Our employers know they are violating the law, that workers have a right to clean, safe living quarters. We write letters and petitions, and because there are so many people in each dormitory, we can get from 1,000 to 2,000 signatures really fast. We send them to the brands, the corporate and factory management, and the union. When we win, we feel empowered!

Building a housing cooperative

The St. Peter Claver Free Zone Women's Group was organized by women workers in Jamaica's export factories as a place to share their experiences, both at home and at work, with other workers. We offer counseling on labor issues as well as psychological and mental health issues, classes, and workshops. As women began to trust us and the other workers they met, the group has become stronger and more involved.

As time passed we began to take action on some of the issues that were the biggest concerns for women. One of these issues was housing. The export factories do not provide housing and the boarding houses in the area were not trustworthy or safe for women. We asked for funds from the Canadian International Development Agency to organize a housing cooperative for women. The project is so successful that we now have several boarding houses around the export processing zone. Our boarding houses are affordable, clean, and safe for women. They are also places where women can connect with other workers. We hold our workshops and classes there, too.

Transportation

Getting to and from work is a serious concern for many factory workers. Buses often do not operate early or late enough to accommodate long working hours. Traveling late at night or early in the morning can be dangerous around many factories, especially for women workers. Too many women workers have been raped or killed after they leave the factory with no safe transportation home. Many workers have to spend many hours to get to work, adding to their already very long workday.

Safe transportation between home and work is one way to protect workers from assault, robbery, and rape. Making transportation available also reduces stress and exhaustion by giving workers more time to rest, shop and prepare food, and take care of personal needs.

Here are some ideas that different groups have tried:

- **Convince owners to provide free, subsidized, or low cost transport** for workers to and from the factory, especially after dark and before sunrise.
- **Persuade local government to start a community bus service** for workers going to and from the factory zone.
- **Expand community bus service** with more and better routes that run during the hours workers need them so workers can get to and from work on time and safely.

Work directly with the bus drivers — if many workers use their services, it might be good business for them to offer better routes and times of service.

While organizing for better transportation, groups have also organized campaigns for workers to be safer going to and from work. Make a map of where your co-workers live to help you create a buddy system for walking, biking, or riding public transportation together.

Workers organize for safer streets

Thousands of young women workers in Sri Lanka's Katunayake Free Trade Zone migrated from the countryside to a vast community of boarding houses outside the Zone. Union organizers surveyed workers in the boarding houses about their concerns. They learned that the women did not feel safe traveling to and from the factories late at night because there were a lot of robberies and rapes in that area.

The organizers brought the women together to talk about the problem, discuss solutions, set priorities, and plan actions. The workers took up a series of campaigns and won several important changes:

Police reforms: Male police were unresponsive to women's concerns and unwilling to investigate attacks. Women did not report attacks expecting only disrespect from the male officers. Workers convinced the police station to set up a women's desk, staffed by women 24 hours a day. There are still problems with the police, but the situation is much better now.

Streetlights: Streetlights had been put in around the Zone and boarding houses, but they did not work everywhere. Some broke from weather and wear, others were broken by people who wanted to make the street dark. Repairs were rarely made. Workers got the government to fix the broken lights and agree to make repairs when problems are reported.

Local bus service: Workers pressured the government to start local bus service between the Zone and the boarding house community. The bus route was so popular that later the union convinced the factory owners to buy 2 more buses for the service. Not only did the women feel safer, they also did not have to walk an extra 3 kilometers each day.

These changes reduced violence and rape, and also helped the women learn a lot about organizing and creating change in their community. It built more of a community feeling among the workers. Now workers watch out for each other more, especially at night when leaving the factory.

Pollution from factories

Factories make useful products, but they also make waste. Unfortunately, factory owners do not always dispose of waste safely. Factories often put dangerous chemicals and other dangerous materials into the air, water, and ground. Pollution from factory waste causes serious health problems for everyone in the community, and when it travels in air and water, can even cause illness for people who live hundreds of miles away. (See Pollution from garment factories on page 106, and Pollution from shoe factories on page 119.)

Factories must provide workers and people in the communities around the factory with:

- information on the chemicals and materials used in the plant, and how they are disposed of.
- results of regular government or independent testing of waste disposal through smokestacks, ventilation systems, pipes, burial pits, etc.
- proof that machinery and installations in the factory are safe, in good condition, and that evacuation plans and resources for the area are ready in case of natural disaster or serious accident.

Factory products themselves can be dangerous to our health when they are poorly designed or cannot be recycled or disposed of safely. Workers and their organizations need to work together with environmental and consumer organizations to protect both jobs and health.

Health problems caused by pollution

Illnesses caused by pollution are not the same for each person or each community. Children often have more health problems than adults, because their bodies are small and still developing. Some problems affect women more than men. Inside or outside the factory, at work or at home, health problems caused by chemicals depend on the type of chemical, the way people are exposed to it, and how often or for how long. To learn more, see chapter 8: Chemical dangers and Appendix B: Common chemicals and materials.

Harm caused by pollution can also depend on the environment around the factory, such as the direction of winds, the kind of soil, the number of trees, the location of water sources, or the depth of groundwater. Some pollution can travel through water and air, and can also harm fish, birds, animals, plants, and people in communities far away from the factory.

Air pollution

Factories contaminate the air by blowing chemical vapors and smoke out through vents and smokestacks, and by burning waste in open dumps or incinerators. Exhaust from generators, diesel trucks, and buses also fill the air with dangerous gases.

Air pollution can cause skin, heart, and breathing problems, and eye irritations and infections. Dangerous chemical gases in the air can also cause cancer and other serious illnesses, problems with fertility and pregnancy, miscarriages, and harm to babies before they are born. Some chemicals harm children's ability to think and learn.

Air pollution that harms people can also harm other living things. For example, soot from the smoke of motor exhaust can cover the leaves of a plant and change the way the plant grows, or cause the plant to produce less fruit, or even die.

Close the dump!

When new factories were built near Nogales, a Mexican city on the USA border, people on both sides of the border welcomed the jobs they brought. The factories had no smokestacks, so nobody worried about pollution. But after a while, many people started getting sick with cancer and other serious illnesses. A group of sick people got together to support each other and named their group LIFE — Living Is For Everyone. They decided to find out why so many people were sick.

LIFE members surveyed their neighborhoods and made a map showing where sick people lived. They found that people living near certain wells were sick much more than people in other parts of the community. They were also concerned about a dump where factories burned waste.

LIFE took pictures of the dump and contacted the media.

They wanted the dump closed, and they wanted help proving that factory pollution was making them sick. But others in the community were worried that all this attention was going to scare the factory owners into leaving Nogales. They held many meetings where everybody got to discuss their fears and frustrations. After many weeks, the community decided to back LIFE. LIFE's campaign convinced the government to study the water, ground, and air in Nogales. The studies found high levels of chemicals that cause cancer.

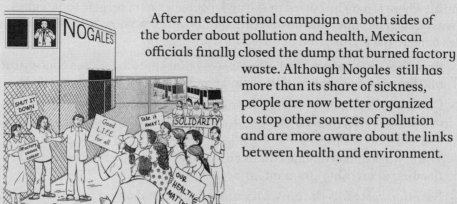

After an educational campaign on both sides of the border about pollution and health, Mexican officials finally closed the dump that burned factory waste. Although Nogales still has more than its share of sickness, people are now better organized to stop other sources of pollution and are more aware about the links between health and environment.

Water pollution

Factories often dump dirty water, used chemicals and oils, sewage, and cafeteria waste directly into the ground or into a community water source, such as a river, lake, or stream. Waste dumped into the ground can poison the groundwater that feeds other water sources, such as wells and ponds. Electronics companies sometimes store very dangerous chemicals in underground tanks. In many countries, including the United States, these containers have leaked, contaminating the soil and groundwater with toxic chemicals.

Using polluted water for drinking, cooking, washing, and bathing can cause many health problems, including stomach infections and diarrhea, skin infections and rashes, eye infections, reproductive problems, cancer, and other serious illnesses.

Water pollution can harm fish and other plants and animals that live in or near the water. Eating fish and plants from contaminated water can also cause health problems. Polluted groundwater or irrigation water can ruin soil for growing crops and it can poison food grown in the soil.

Pollution from solid waste

Factories also produce solid waste, such as spoiled parts, metal filings, scraps, empty chemical containers, used cardboard boxes, wood pallets, plastic, wire, paper, and other trash. Some companies transport waste to a local dump or landfill where it may be buried or burned. Factories may recycle some types of waste, such as paper and cardboard, but too often waste is just dumped in piles outside the factory and in the community.

- Rats, flies, mosquitoes, and other insects that spread diseases concentrate and breed in waste piles, dumps and ponds.
- Children playing near waste piles and people collecting waste to use or sell can easily get diarrhea, scabies and other skin infections, eye infections, tetanus, and other health problems.
- Waterways and drainage canals can clog with dumped waste, causing flooding or creating stagnant, unhealthy pools.
- Burning waste fills the air with smoke, fumes, and dangerous chemicals. Poisonous ash drops onto plants, soil, and water. Burning plastic and batteries are especially harmful.

Tragedy in Bhopal

On the night of December 2, 1984, 40 tons of deadly chemical vapors spread through Bhopal, India, a city of about 1 million people. The chemical came from a leak inside a pesticide factory owned by Union Carbide, a large corporation from the United States. The factory had an alarm system to warn if there was a leak, but the owners of the factory had disconnected it. Within an hour, the deadly gas covered the entire city. Many people died in their sleep that night, and over 8,000 people died in the days that followed.

The harm from that night 30 years ago still continues. More than 20,000 people have died and more than 150,000 people live with serious health problems that include lung damage, loss of vision, and cancers. The poisoning affects children born to survivors of the disaster. Many children in Bhopal have been born with misshapen bodies and are unable to grow, learn, and talk like healthy children. Even people who moved to Bhopal afterwards are affected because they drink poisoned water and eat food grown in the area.

Union Carbide and the company that now owns it, Dow Chemical, have refused to take responsibility for the disaster. But the people of Bhopal have organized to demand justice and win compensation for survivors and their families. They are fighting for the Indian government to supply their communities with clean water, and to clean up and remove poisonous materials and contaminated soil from the factory site.

The Bhopal disaster shows what can happen when we trust a company to keep us safe from the extremely dangerous chemicals used in their factories. Because companies routinely ignore basic safety precautions to increase profits, they and their hired experts cannot be allowed to evaluate the benefits and risks by themselves. Disasters will be prevented only when workers and neighbors have the information they need and the power to participate in decisions about their community's safety.

Leaks, spills, and fires

A large chemical leak or spill can suddenly harm the whole community, as did the disaster in Bhopal. The leak or spill can come from machinery inside the factory, from a break or explosion in containers and pipes that hold dangerous liquids or gases, or from trucks or trains carrying chemicals or waste.

Chemical explosions or fires can spread poisonous smoke through the air. The water used to fight a fire can carry chemicals into lakes or streams, or into the ground where it can contaminate wells and other water sources.

Electronics recycling

Electronics contain hundreds of dangerous substances that can harm workers' health when they are being produced. When these products are no longer useful and are thrown away or recycled, they often end up poisoning even more people.

Workers, and sometimes entire families, disassemble electronics waste. People smash, burn, and often work with their bare hands to separate the pieces. This releases dangerous and toxic chemicals into the air, soil and water. The workers, their families, and their communities are directly exposed to cadmium, lead, and hundreds of other chemicals known to cause serious health problems, cancers, and death.

Organizing against factory pollution

Gathering information about pollution from factories can be as simple as asking some questions and taking a walk around the area, or it may be more complex, involving formal interviews and scientific studies. In either case, if you organize well you may be able to find the sources of pollution and change things for the better.

| Activity | Community pollution survey |

This activity has 2 parts. Your group may need to meet a few times to plan and to evaluate each part. It may take several weeks to complete.

1. Talk to people in the community

Ask your neighbors and older residents of the community to think back to a time before the factory opened. What has changed since then?

Ask your neighbors what signs of factory pollution they have seen or smelled. Ask them about illnesses they or their family members may be suffering, especially miscarriages and birth defects, as many toxics cause reproductive problems. Write down the information about illnesses, dates, and the location of their homes in relation to the factory. You can also use this information to make a map.

For ideas about making and using surveys, see chapter 3.

Ask workers and former workers what kind of waste the factory produces and where it goes. Try to find out what chemicals are used in the factory, how they are used, and how those chemicals get into the air, water, food, and homes outside the factory. Find out where the wastewater from the factory goes. Companies often dump many of the chemicals they use into local sewers, rivers, lakes, and so forth. This information will help you plan the next part of the activity.

2. Take a walk

As a group, or in several small groups, you can walk around the community using your eyes, nose, and ears to detect strange colors, smells, and sounds that may be signs of pollution. Follow up on the information people in the factory and community told you. Write down what you learn and take photographs of what you see. This will help you share the information later and will help the group decide what action to take.

Ask questions about what you don't see. For example, if there are no trucks leaving the factory with chemical waste, it is either going into the air, being dumped into the ground, or piped into a sewer or stream. Are smells, illnesses, or other signs of pollution greater downwind or downstream from the factory?

(continued)

| Activity | Community pollution survey (continued) |

Decide as a group where to walk and what to look for. Here are some suggestions of things to observe:

- **Look for signs of air pollution**

    Is there smoke, dust, or smog in the air around the factory? Do trucks often park on streets with the motor running?

    Walk downwind from the factory and look for dust in the air or signs of chemicals on the ground, building, or plants.

    Use your sense of smell to detect strange odors. Sniff around for a chemical smell or a burning smell. You may have to walk the area more than once and at different times, because burning may happen only at certain times of the day or week.

- **Look for signs of water pollution**

    Visit nearby creeks, canals, and ponds, and notice the color and the smell of the water. Look for signs of oily, foamy, or sticky residues in the water or on the plants, rocks, or sand next to the water. Observe the plants, fish, animals, and insects living in and around the water. Do they seem healthy?

- **Look for signs of other waste**

    Can you see liquid waste flowing out of the factory, or a trench where barrels of chemicals are emptied onto the ground? Are there piles of empty containers or other trash?

3. Discuss what you learn

The most important step is sharing all the information with the group or entire community. You may want to make a map of the area around the factory and mark where you observed signs of pollution.

On a wall or a chalkboard, make a list of all the kinds of pollution coming from the factory, possible health effects of each type of pollution, and possible solutions. Using these lists, ask questions that will help the group decide what action to take. For example, which kind of pollution is causing the most problems? Which kind of pollution may be the easiest to stop or to clean up? See more about how to make a community map on page 44.

Taking action to clean it up

The Metales y Derivados battery recycling plant in the Chilpancingo neighborhood of Tijuana, Mexico, did not take care with its toxic waste. The factory stored it in badly-made containers that leaked chemicals into the soil and water. The wind blew waste into the community. People complained about skin rashes, stomach problems, and asthma.

Pressure from the community and environmentalists finally pushed the Mexican government to close the plant. But instead of cleaning up the extremely dangerous chemicals, the factory owner fled across the border to San Diego, USA. He knew the Mexican government could not touch him there. The plant was abandoned with 23,000 tons of waste, including 7,000 tons of a very toxic lead mixture.

The people of Chilpancingo, with help from the Environmental Health Coalition (EHC) activists from the USA and Mexico, campaigned to clean up this toxic waste site left by Metales y Derivados. After more than a decade, the Mexican government finally signed a cleanup agreement and formed a bi-national community/government working group. The cleanup was completed in 2008 and included independent community monitoring. Key to their success was:

- **getting organized and connecting** with environmental, labor, and human rights groups. They held rallies, sent letters to government officials, and kept media attention focused on their problem.

- **testing, monitoring and publicizing the pollution**. Local laboratories tested the water and soil, and university students in the border region gave technical support.

- **organizing educational campaigns** about pollution and health. They developed a grass-roots training program for women on how to identify and eliminate toxics in the household, how industrial contamination affects the community, and how to create action plans for change.

- **using local, national, and international laws and regulations**. When the Mexican government said it was not responsible and would not pay for the clean-up, the people appealed. After 3 years, the bi-national environmental agency determined that the Chilpancingo site was a "grave risk to human health." They also got the UN Special Rapporteur on the Right to Adequate Housing to tour the area, and the UN High Commission for Human Rights to speak on their behalf.

All these actions increased pressure on the Mexican government to finally clean up Chilpancingo.

PART 5
Appendices

APPENDIX A

Laws and the struggle for decent, healthy, and fair work

All people deserve to be treated fairly, in a way that protects and promotes their dignity and their physical, mental, and social well-being. These are basic human rights. To achieve them, people who work need a healthy and safe workplace, free of violence and discrimination, where they can form unions and negotiate as a group for fair conditions and a living wage.

The United Nations and the International Labour Organization are two of the largest global organizations that make recommendations on worker rights. Your government, and the other governments of the world that are part of the United Nations and the International Labour Organization, have signed treaties and agreements designed to protect workers.

International and national laws by themselves do not protect workers. Without responsible employers, ways to ensure laws are enforced, and organized workers and communities, laws are only promises on paper and nothing more.

Using the law to support your campaign

Workers gain the power to change their workplace when they know their rights and can organize to win them. Organizing requires ongoing discussion and problem-solving among workers, as well as bargaining with the employer.

Be familiar with your national labor law. Some countries have very specific labor laws created in response to worker organizing, while other countries have hardly any labor law. How your demands relate to the law can determine how, when, and about what you organize. When workers demand more than current labor law allows, it does not mean the demands are impossible to win, but that it will require more unity from the workers to win them.

So first learn about your labor law, and how it can help or harm you. Then talk with your co-workers and hold meetings to discuss everyone's concerns.

Unions are often the only type of worker group recognized in labor law. The law may set requirements on how unions are run (rules for elections, who can be members, and so forth) and may regulate how unions and employers relate with each other. Community and womens' groups are often easier to form and run. They can gain national and international recognition, especially if they are legally established as a non-governmental organization (NGO). Usually only a union can negotiate and enforce a collective bargaining agreement between workers and employers. But this does not prevent workers in a community organization from trying to negotiate with an employer over issues of mutual concern not covered in the workers' contract.

Discussing changes you want to see in the factory and agreeing upon demands require good organizing and fluid communication among workers. Regular meetings, open discussions, and making compromises with your co-workers are important. Two people who work in the same factory may want to address different concerns about working conditions, and both may be equally important. Patience and a commitment to unity are important characteristics for an organizer. See chapter 2: Learning and teaching about health at work.

And again, what the law says may be one thing and the enforcement of the law may be another. Despite the rights you may have on paper, the police or military may be used by the government and factory owners to prevent or break your organizing efforts. A hard lesson that many unions and organizers have learned is that the law is usually on the side of those with the most power.

The ILO can recommend changes to national labor laws, but achieving them is a long process. Organizing workers is the most fundamental condition in changing national labor law. Organizing makes your voices heard and demands that the employer, the brand, and the government protect the rights of workers and enforce good and just working conditions.

National labor laws

Every country has its own national labor law that regulates the relationship between workers, trade unions, employers, the government, and the international companies or "brands." Worker health and safety might be part of the labor law or it might be part of the laws that regulate health.

To learn what the labor laws are in your country and how you can use them to fight for better conditions, ask a union, a law professor at a university, the labor department of your government, a lawyer at a legal aid organization or clinic, or the staff at a workers' center. Do research on the Internet, too. Legal documents are often written in a way that is hard to understand, but you will likely find groups that have summarized and translated the law into words that are easier to understand.

Labors laws are sometimes written to protect workers and sometimes to protect business. Well-organized workers' groups have been successful at influencing their governments to create or change laws to ensure workers are guaranteed safe and healthy work at a fair wage. It is just as likely, however, that what laws are passed and how they are enforced is heavily influenced by business interests. Having good laws on paper does not mean these laws are put into practice. That depends on how well you organize.

Bangladesh Labor Act

In many countries, workers must wait a long time for the government to legally define their rights. In Bangladesh, the first consolidated Labor Act was passed in 2006. While better than nothing, it did not sufficiently address many important issues, including insurance and compensation for injury or death, child labor, emergency exits in factories, and many others. Unions, worker organizations, employers, and legislators began meeting to expand and improve the Labor Act.

The Bangladesh Occupational Safety, Health, and Environment Foundation (OSHE) was one of the groups that lobbied the government and drafted suggestions for improved labor laws. In July 2013, a few months after the Rana Plaza factory collapse, the government came under enough international pressure to finally amend the existing labor law. OSHE printed copies of the law to help distribute it among workers and students. OSHE also produced a poster about health and safety committees required by the new law, and began a 10-part training program for workers. As in other countries, the Bangladesh labor law still requires improvement. It also needs to be better respected by factory owners and better enforced by the Ministry of Labor and Employment. But workers now have a legal way to fight for their rights.

International labor laws

The United Nations (UN) is an international institution made up of national governments. The UN is responsible for setting the standards regarding people's basic human rights, as reflected in the Universal Declaration of Human Rights. The UN has also proposed and approved many conventions that describe the rights people have won through organizing and struggle.

Two important UN documents that are particularly helpful when organizing around labor and work health issues are the International Covenant on Economic, Social and Cultural Rights (ICESCR) and the International Covenant on Civil and Political Rights (ICCPR). The Convention on the Elimination of All Forms of Discrimination against Women (CEDAW, see page 11) has also been used by groups supporting migrant women workers and domestic workers.

 Two UN covenants to inspire labor organizing

The **UN International Covenant on Economic, Social and Cultural Rights (ICESCR),** especially articles 6, 7, 8, and 10, focuses on the right to work. People have the right to:

- earn a living from their work and get a fair wage.
- have working conditions that are safe, healthy, and dignified.
- be free from discrimination at work, including the right to equal pay for equal work.
- have paid holidays.
- organize and bargain collectively.

The **UN International Convenant on Civil and Political Rights (ICCPR)** makes the case that worker rights are human rights. The articles most relevant to workers affirm:

- the right to equality between men and women in the workplace.
- freedom from inhumane or degrading treatment or punishment.
- freedom of association.
- the right to peaceful assembly.

The UN's International Labour Organization

The International Labour Organization (ILO) is the part of the UN dedicated to workers' rights. It is an organization representing workers, employers, and governments that sets guidelines that every workplace, company, and country should implement and enforce to protect workers. ILO labor standards, conventions, and recommendations must be ratified and signed by each participating country. Not all countries ratify all conventions, and a country can choose which parts of each convention it will accept and which it rejects. See the Ratification by Country page on the ILO website (ilo.org) to learn which conventions your country has signed, and what "adaptations" they have made to the conventions. Once a country has signed a convention, its government is expected to make its labor law match or exceed the standards set by the ILO.

Unfortunately, the ILO has no means to enforce these labor standards. The only way to ensure that labor rights are enforced is for workers to organize and pressure their governments, the brands, and the employers to accept their responsibility to improve and enforce labor standards.

The "workers' rights" boxes included throughout this book highlight basic workers' rights as recognized by the ILO and UN. (They are listed by topic on page xi and by name on pages 457 to 458.) Use them to compare your current working conditions with international labor law. The ILO and UN conventions can be motivational tools for organizing and demanding changes in your workplace that international agreements and your government say you should have.

ILO 40-Hour Week Convention:

work week --> 40 hours

regular working hours

Some ways to use international labor law

- Educate workers about how their desires and demands for a healthy, safe, and fair workplace are supported by international law. People often feel more justified in organizing when they know this is true.

- Push local officials to enforce already existing labor law. If national laws are backed by international law, then workers have twice as much right to demand enforcement.

- Compare your national labor laws to international standards to show how they do not meet them and why it would be good if they did. Governments do not like to be embarrassed, especially in front of other governments.

- If your government has not signed international conventions on labor rights, organize with other labor and community groups to influence the government to do so. They might agree to sign a convention because it would make them look good. But you will probably have to organize further to get them to create systems to enforce these conventions.

- Convince your employer that complying with labor laws will make workers healthier, happier, and more productive. The international companies the factory sells to will value the good reputation they earn by following the laws, and their ability to meet production schedules because their workers are happier, more efficient, and less likely to strike or stop production.

- Let the international companies ("brands") who purchase from your factory know when and in what ways their suppliers are breaking international laws. Brands often worry a lot about their image and reputation and do not want to jeopardize that. Also, they may be breaking laws in their home country if they ignore labor rights where their goods are made.

See more about organizing a campaign and how to find allies and supporters in chapter 3.

ILO Core Labor Standards

If your country does not have a labor law or the national labor law does not address your concerns, you can propose that the government use the ILO's Codes of Conduct as guidelines to create new labor law. The Codes of Conduct are based on the 4 Core Labor Standards (CLS):

1. The right to free association and collective bargaining

2. The elimination of forced labor

3. The abolition of child labor

4. The elimination of discrimination in the workplace

By themselves, the Core Labor Standards are not sufficient to protect workers. Other ILO Conventions (see pages 457 to 458) cover hours and wages, health and safety, working conditions, and dozens of other work-related situations.

The commitment to equal rights for men and women in economic, social, and political matters is also clearly stated in many ILO, UN, and other agreements. Governments are obligated to make sure women have the right to work in any profession and have the same rights at work as men. These rights include the right to receive equal pay for similar work, equal training and promotions, and freedom from discrimination as women or mothers.

How to influence the ILO

Each year, the ILO holds an International Labour Conference (ILC) where delegates from each member-country, as well as representatives from employer and worker groups, meet to discuss complaints, draft new conventions, and change existing conventions. If there is a convention you would like to add or change, you can submit a proposal to the ILC or the representative of the workers' group from your country for review. But be prepared: it can take many years, many lawyers, and a lot of financial resources for a proposal to become a Resolution or Convention. Because it is so expensive, difficult, and time-consuming, for the most part only global union federations take this on.

But change does happen. In 2011, the ILO adopted a new Domestic Workers Convention (No. 189) setting the first global standards for domestic work. This convention is providing workers support and leverage to push their national governments to adopt similar changes to national labor law in many countries, including the United States, the countries of the European Union, the Philippines, Haiti and elsewhere.

Filing a complaint

If your country has signed an ILO convention but does not make or enforce changes in national labor law, filing a complaint is one way to pressure the national government, the brand, and your employer to improve labor conditions. A workers' group can submit a complaint directly to the International Labor Conference to be reviewed by the ILO, or can reach out to delegates from the organizations of your country that attend the Conference and ask them to ensure your complaint is reviewed there.

The ILO's governing body will then decide whether to review your complaint. If it does, a Commission of Inquiry will be appointed to investigate the complaint in your country, review your labor law and its implementation, and inspect factory conditions. After the investigation, the ILO will write a report encouraging the national government to accept the ILO's recommendations, improve the law, and to enforce it.

Filing a complaint and receiving international support to enforce national labor law is useful, but the process of investigation and writing a report usually takes five to seven years. You may want to consider other ways of using international labor law to apply pressure for change that are more effective and time efficient. And if you do decide to file a complaint with the ILO, or another international governing body, such as the Inter-American Court of Human Rights, you will want to continue to push for enforcement of labor law and negotiate for better working conditions and rights by approaching your employer directly, appealing to the brand, and confronting your government.

ILO Better Work program

What would happen if a factory was run according to the ILO core labor standards? The ILO created the Better Work (BW) program to find out. Based on its pilot project, Better Factories Cambodia, BW inspects and monitors member factories in 8 countries to see if they follow basic ILO conventions that protect workers, and reports the results. BW also trains workers, union leaders, and factory managers on workers' rights, health, and safety, and coordinates with the government, manufacturers' association, and the brands.

The factories in the BW programs tend to be safer than before, and safer than other local factories. However, many challenges remain:

- Worker participation and empowerment is downplayed, and workers are discouraged from taking action to improve health and safety in the factory.
- Factory inspections are often known ahead of time, and workers fear losing their jobs if they speak with inspectors.
- Violations are not made public.
- BW and its inspectors have no power to enforce suggested changes.
- BW does not target brands that contract factories to make their clothes but ignore their responsibility for working conditions.
- BW does not report on wages (many factories do not pay a living wage), too many hours, violations of labor and union rights, or mass faintings (a big problem in Cambodia).

To achieve its goals of achieving a healthier, sustainable workplace, the ILO Better Work program must change to:

- Encourage worker participation and empowerment.
- Support the formation of factory-level health and safety committees with elected worker representatives.
- Give health and safety committees power to make improvements and stop dangerous work.
- Address labor rights issues such as respecting unions, negotiating contracts, and paying a living wage.

International conventions on workers' rights

There are many international workers' rights conventions and agreements. We have chosen to include in this book some of the most important and relevant to the topics we cover. You can find all the UN Conventions by going to this website: treaties.un.org. You can find all of the ILO Conventions here: ilo.org/global/standards. It might be helpful to do more research on the convention you want, to see how it is implemented, how it can be useful for your campaign, and if your country has ratified it.

 International agreements in this book

continued

International agreements in this book
(continued)

Other international agreements

Trade agreements and international law

Trade agreements create the rules by which companies and governments do business across borders. Most trade agreements limit the restrictions governments can place on companies. Laws that protect people and the environment are seen as obstacles to trade, so many companies and governments negotiate agreements that lower labor standards rather than improve them.

Some trade agreements and membership requirements of trade organizations stop governments from making and enforcing policies that protect the environment and public health. The World Trade Organization (WTO) sets the standards for global trading practices and regulates national trade policies. If a country is a member of the WTO, its national laws must follow WTO trade rules.

Workers are not fairly represented in the WTO. International trade unions have requested that the WTO adopt ILO labor standards and promote labor rights by including a worker rights clause within the global trade system. The WTO has so far refused to do this.

Some trade agreements address labor rights. For example, in 1992 the North American Free Trade Agreement (NAFTA) became the first trade agreement to include an agreement on labor, the North America Agreement on Labor Cooperation (NAALC). Unfortunately, it has not been effective. The NAALC did not establish an international court or monitoring system to ensure the implementation of labor standards. It did not require each participating country to improve its labor law. And it has not promoted or protected workers' rights.

Trade agreements do occasionally improve occupational health in countries where labor and occupational health laws are lacking. In Peru, for example, a trade agreement with the USA promoted a law requiring workplaces to form joint health and safety committees. But the agreement did not include recognition of the most basic labor right — that workers could organize and bargain collectively.

The UN's Principles on Business and Human Rights were developed to protect workers from the business rules in international trade that put "profits over people." These principles put pressure on companies to respect international human rights and follow the labor laws of the country where the factory is located as well as the labor standards of the international brand's home country. However, it has been impossible to implement these principles because the Principles on Business and Human Rights have no enforcement mechanism.

Using trade agreements to protect labor rights

After the Dominican Republic-Central America-United States Free Trade Agreement, known as CAFTA-DR, was signed by Guatemala in 2006, the short period of employer good behavior while the treaty was being negotiated came to an abrupt end. Returning to practices of previous decades, workers who tried to assert their rights were harassed, fired, and even murdered. In the years since the signing of the agreement, 68 union members were killed, with little government response and no arrests until 2014.

In 2008, 6 Guatemalan unions and the AFL-CIO, the federation of US unions, filed a complaint with the US Office of Trade against Guatemala's violation of its own labor laws and international labor standards. In 2009, the US government found that Guatemala was violating its laws by not letting workers organize unions, not paying lawful wages, and not paying workers' health insurance even though money was deducted from their wages, among other legal violations.

Unions and other organizations launched an international campaign to get the USA to pressure Guatemala to respect workers' rights. It took 5 years of campaigning in the USA and Guatemala before the governments agreed to sign an enforcement plan which required both governments to respect labor law in their countries. But even after the agreement was signed, employers continued to deny workers their rights.

Conditions worsened in Guatemala. Violence and lack of work forced more men, women, and children to migrate to the USA. Finally, for the first time ever, the US Trade Representative moved for arbitration in September 2014. This increases the pressure on Guatemala (and the USA) to live up to its agreements. While this may not improve workers lives immediately, it is important for workers because it shows that labor rights can have an effect on trade agreements. The lesson of CAFTA-DR is that while these trade agreements are overall bad for workers, their labor provisions can be used to draw international attention to and exert pressure on bad employers and the governments that allow companies to violate labor rights.

APPENDIX B
Common chemicals and materials

Many workers do not know the names of all the chemicals they come in contact with. Sometimes chemicals are put into small containers without labels. Other times employers hide the chemical information or call the chemical by other names and not its chemical name. Also, most factories do not track how chemicals applied earlier in the process can affect workers down the line or how much and what kind of byproducts are produced when a chemical is used. But all these chemicals can affect your health and you have a right to know about them.

The charts in this section will help you use the information you know about a chemical to identify it or learn more about its effects.

- **What are they?** will tell you what it looks, smells, or tastes like.
- **Do you work with them?** gives information about its uses in garment, shoe, or electronics factories.
- **When they come in contact with your body** gives information about how a chemical can hurt your eyes, skin, nose, lungs, mouth, and belly.
- **When you are exposed over time** explains how the chemical can hurt your body in the long term, for example, if it causes sexual and reproductive health problems or cancers.

The charts include **what kind of protective equipment** you should wear if your factory does not have good ventilation, if the controls do not work well, or if you are concerned that they are not protecting you. The only real solution to chemical dangers is to not use chemicals that can harm people, but to substitute safer chemicals. In the meantime, it is important that people have ways to protect themselves. If you are concerned about the ventilation in your factory or workstation, see chapter 17 to learn how good ventilation keeps chemicals out of the air. If you are concerned about a chemical touching your skin or eyes, see chapter 18: Personal protective equipment.

Use these charts to talk with other workers about the health dangers they are experiencing or worrying about. The charts can help you organize to demand better protection from the chemicals you are using and to demand that the worst chemicals be banned and removed from your factory.

Too many chemicals, too little information

Coming in contact with chemicals makes it more likely that you will have health problems. However there is too little information about how chemicals hurt people because they have not been studied. Of the 90,000 chemicals in use today, only a few thousand have been studied for **some** health effects! And although we know that chemicals are more harmful in combination with other chemicals than they are alone, there have been even fewer studies of how multiple chemicals affect us.

Until a chemical is studied for health effects (acute and chronic), how it affects the environment, and how it interacts with other chemicals, we should consider it dangerous. Many people believe that it is **not fair to chemicals** to say they are dangerous until proven safe. But we say it is **not fair to people,** to workers and their families, to work with chemicals not proven absolutely safe. If you cannot find information about a chemical, treat it as dangerous and protect yourself from coming in contact with it (see chapter 8: Chemical dangers, chapter 17: Ventilation, and chapter 18: Personal protective equipment).

These charts do not include information about how chemicals pollute the environment and harm people's health outside the factory. Often we are exposed multiple times to dangerous chemicals: first, inside the factory, and then again through polluted air, water, and soil in our communities. If you cannot find out if chemical wastes are being disposed of safely, assume that they are not. See chapter 33: Pollution from factories, for information about good disposal and how to organize against factory pollution.

These charts contain only about 100 common chemicals used in shoe, garment, and electronics factories. There are just too many in use to list them all. We did not include chemical mixes since mixes often change, are different from factory to factory and brand to brand, and their ingredients are often kept secret. To find out about a chemical not included in these charts or other information, see pages 178 to 184, and page 464 for other resources that can help you. You may know the same chemical by a different name; see the Index of chemical names on page 467.

Where did this information about chemicals come from?

Of the thousands of chemicals in use, few have been studied fully to know how they affect our health when used alone or when they mix with other chemicals. Concerns such as acute effects, flammability, and proper storage have been well-investigated and the information we have is mostly accurate and good. But we know little about long-term health and environmental effects.

In developing this book, we consulted many resources, including materials produced by international agencies that classify chemicals, government agencies that regulate chemicals, nonprofits that work to protect people from chemicals, and chemical companies that make and sell chemicals.

The information we found varied among all the trustworthy sources we consulted (see the list on page 464). The information we included in the book and in these charts is based on the following principles of when to recognize a danger:

- The chemical has been found to cause harm. Sometimes different health problems were listed in different resources. To be safe, we included all problems found in every source.

- The lowest level at which a chemical can cause harm, for example, when the smell of a chemical indicates a level of exposure. Levels of exposure considered to be safe vary from one country and one resource to another. When we include a level of exposure, we choose the lowest level that was found to be the border between safe and unsafe.

- The chemical has been found to be a probable or possible cause of cancer or reproductive health problems. If a chemical could possibly or probably cause cancer or reproductive health problems, or if it was found to cause them in animals, we say it "may cause" the problem.

- The chemical has been found to cause cancer or reproductive health problems. If any source said that it caused cancer in people, that is how we categorized it.

To find information about chemicals and materials, use these sources we consulted

Canadian Center for Occupational Health and Safety (CHEMINDEX), ccinfoweb.ccohs.ca/chemindex/search.html

Chemical Hazard and Alternatives Toolbox (ChemHAT), chemhat.org

European Chemicals Agency Information on Chemicals, echa.europa.eu/information-on-chemicals

International Agency for Research on Cancer (IARC), monographs.iarc.fr/ENG/Classification/index.php

International Labour Organization (ILO) International Chemical Safety Cards, ilo.org/safework/info/publications/WCMS_113134/lang--en/index.htm

International Programme on Chemical Safety (INCHEM), inchem.org

New Jersey (USA) Fact Sheets, web.doh.state.nj.us/rtkhsfs/search.aspx

PubMed, ncbi.nlm.nih.gov/pubmed

RISCTOX Database, istas.net/risctox/en

Toxipedia, toxipedia.org

ToxNet, toxnet.nlm.nih.gov

ToxTown, toxtown.nlm.nih.gov

US Agency for Toxic Substances and Disease Registry (ATSDR), www.atsdr.cdc.gov

US National Institute on Occupational Safety and Health (NIOSH), cdc.gov/niosh/npg

World Health Organization (WHO) International Program on Chemical Safety, who.int/ipcs/assessment/en

We also consulted Safety Data Sheets (SDS) produced by the manufacturers of individual chemicals.

Find a chemical in the charts

The chemicals and materials on the following pages are grouped in families. These families show you how similar chemicals relate to each other. If your boss adds or replaces a chemical with an unknown new one, look at what category it belongs to and see if the new chemical has any of the characteristics of other chemicals on the chart.

The chemical families appear in the order of the alphabet. The chemicals inside each family are also listed in the order of the alphabet. Chemicals that start with a number (such as 2-butanone) come before chemicals that start with letters (such as acetone):

1 2 3 4 A B C D E F G H I J K L M N O P Q R S T U V W X Y Z

Sometimes chemical names are very similar. The difference may be only a few letters or a number. But these small differences can make a great difference in how the chemical acts. To avoid confusion or mistakes, each chemical also has a unique number called a CAS number. The chart shows the CAS number for each chemical. A few chemicals in this list do not have CAS numbers because they represent a category of chemicals. There are many azo dyes, for example, and each one has a CAS number, but azo dyes as a category do not have a CAS number so you will not find one listed.

If the chemical name you want to look up is not in the chart, use the Index of chemical names on page 467 to see if it has a different name in the chart. For example, the chemical "chlorine bleach," used to acid-wash jeans, is sometimes called "Clorox" and sometimes called "sodium hypochlorite."

We have listed this chemical as "chlorine bleach" in the chart. If you look for "Clorox" in the Index of chemical names, you will find this:

Clorox. . . . . *see* Chlorine bleach. . . . . page 478

If you look for "sodium hypochlorite" in the Index, you will find this:

Sodium hypochlorite. . . . . *see* Chlorine bleach . . . . page 478

If you cannot find a chemical, see pages 178 to 184, and page 464 for resources that can help you find more information.

What the symbols mean

The symbols below appear next to the chemical name at the top of the chart. They tell you which chemicals are more dangerous (more and darker symbols mean more danger). But even if a chemical does not have symbols it does not mean it is safe.

 This symbol means that the chemical or material has been banned or is soon to be banned in one or more countries because it is harmful to people's health and the environment. If it is banned in one country, it should be banned in all.

 This symbol means that the chemical or material is likely to catch on fire or explode. Pay attention to chemicals or materials it might react with, and keep it away from heat or a possible spark.

These 2 symbols mean that the chemical may or can cause reproductive health problems:

 The man and woman with a **white background and a question mark** means that there is a possibility it may cause reproductive health problems.

 The man and woman with a **black background** means that this chemical has been proven to cause reproductive health problems.

The chart text explains **what kind** of reproductive health problem it can cause, such as reduced fertility in men, women, or both, miscarriages, and damage to a baby inside the womb. For more information about reproductive health problems, see page 161 and chapter 26: Sexual and reproductive health.

These 2 symbols mean that the chemical may or can cause cancer:

 The person in bed with a **white background and a question mark** means that there is a possibility it may cause cancer.

 The person in bed with a **black background** means that this chemical has been proven to cause cancer.

The chart text explains what kinds of cancers it may or can cause, if that is known.

 This symbol means that the chemical can cause immediate death if you are exposed to it. Although most of the chemicals can cause death if you are exposed to high doses or for a long time, we used this symbol only for the ones that would kill you immediately.

Index of chemical names

A

D

E

Chemical charts

Acids

Acids come in liquid form and are used to clean electronic parts and metals, added to fabric dyes, and used in leather treatment.

Acids release fumes that can be toxic when inhaled, sometimes causing lung problems immediately. Absorbing acids through the skin is also a common and dangerous form of exposure. As a group, acids are very reactive chemicals and can be extremely harmful when they touch your body. Even small amounts or very diluted acids can cause severe burns and penetrate your skin.

The charts include only some of the acids that exist. See pages 178 to 184 and page 464 for how to find information about other acids. See the Index of chemical names on page 467 to find alternative names for chemicals.

Prevent or reduce exposure:

- Have ventilation systems that extract fumes and replace or dilute dirty air with clean air (see chapter 17: Ventilation).
- Enclose operations where possible.
- Do not mix or pour acids by hand.
- Wear acid-resistant gloves, acid-resistant long aprons, eye-protective glasses and a face shield. Wear correct respirators that fit you. All protective clothing should be clean, available each day, put on before work, and never taken home with you (see chapter 18: Personal protective equipment).
- Have an emergency plan for spills, splashes, and accidental exposures. The plan should include first aid treatment and protective equipment. Keep necessary supplies at the worksite, well stocked, and accessible to workers. For First aid for HF burns, see page 66.
- Work areas where acids are used, stored, and mixed need to be controlled for heat and monitored for concentration of fumes and vapors. They should also have alarms, fire extinguishers, and a fire emergency plan (see chapter 11: Fire).

Acids

Acetic acid – CAS No. 64-19-7

Formic acid – CAS No. 64-18-6

Hydrochloric acid (HCl) – CAS No. 7647-01-0

Hydrofluoric acid (HF) – CAS No. 7664-39-3

Nitric acid – CAS No. 7697-37-2

What are they?

Acids are colorless liquids with strong smells. **Acetic acid** has a vinegar-like smell. **Formic, hydrochloric, hydrofluoric,** and **nitric acid** have pungent, irritating odors. **Acids** release fumes. **Nitric acid** in fume form is red in color.

Do you work with them?

Acids are used in electronics and garment industries. **Formic acid** is used in dyeing and finishing textiles and treating leather. **Hydrochloric** and **hydrofluoric acid** are used to clean wafers, chips, and printed circuit boards. **Nitric acid** in fume form is used to dissolve, etch, and clean metals in the electronics industry.

When they come in contact with your body

Skin: They can severely irritate, burn the skin and cause a rash, pain, redness, ulceration and permanent scarring. When **hydrochloric acid** touches your skin, it will burn quickly, but the skin will feel cold and numb. Treat it quickly as a chemical burn (see pages 175). When **hydrofluoric acid** touches your skin it will burn quickly and deeply. However, **hydrofluoric** burns do not show right away, so it is important to immediately wash off any area that comes into contact with it. If it is absorbed through the skin it can be fatal. See First Aid on page 66.

Eyes: They severely irritate and burn the eyes and can lead to permanent eye damage, corneal scarring and blindness. See First Aid on page 175.

Nose/lungs: The fumes can irritate your nose, throat, and lungs, causing coughing, wheezing and difficulty breathing. Inhaling fumes can cause dizziness and headaches. It can also create a buildup of fluid in the lungs, called lung edema. **Hydrofluoric acid** may be fatal because it can cause irregular heartbeat. See First Aid on pages 66 and 174.

Mouth/belly: They can lead to injury of the gastrointestinal tract and stomach causing loss of appetite, nausea, vomiting, diarrhea and abdominal pain. **Hydrofluoric acid** can burn your mouth and throat and lower your heart rate and blood pressure. See First Aid on pages 66 and 176 and seek medical attention right away.

(continued)

Acids *(continued)*

When you are exposed over time:

Acids can harm your liver, kidneys, and lungs. They can cause chronic bronchitis and pneumonia.

Nitric acid can cause yellowing and erosion of the teeth.

Hydrochloric acid can cause yellowing and erosion of the teeth.

Hydrofluoric acid can cause digestive imbalance, irregular heartbeat, and affect your nervous system leading to seizures. It can also weaken or destroy your bones and cause skin problems.

If you are at risk of exposure:

Use butyl gloves, an apron, and eye/face protection to keep acids off your skin (see chapter 18: Personal protective equipment).

For **HCl**, use tyclem or Teflon gloves.

For **HF**, use double nitrile gloves.

Wear a respirator that can filter **acid** fumes (see Respirators on pages 266 to 270).

Acid wash chemicals

Acid wash chemicals are used to make textiles appear worn and faded. The chemicals strip away the original color. Chlorine and potassium permanganate (PP) bleaches are the most common bleach solutions used for acid washing in textiles.

Chlorine and potassium permanganate are mixed with other chemicals and diluted to make liquid bleach solutions. Both chemicals release fumes.

If chlorine comes in contact with ammonia, it will produce toxic vapors that can explode. Potassium permanganate will produce toxic vapors and can explode if it comes in contact with acids and powdered metals. Acid wash chemicals release very toxic fumes when they catch on fire. Do not store these chemicals near other chemicals or near heat.

The charts include only some of the acid washes that exist. See pages 178 to 184 and page 464 for how to find information about other acid washes. See the Index of chemical names on page 467 to find alternative names for chemicals.

Prevent or reduce exposure:

- Use ventilation systems that remove dust and fumes, and dilute the air (see chapter 17: Ventilation).
- Enclose operations where possible.
- Do not mix or pour acid wash chemicals by hand.
- Wear acid-resistant gloves, acid-resistant long aprons, eye-protective glasses and a face shield. Wear correct respirators that fit you. All protective clothing should be clean, available each day, put on before work, and never taken home with you (see chapter 18: Personal protective equipment).
- Have an emergency plan for spills, splashes, and accidental exposures that includes first aid treatment and protective equipment. Keep necessary supplies emergency at the worksite, well stocked, and accessible to workers.
- Work areas where acid washes are used, stored, and mixed need to be controlled for heat and monitored for concentration of fumes and vapors. They should also have alarms, fire extinguishers, and a fire emergency plan (see chapter 11: Fire).

Acid wash chemicals

Chlorine bleach – CAS No. 7782-50-5

Potassium permanganate bleach – CAS No. 7722-64-7

What are they?

Acid wash chemicals are found in liquid bleaches. **Chlorine bleach** is a pale yellow liquid with a strong smell. **Potassium permanganate bleach** is a purple liquid.

Do you work with them?

Acid wash chemicals are used to make jeans look worn and faded.

When they come in contact with your body

Skin: They irritate and burn your skin. You may develop a skin rash, redness, and dryness. Your skin might start peeling, itching, and cracking. Over time, the skin may swell up and blister. See First Aid on page 175.

Eyes: They irritate and burn your eyes. They can cause conjunctivitis. Signs of conjunctivitis are watery eyes and discomfort. Large amount of acid wash chemicals may permanently damage your eyes and cause blindness. See First Aid on page 175.

Nose/lungs: The fumes can irritate your nose, throat, and lungs, causing congestion, coughing, wheezing, shortness of breath, and chest pain. Inhaling **chlorine bleach** and **potassium permanganate bleach** fumes can cause dizziness, headaches, and create buildup of fluid in the lungs, called lung edema. See First Aid on page 174.

Mouth/belly: If they get into your mouth and belly, they can burn your stomach, cause nausea, vomiting, and diarrhea. See First Aid on page 176 and seek medical attention.

When you are exposed over time:

Acid wash chemicals can make your nose and lungs very sensitive and cause bronchitis, pneumonia, and chronic asthma. Chronic asthma means that even if you stop working with acid wash chemicals, you may still have asthma.

Potassium permanganate bleach damages your liver and kidneys. If it gets in your mouth periodically over a long time period, it can damage your heart and the nervous system. It may decrease fertility in men and women.

If you are at risk of exposure:

Use elbow-length, butyl rubber or nitrile gloves, an apron, and eye protection (see chapter 18: Personal protective equipment).

Use a supplied-air respirator (see pages 268 to 270).

Safer substitutes:

It is better to not add any **acid wash chemicals** to the washing machine and instead use pumice stones by themselves.

Ammonia and ammonium compounds

Ammonia and ammonium compounds come in liquid, gas, and solid forms. Pure ammonia is a gas, but if you're working with cold ammonia, it will be in liquid form. Ammonia and ammonium compounds are used in the electronics, garment, and shoe-making industries. They are used in electroplating, to make rubber, as a solvent to make plastics, and in dyes and fabric finish treatments.

Containers of ammonia may explode when exposed to heat. Store ammonia in pressure-controlled, enclosed containers.

When any amount of ammonia touches any part of your body, rinse it off immediately with cool water for at least 15 minutes. See First Aid on page 175.

The charts include only some of the ammonia compounds that exist. See pages 178 to 184 and page 464 for how to find information about other ammonia compounds. See the Index of chemical names on page 467 to find alternative names for chemicals.

Prevent or reduce exposure:

- Use ventilation systems that remove fumes and dilute the air (see chapter 17: Ventilation).

- Enclose operations where possible.

- Do not mix or pour ammonia or ammonium compounds by hand.

- Wear gloves. Wear correct respirators that fit you. All protective clothing should be clean, available each day, put on before work, and never taken home with you (see chapter 18: Personal protective equipment).

- Have an emergency plan that includes first aid treatment and protective equipment for spills, splashes, and accidental exposures. Keep necessary emergency supplies at the work site well stocked and accessible to workers.

- Work areas where ammonia compounds are used, stored, and mixed need to be controlled for heat and monitored for concentration of fumes and vapors. They should also have alarms, fire extinguishers, and a fire emergency plan (see chapter 11: Fire).

Ammonia and ammonium compounds

Ammonia – CAS No. 7664-41-7

Ammonium chloride – CAS No. 12125-02-9

Ammonium hydroxide – CAS No. 1336-21-6

What are they?

Ammonia is a colorless gas or liquid with a strong, irritating smell. It smells even at low amounts. **Ammonium hydroxide** is a colorless liquid mixture of ammonia and water. It has a strong smell. If you smell ammonium hydroxide, you are exposed to amounts that may harm you. **Ammonium chloride** is a solid white powder with no smell.

Do you work with them?

Ammonium compounds are used in electronics, shoes, and garment production. **Ammonia** is used in making silicon layers. Liquid ammonia is used in fabric treatment and in dyes. **Ammonium hydroxide** is used in the preparation of dyes and rubber. **Ammonium chloride** is used to make batteries and in electroplating.

When they come in contact with your body

Skin: They irritate and burn your skin. You may develop a skin rash, redness, and dryness. Your skin might start peeling, itching, and cracking. If liquid ammonia touches you, it will burn quickly, but the skin will feel cold and numb. See First Aid on page 175.

Eyes: They irritate and burn your eyes. Contact with large amounts can lead to blindness. See First Aid on page 175.

Nose/lungs: The fumes irritate your nose, throat, and lungs, causing congestion, coughing, wheezing, shortness of breath, and chest tightness. If you continue to be exposed, it can cause severe asthma attacks. Inhaling high amounts of fumes can create buildup of fluid in the lungs, called lung edema. See First Aid on page 174.

Mouth/belly: They can burn your mouth, throat, and stomach and cause nausea, vomiting, and diarrhea. See First Aid on page 176 and seek medical attention.

When you are exposed over time:

Ammonium compounds irritate your respiratory tract and can cause bronchitis, pneumonia, and asthma.

Ammonia and **ammonium chloride** can make your nose and lungs very sensitive and cause chronic asthma.

Ammonium chloride may affect your kidneys. It may damage a baby in the womb.

(continued)

Ammonia and ammonia compounds (continued)

If you are at risk of exposure:

Use elbow-length, butyl rubber or nitrile gloves, an apron, and eye/face protection (see chapter 18: Personal protective equipment).

Use a supplied-air respirator (see pages 268 to 270).

Safer substitutes:

Ammonium hydroxide is diluted and is a little safer than pure **ammonia**.

Dopant gases

Dopant gases are used to add layers to the wafer (implant ions) to make the wafer conduct electricity better. Arsine, diborane, and phosphine are the most commonly used dopant gases. Arsine gas comes from the element arsenic, diborane from boron, and phosphine from phosphorous.

As gases they are more dangerous than as solids because they can get on and inside you easily. Arsine, diborane and phosphine gases are stored in containers that also contain their liquid forms. While most exposure occurs by breathing in fumes, a leak from a container can be liquid or gas.

Workers who load and unload wafers, replace gas cylinders, and clean and maintain the ion implantation machines can come into contact with dopant gases. So can other workers in the area.

If you accidentally swallow a dopant liquid, it can be released in your stomach as a gas and damage your digestive tract.

The charts include only some of the dopant gases that exist. See pages 178 to 184 and page 464 for how to find information about other dopant gases. See the Index of chemical names on page 467 to find alternative names for chemicals.

Prevent or reduce exposure:

- Use ventilation systems that extract fumes and dilute the air. Machines need exhaust vents inside so that no gases escape (see chapter 17: Ventilation).

- Enclosed equipment that is remotely controlled reduces workers' exposure where the possibility of an accident is greatest.

- Wear protective equipment such as chemical goggles, gloves, chemical splash aprons, and respirators especially when in direct contact with gas cylinders and parts of the ion implanting machine, such as vacuum pumps and the ion source (see chapter 18: Personal protective equipment).

- Have an emergency plan that includes first aid treatment and protective equipment for spills, splashes, and accidental exposures. Keep necessary emergency supplies at the worksite, well stocked, and accessible to workers.

- All dopants are extremely flammable and can explode. Areas where they are stored and used must be kept cool and the air must be monitored. The areas should also have alarms, fire extinguishers, and an emergency plan (see chapter 11: Fire).

Dopant gases

Arsine – CAS No. 7784-42-1

Diborane – CAS No. 19287-45-7

Phosphine– CAS No. 7803-51-2

What are they?

Dopants are colorless gases. **Arsine** and **phosphine** smell unpleasantly like garlic or rotten fish. **Diborane** has an unpleasant sweet smell. If you can smell them, you are being exposed to amounts high enough to harm you.

Do you work with them?

Dopants are used in the electronics industry, in the process called "ion implantation" to make wafers conduct electricity better.

When they come in contact with your body

Skin: They may irritate your skin. In gas form they are not toxic to the skin, but if the liquid form touches you, it will burn quickly, even though the skin will feel cold and numb. Treat it quickly as a chemical burn. See First Aid on page 175.

Eyes: The fumes may irritate your eyes. The liquid form can cause severe eye burns. See First Aid on page 175.

Nose/lungs: The fumes can irritate your nose, throat, and lungs, causing coughing and wheezing. Breathing in these gases can cause you to feel weak, dizzy, lightheaded, short of breath, and pass out. Some signs are similar to "metal fume fever," which feels like a flu with a combination of these signs: headache, fever and chills, body aches, chest tightness, and cough. Higher exposures can also create a buildup of fluid in the lungs, called lung edema. See First Aid on page 174.

Mouth/belly: A dopant gas can be released in your stomach and cause damage to your digestive tract and lead to abdominal pain, nausea, vomiting, and diarrhea. See First Aid on page 176 and seek medical attention.

When you are exposed over time:

All **dopants** can harm your liver, kidneys and the nervous system causing weakness, muscle cramps, and poor coordination in the limbs.

Arsine kills red blood cells (hemolysis), which leads to anemia. Continuing to breathe **arsine** kills more red blood cells and can result in kidney failure. Skin and eyes that become yellow are danger signs and you should seek medical attention immediately. **Arsine** may cause skin, liver, kidney, lung, and bladder cancer.

(continued)

Dopant gases (continued)

Diborane can harm your lungs and cause chronic bronchitis and breathing problems.

Phosphine can harm your lungs and cause chronic bronchitis and breathing problems. High amounts of **phosphine** at once can cause heart and kidney failure. Skin and eyes that become yellow are danger signs and you should seek medical attention immediately.

If you are at risk of exposure:

Use both neoprene and nitrile gloves, an apron, and eye/face protection when changing vacuum pump oils and gas containers (see chapter 18: Personal protective equipment). This equipment must be well-cleaned or disposed of after use.

Use a supplied-air respirator if you are cleaning the ion source, changing vacuum pumps, or doing other maintenance work on the machine, or if you are replacing gas containers (see Respirators on pages 268 to 270).

Safer substitutes:

Mono ethyl arsine is a less toxic substitute for **arsine**.

Dyes

Dyes give color to fabric. Dyes consist of many groups of chemicals and each group has many individual chemicals. Azo is the largest group of dyes. Twenty-two of the hundreds of azo dyes are banned because there is no doubt that they harm people's health.

Solvents, acids, bases, metals, and other toxic chemicals are often added to dyes to help fabric take in the coloring. Some dyes come in powder form and must be mixed with a solvent before dyeing the cloth.

There are two ways dyes can be classified and identified: based on their application or based on their chemical structure. Application-based dyes are acid, basic, direct, disperse, mordant, reactive, pigment, and vat dyes. Different dyes are used for different fabrics and dye processes. Structure-based dyes include nitro, azo, carotenoid, triarylmethane, xanthene, acridine, quinoline, indamine, sulphur, amino- and hydroxyl- ketones, anthraquinone, indigoid, phthalocyanine, inorganic pigment, and others. Most dyes are identified with a "color index" (CI) name and number.

Dyes create dust and fumes that are easily inhaled and that can harm your mouth, throat, and lungs.

The charts include only some of the dyes that exist. See pages 178 to 184 and page 464 for how to find information about other dyes. See the Index of chemical names on page 467 to find alternative names for chemicals.

Prevent or reduce exposure:

- Use ventilation systems that remove fumes and dilute the air (see chapter 17: Ventilation).

- Enclose operations where possible.

- Do not mix or pour dyes by hand.

- Wear gloves. Wear correct respirators that fit you. All protective clothing should be clean, available each day, put on before work, and never taken home with you (see chapter 18: Personal protective equipment).

- Have an emergency plan that includes first aid treatment and protective equipment for spills, splashes, and accidental exposures. Keep necessary emergency supplies at the work site, stocked, and accessible to workers.

- Work areas where dyes are used, stored, and mixed need to be controlled for heat and monitored for concentration of fumes and vapors. The areas should also have alarms, fire extinguishers, and a fire emergency plan (see chapter 11: Fire).

- Wash hands only with soap and water. Do not use solvents on skin to remove dye stains.

Dyes

Anthraquinone dyes

Azo dyes

Indigoid dyes

Sulfur dyes

Triarylmethane dyes

What are they?

Dyes are liquid or solid chemicals that come in different colors. **Solid dyes** usually come as sand-like powders or crystals. Some **dyes** have a strong smell, but others have no smell at all. Some **azo dyes** release toxic aromatic amine chemicals that have an unpleasant, fishy smell.

Do you work with them?

Dyes are used in the garment and shoe industries to dye cloth, fur, and leather. **Anthraquinone dyes** are most commonly used for violet, blue, and green colors. **Azo dyes** are used on cotton, wool, silk, and nylon to make them red, orange, and yellow. **Indigoid** dyes are used for dark colors and are often used to dye jeans. **Sulfur dyes** are used on cotton and rayon. They are commonly used for dark colors such as black, brown, dark blue, and violet. **Triarylmethane dyes** make very bright colors.

When they come in contact with your body

Skin: They irritate and dye your skin. You may develop a skin rash, redness, and dryness. Your skin might start peeling, itching, and cracking. Most often, a rash appears between your fingers or on the back of hands and wrists. See First Aid on page 175.

Eyes: They irritate and burn your eyes. They can cause itching, watery eyes, and swelling of the eyelids. See First Aid on page 175.

Nose/lungs: The dust and fumes can irritate your nose, throat, and lungs, causing congestion, coughing, wheezing, shortness of breath, and chest tightness. The longer you are exposed the more sensitive your nose and lungs become, which can lead to severe asthma attacks. Inhaling high amounts of pigment and dye dust and fumes can create buildup of fluid in the lungs, called lung edema. See First Aid on page 174.

Mouth/belly: They cause nausea, vomiting, and diarrhea. See First Aid on page 176 and seek medical attention.

(continued)

Dyes *(continued)*

When you are exposed over time:

Dyes harm your immune system, liver, kidneys, and urinary tract. They can make your nose and lungs very sensitive and cause chronic asthma. **Dyes** damage your red blood cells so they can no longer deliver oxygen to your organs. This is called methemoglobinemia. Signs of methemoglobinemia are blue skin and lips, headache, weakness, difficulty breathing, and lack of energy. If it's not treated, you may go into a coma and your heart may stop.

Azo dyes may affect fertility. They can cause liver cancer and especially bladder cancer.

Anthraquinone dyes may cause liver, colon, kidney, and bladder cancer.

Triarylmethane dyes may cause cancer.

If you are at risk of exposure:

Use elbow-length, butyl rubber gloves and eye/face protection (see chapter 18: Personal protective equipment).

Use a supplied-air respirator (see pages 268 to 270).

Safer substitutes:

Dyes that do not create dust are safer, such as **granular** or **liquid-form dyes**. **Natural dyes** are usually safer than **synthetic dyes**.

Flame retardants

Flame retardants are added to plastics, electronic parts, wire coverings, rubber, textiles, wood, and furniture to make them less likely to burn. There are two classes of flame-retardants: **halogenated** and **non-halogenated**. Sometimes a flame retardant is used by itself, and sometimes in combination with other flame retardants.

Halogenated flame retardants contain chlorine or bromine. Bromine-based flame-retardants are used more often because they are cheap.

Non-halogenated flame retardants contain nitrogen, phosphorous, or metals such as aluminum, magnesium, and antimony. The nitrogen-based and phosphorous-based flame retardants are often used in combination with each other.

Halogenated flame retardants are considered more dangerous to people's health than non-halogenated ones. Several have been banned in many countries. However, many non-halogenated flame retardants are just as dangerous to your health.

The chart includes only some of the flame retardants that exist. See pages 178 to 184 and page 464 for how to find information about other flame retardants. See the Index of chemical names on page 467 to find alternative names for chemicals.

Prevent or reduce exposure:

- Use ventilation systems that remove fumes and dilute the air (see chapter 17: Ventilation).
- Enclose operations whenever possible.
- Do not mix or pour flame retardants by hand.
- Use gloves when handling flame retardants. Wear correct respirators that fit you. All protective clothing should be clean, available each day, put on before work, and never taken home with you (see chapter 18: Personal protective equipment).
- Have an emergency plan that includes first aid treatment and protective equipment for spills, splashes, and accidental exposures. Keep necessary emergency supplies at the work site, stocked, and accessible to workers.
- Work areas where flame retardants are used, stored, and mixed need to be controlled for heat and monitored for concentration of fumes and vapors. The areas should also have alarms, fire extinguishers, and a fire emergency plan (see chapter 11: Fire).

Halogenated flame retardants

BROMINATED FLAME RETARDANTS

⊘ **Polybrominated biphenyls (PBBs)**
– CAS No. 59536-65-1

Polybrominated diphenyl ethers (PBDEs)

Tetrabromobisphenol A (TBBPA) – CAS No. 79-94-7

CHLORINATED FLAME RETARDANTS

⊘ **Polychlorinated biphenyls (PCBs)**
– CAS No. 1336-36-3

What are they?

Polybrominated biphenyls are white powders. **Polybrominated diphenyl ethers** are pale yellow or white powders. **TBBPA** is a white, sandy powder. **Polychlorinated biphenyls** are light yellow or colorless thick, oily liquids.

Do you work with them?

Halogenated flame retardants are added to fabric in garment factories. They are used in electronics factories in plastics, electronic coatings, and wires.

When they come in contact with your body

Skin: They may irritate your skin. You may develop a skin rash, redness, and dryness. Your skin might start peeling, itching, and cracking. See First Aid on page 175.

Eyes: They may irritate your eyes. See First Aid on page 175.

Nose/lungs: The fumes may irritate your nose, throat, and lungs, causing congestion, coughing, wheezing, shortness of breath, and chest pain. See First Aid on page 174.

Mouth/belly: They can cause nausea, vomiting, and diarrhea. See First Aid on page 176 and seek medical attention.

When you are exposed over time:

Halogenated flame retardants damage your immune system, mental development, and lower your memory and learning ability. They may damage your thyroid. Signs of hypothyroidism include constipation, sensitivity to cold, weakness, thin hair and nails, and weight gain.

Polybrominated biphenyls may reduce fertility in men and women and slow down a child's development. They may cause cancer.

Polybrominated diphenyl ethers can reduce fertility in men and women, enter into mother's milk and pass to a baby through breastfeeding, and slow down a child's development. They may cause cancer.

(continued)

Halogenated flame retardants *(continued)*

Tetrabromobisphenol A may reduce fertility in men and women.

Polychlorinated biphenyls can reduce fertility in men and women and slow down a child's development. They can cause cancer.

If you are at risk of exposure:

Use elbow-length, nitrile gloves, an apron, and eye/face protection (see chapter 18: Personal protective equipment).

Use a supplied-air respirator (see pages 268 to 270).

Safer substitutes:

Non-halogenated flame retardants are safer alternatives to **halogenated flame retardants**. **Tetrabromobisphenol A (TBBPA)** is one of the less dangerous **halogenated flame retardants**.

Non-halogenated flame retardants

INORGANIC FLAME RETARDANTS

Aluminium hydroxide – CAS No. 21645-51-2

Antimony trioxide – CAS No. 1309-64-4

NITROGEN-BASED FLAME RETARDANTS

Melamine cyanurate – CAS No. 37640-57-6

PHOSPHOROUS-BASED FLAME RETARDANTS

Red phosphorus – CAS No. 7723-14-0

Triphenyl phosphate (TPP) – CAS No. 115-86-6

What are they?

Aluminium hydroxide is a white powder similar to flour without smell. **Antimony trioxide** and **melamine cyanurate** are powders like sand without smell. **Red phosphorus** is red powder without smell. **Triphenyl phosphate (TPP)** is a white, crystalline powder with a sweet smell.

Do you work with them?

Phosphorous-based and **nitrogen-based flame retardants** are added to fabric in garment factories. They are also added to circuit board coatings and electronic parts. **Inorganic flame retardants** are added to plastics during melting and extrusion.

When they come in contact with your body

Skin: They may irritate your skin. You may develop a skin rash, redness, and dryness. Your skin might start peeling, itching, and cracking. See First Aid on page 175.

Eyes: They may irritate your eyes. **Red phosphorus** may damage the cornea (the tissue that covers the front of the eye). See First Aid on page 175.

Nose/lungs: The dust may irritate your nose, throat, and lungs, causing congestion, coughing, wheezing, shortness of breath, and chest pain. Inhaling **antimony trioxide** can cause throat ulcers. See First Aid on page 174.

Mouth/belly: They can cause stomach pain, nausea, and vomiting. **Antimony trioxide** can cause metallic taste in the mouth. See First Aid on page 176 and seek medical attention.

(continued)

Non-halogenated flame retardants (continued)

When you are exposed over time:

Non-halogenated flame retardants damage your liver and kidneys.

Aluminium hydroxide dust can scar your lungs, cause pneumoconiosis, weaken your muscles and soften your bones. Signs of pneumoconiosis are cough and shortness of breath.

Antimony trioxide damages your heart and lungs. It may reduce fertility in men and women, cause miscarriages, and hurt a baby in the womb. It may cause lung cancer.

Melamine cyanurate affects your urinary tract and may cause bladder stones.

Red phosphorus damages your heart and lungs. It can cause bronchitis and anemia.

Triphenyl phosphate may affect the nervous system, causing weakness and poor coordination in the arms and legs.

If you are at risk of exposure:

Use elbow-length, butyl rubber gloves, an apron, and eye/face protection (see chapter 18: Personal protective equipment).

Use a respirator with a particle filter designed for solid particle filtration (see pages 266 to 270).

Safer substitutes:

Alternative materials for computer devices and plastics that do not require **flame retardants** at all, such as glass, metal and low voltage wires, should be used.

Fluxes

Flux chemicals are used to clean electronic parts during the soldering, brazing, and welding of metal parts. When clean, metal parts stick together much better.

Different fluxes are used for different metals. Rosin and ammonium chloride are used with tin and tin/lead in electronics. Hydrochloric acid and zinc chloride are used with zinc-coated iron. Sodium borate is used with any metal containing iron. Flux chemicals are sometimes dissolved in other chemicals, such as isopropyl alcohol, to make a liquid flux solution.

Lead solder was very common before it was banned by the European Union. Water-soluble fluxes are used with lead-free solder.

Fluxes release dangerous fumes when heated during soldering. Extractors must be close to the soldering source to remove all the fumes.

Many chemicals are used in fluxes. For more on ammonium chloride, see Ammonia and Ammonium Compounds on page 479; for hydrochloric acid, see Acids on page 474.

The chart includes only some of the flux chemicals that exist. See pages 178 to 184 and page 464 for how to find information about other fluxes. See the Index of chemical names on page 467 to find alternative names for chemicals.

Prevent or reduce exposure:

- Use extraction ventilation to remove flux fumes as close to the soldering process as possible. Use ventilation systems that remove fumes and dilute the air (see chapter 17: Ventilation).
- Enclose operations whenever possible.
- Avoid manual hand soldering if there is an alternative automated manufacturing process available.
- Do not mix or pour fluxes by hand.
- Use gloves when handling fluxes. Wear correct respirators that fit you. All protective clothing should be clean, available each day, put on before work, and never taken home with you (see chapter 18: Personal protective equipment).
- Have an emergency plan that includes first aid treatment and protective equipment for spills, splashes, and exposures. Keep necessary emergency supplies at the work site well stocked and accessible to workers.
- Work areas where fluxes are used, stored, and mixed need to be controlled for heat and monitored for concentration of fumes and vapors. The areas should also have alarms, fire extinguishers, and a fire emergency plan (see chapter 11: Fire).

Fluxes

Ammonium chloride – CAS No. 12125-02-9

Hydrochloric acid (HCl) – CAS No. 7647-01-0

Rosin – CAS No. 8050-09-7

Sodium tetraborate decahydrate – CAS No. 1303-96-4

Zinc chloride – CAS No. 7646-85-7

What are they?

Ammonium chloride is a solid white powder that has no smell. **Hydrochloric acid** is a colorless liquid with a sharp smell. **Rosin** is a yellow-orange powder and can have a slight pine smell or no smell at all. **Sodium tetraborate decahydrate** and **zinc chloride** are white, sand-like powders with no smell.

Do you work with them?

Flux chemicals are used in the electronics industry during soldering, welding and brazing of electronic parts.

When they come in contact with your body

Skin: They irritate your skin. You may develop a skin rash, redness, dryness, and blisters. Your skin might start peeling, itching, and cracking. When **hydrochloric acid** touches your skin, it will burn quickly, but the skin will feel cold and numb. Treat it quickly as a chemical burn. **Zinc chloride** causes burns and ulcers. See First Aid on page 175.

Eyes: They irritate your eyes. Your eyes become watery and red. See First Aid on page 175.

Nose/Lungs: They irritate your nose, throat, and lungs, causing coughing, wheezing, shortness of breath, and chest pain. **Sodium tetraborate decahydrate** causes sore throats and nosebleeds. **Zinc chloride** can create buildup of fluid in the lungs, called lung edema. See First Aid on page 174.

Mouth/Belly: If ingested, they can cause nausea, stomach pain, vomiting, and diarrhea. Swallowing **sodium tetraborate decahydrate** can cause weakness and convulsions. **Zinc chloride** burns your digestive tract. See First Aid on page 176 and seek medical attention.

(continued)

Fluxes (continued)

When you are exposed over time:

Ammonium chloride and **rosin** can make your nose and lungs very sensitive and cause chronic asthma. Even after you stop working with these chemicals, they can give you an asthma attack.

Ammonium chloride may affect your kidneys and may damage a baby inside the womb.

Hydrochloric acid can damage and cause yellowing of the teeth.

Sodium tetraborate decahydrate can damage your liver, kidneys, and nervous system. It may damage a baby inside the womb and may reduce fertility in men and women.

Zinc chloride can scar your lungs and may damage a baby inside the womb.

If you are at risk of exposure:

Use gloves and a face shield when soldering and handling **flux** chemicals (see chapter 18: Personal protective equipment).

Use a respirator with a filter (see pages 266 to 270).

Safer substitutes:

Sometimes soldering and the need for **flux** can be eliminated by using screws and wire to join metal parts. Use no-clean, rosin-free, and water-soluble flux alternatives if possible.

Formaldehyde

Formaldehyde is a gas with a very suffocating smell. It often comes as a liquid mixture of formaldehyde, water, and methanol called "formalin." For more information about methanol, see Alcohol solvents on page 518.

Formaldehyde is used in the electronics, shoe, and garment industries. It is used to keep fabric from wrinkling. It is also commonly used in plastics, glues, and coatings to make them stronger.

Formaldehyde is extremely flammable! It also reacts strongly with acids. Keep formaldehyde away from acids, other chemicals, and heat. See the Index of chemical names on page 467 to find alternative names for formaldehyde.

Prevent or reduce exposure:

- Use ventilation systems that remove fumes and dilute the air (see chapter 17: Ventilation).
- Enclose operations whenever possible.
- Do not mix or pour formaldehyde by hand.
- Use gloves when handling formaldehyde. Wear correct respirators that fit you. All protective clothing should be clean, available each day, put on before work, and never taken home with you (see chapter 18: Personal protective equipment).
- Have an emergency plan that includes first aid treatment and protective equipment for spills, splashes, and exposures. Keep necessary emergency supplies at the work site well stocked and accessible to workers.
- Work areas where formaldehyde is used, stored, and mixed need to be controlled for heat and monitored for concentration of fumes and vapors. The areas should also have alarms, fire extinguishers, and a fire emergency plan (see chapter 11: Fire).

Formaldehyde

 Formaldehyde – CAS No. 50-0-0

What is it?

Formaldehyde is a colorless gas that has a very strong, sharp smell. The smell is so strong that it is difficult to breathe. It often comes mixed with water and methanol. If you can smell it strongly in the air, you are exposed to a dose high enough to harm you.

Do you work with it?

Formaldehyde is used in garment factories in dyes, fabric treatments, and pressing. It is used in shoe factories in plastic production and glues. It is used in electronics in coatings of circuit boards.

When it comes in contact with your body

Skin: It irritates your skin. You may develop a skin rash, redness, dryness, and pain. Your skin might start peeling, itching, and cracking. See First Aid on page 175.

Eyes: It severely irritates and burns your eyes. It may cause watery and red eyes, pain, and blurred vision. Direct contact with a large enough amount may cause blindness. See First Aid on page 175.

Nose/lungs: It irritates your nose, throat, and lungs, causing sore throat, coughing, wheezing, shortness of breath, and chest pain. It can create buildup of fluid in the lungs, called lung edema. See First Aid on page 174.

Mouth/belly: If it gets into your mouth and belly, it can cause severe pain, vomiting, and diarrhea, and can be fatal. See First Aid on page 176 and seek medical attention.

When you are exposed over time:

Formaldehyde damages your lungs and can cause bronchitis. It can irritate your throat and lungs and cause chronic asthma. It may damage a baby inside the womb, may cause miscarriages and may reduce fertility in women. It can cause blood cancer and cancers of the nose and throat.

If you are at risk of exposure:

Use natural or butyl rubber, nitrile or neoprene gloves, an apron, and eye/face protection (see chapter 18: Personal protective equipment).

Use a respirator that can filter **formaldehyde** (see pages 266 to 270).

Safer substitutes:

Silicone-based fabric finishing treatments for pressing are considered a safer alternative to **formaldehyde.**

Isocyanates

Isocyanates are liquids used in glues, rubber, and coatings in shoe manufacturing. Isocyanate (water-based) glues were once considered safer than solvent-based glues, but more and more health problems in workers show that these glues are not safe. The most common and dangerous isocyanates are diisocyanates. In the chart on the next page we only list diisocyanates.

Mixing isocyanates and water or acids in a closed container can be very dangerous. It can create high pressure that might explode the container.

Isocyanates are often combined with other chemicals such as alcohols, acids, and polyurethanes. They are mixed with alcohols to create polyurethane plastic and with acids to make polyurea coatings. For more information on alcohols, see page 518. For acids, see page 474. For polyurethane, see page 512.

One of the biggest health problems caused by working with isocyanates is asthma. If you feel chest tightness, difficulty breathing, or begin to have asthma attacks, leave the work area and stop working with the isocyanates. If you continue to work with isocyanates, you might have a more serious asthma attack that could kill you. Talk to a health worker and try to transfer to a different job in your factory.

The charts include only some of the isocyanates that exist. See pages 178 to 184 and page 464 for how to find information about other isocyanates. See the Index of chemical names on page 467 to find alternative names for isocyanates.

Prevent or reduce exposure:

- Use ventilation systems that extract fumes and dilute the air (see chapter 17: Ventilation).
- Enclose equipment where possible.
- Do not mix or pour isocyanates by hand.
- Wear butyl rubber gloves. Wear correct respirators that fit you. (See chapter 18: Personal protective equipment.)
- Have an emergency plan that includes first aid treatment and protective equipment for spills, splashes, and exposures. Keep necessary emergency supplies at the worksite, well stocked, and accessible to workers.
- Work areas where isocyanates are used, stored, and mixed need to be controlled for heat and monitored for concentration of fumes and vapors. The work areas should also have alarms, fire extinguishers, and a fire emergency plan (see chapter 11: Fire).

Isocyanates

Isophorone diisocyanate (IPDI) – CAS No. 4098-71-9

Methylene bisphenyl diisocyanate – CAS No. 101-68-8

Naphthalene diisocyanate (NDI) – CAS No. 3173-72-6

Toluene diisocyanate (TDI) – CAS No. 26471-62-5

Hexamethylene diisocyanate (HDI) – CAS No. 822-06-0

What are they?

Isocyanates are clear, colorless, or slightly yellow liquids that have a strong, fruity smell. If you can smell them, they can harm you.

Do you work with them?

Isocyanates are used in shoe making in glues, rubber, and finish coatings.

When they come in contact with your body

Skin: They irritate and burn the skin. You may develop a rash, redness, and dryness. Your skin might start peeling, itching, and cracking. Your skin may become so sensitive that even a very small amount causes skin irritation. See First Aid on page 175.

Eyes: They irritate and burn your eyes. They cause conjunctivitis: watery eyes and discomfort. High amounts of **isocyanate** can permanently damage your eyes. See First Aid on page 175.

Nose/lungs: The fumes can irritate your nose, throat, and lungs, causing congestion, coughing, wheezing, shortness of breath, and chest tightness. The longer you are exposed, the more sensitive you become, which can lead to severe asthma attacks. Inhaling a lot of **isocyanate** fumes can create buildup of fluid in the lungs, called lung edema. See First Aid on page 174.

Mouth/belly: They can irritate your gastrointestinal tract, and cause nausea and vomiting. See First Aid on page 176 and seek medical help.

When you are exposed over time:

Isocyanates can make your nose and lungs sensitive and cause chronic asthma and pneumonitis. After some time you may develop chronic asthma that continues even if you stop working with **isocyanates**.

Toluene diisocyanate may cause cancer.

(continued)

Isocyanates *(continued)*

If you are at risk of exposure:

Use elbow-length, butyl rubber gloves, an apron, and eye/face protection (see chapter 18: Personal protective equipment).

Use a supplied-air respirator. Negative pressure air-purifying respirators are not recommended for **isocyanates** (see Respirators on pages 266 to 270).

Safer substitutes:

Methylene bisphenyl diisocyanate and **naphthalene diisocyanate** are safer than other **isocyanates** because they evaporate more slowly.

Mercapto-based rubber accelerators

Rubber accelerators are used to make rubber material more durable and flexible. They are added to the rubber used to make shoe soles.

Accelerators that contain sulfur are called mercapto-based accelerators. Sulfur acts as a type of glue that makes the rubber more compact and keeps it from breaking easily. Rubber accelerators often come in a mix. Since there may be several mercapto-based accelerator chemicals in a mix, it can be difficult to know which chemicals are present and how much of each you are working with.

Mercapto-based rubber accelerators release very toxic fumes when they burn. Do not store these chemicals near heat or near acids.

The charts include only some of the mercapto-based rubber accelerators that exist. See pages 178 to 184 and page 464 for how to find information about other accelerators. See the Index of chemical names on page 467 to find alternative names for chemicals.

Prevent or reduce exposure:

- Use ventilation systems that remove fumes and dilute the air (see chapter 17: Ventilation).
- Enclose operations where possible.
- Wear gloves when handling rubber accelerator compounds. It is very important to avoid skin contact with these chemicals because mercapto-based rubber accelerators are known to severely irritate your skin and cause allergic reactions. Wear correct respirators that fit you (see chapter 18: Personal protective equipment).
- Do not mix or pour mercapto-based rubber accelerators by hand.
- Have an emergency plan that includes first aid treatment and protective equipment for spills, splashes, and exposures. Keep necessary emergency supplies at the work site well stocked and accessible to workers.
- Work areas where mercapto-based rubber accelerators are used, stored, and mixed need to be controlled for heat and monitored for concentration of fumes and vapors. Work areas should also have alarms, fire extinguishers, and a fire emergency plan (see chapter 11: Fire).

Mercapto-based rubber accelerators

2-Mercaptobenzothiazole (MBT) – CAS No. 149-30-4	
2,2-Mercaptodibenzothiazyl disulphide (MBTS) CAS No. 120-78-5	
Zinc-2-mercaptobenzothiazole (ZMBT) CAS No. 155-04-4	

What are they?

MBT comes in yellow crystals. **MBTS** and **ZMBT** are pale yellow powders. **Mercapto-based rubber accelerators** have an unpleasant, rotten-egg smell, or no smell at all. They have a bitter taste.

Do you work with them?

Mercapto-based rubber accelerators are used in rubber for shoe soles. They make natural and synthetic rubber more durable and flexible .

When they come in contact with your body

Skin: They irritate and burn your skin. You may develop a skin rash, redness, and dryness. Your skin might start peeling, itching, and cracking. See First Aid on page 175.

Eyes: They irritate and burn your eyes. See First Aid on page 175.

Nose/lungs: The dust can irritate your nose, throat, and lungs, causing sore throat, congestion, and coughing. Inhaling the dust can cause headaches and dizziness. See First Aid on page 174.

Mouth/belly: They can irritate your gastrointestinal tract and cause nausea, vomiting, and diarrhea. If you swallow **mercapto-based rubber accelerators**, take activated charcoal with water if available. See First Aid on page 176 and seek medical help.

When you are exposed over time:

Mercapto-based rubber accelerators can make your skin very sensitive and cause skin allergies after repeated contact. You can have a skin reaction if you come in contact with even very small amounts of these chemicals.

MBT may cause colon, bladder, and bone marrow cancer.

If you are at risk of exposure:

Use elbow-length, butyl rubber gloves, an apron, and eye/face protection (see chapter 18: Personal protective equipment).

Use a supplied-air respirator (see pages 268 to 270).

Safer substitutes:

Benzoyl peroxide is a less harmful rubber additive than **mercapto-based accelerators**, but this alternative is not completely safe either.

Metals

Metals usually are solids, although mercury is a metal that is a liquid. Larger amounts of metals are harmful. Heavy metals are dangerous at any level of exposure because they accumulate in your body. Even though you might be exposed to only small amounts each day, it adds up over time to dangerous levels.

Toxic exposure to metals occurs primarily through inhaling metal dust and fumes when metals are heated, soldered, or cut. After you work with them, particles of metal or metal dust on your fingers and hands may also rub off onto food or drop into water and get into your body. Metals are most heavily used in the electronics industry in batteries, welding, recycling, and coatings. In the garment and shoe industries, metals are used in dyeing fabrics and tanning leather.

The charts include only some of the metals that exist. See pages 178 to 184 and page 464 for how to find information about other metals. See the Index of chemical names on page 467 to find alternative names for metals.

Prevent or reduce exposure:

- Use ventilation systems that remove dust and fumes, and dilute the air (see chapter 17: Ventilation).
- Enclose operations where possible.
- Wear metalworking gloves when working with metals. Use a face shield when heating, soldering, or cutting metals. Wear correct respirators that fit you, especially when heating metals. All protective clothing should be clean, available each day, put on before work, and never taken home with you (see chapter 18: Personal protective equipment).
- Have an emergency plan that includes first aid treatment and protective equipment for spills, splashes, and accidental exposures. Keep necessary emergency supplies at the worksite, well stocked, and accessible to workers.
- Wash your hands and face carefully before eating, drinking, or smoking.

Metals

⊘ Cadmium (Cd) – CAS No. 7440-43-9	
⊘ Chromium hexavalent – CAS No. 18540-29-9	
⊘ Copper (Cu) – CAS No. 7440-50-8	
⊘ Lead (Pb) – CAS No. 7439-92-1	
Mercury (Hg) – CAS No. 7439-97-6	
Nickel (Ni) – CAS No. 7440-02-0	
Tin (Sn)– CAS No. 7440-31-5	

What are they?

Metals are usually solids of various colors and without odors. But some metals, such as **mercury,** are liquid. Others, such as **chromium hexavalent** can be solid or liquid. Solid **chromium hexavalent** is usually yellow, orange, or red. **Cadmium** is blue-tinged and shiny. **Copper** is red-orange and turns a dull, brown color when exposed to air. **Lead** is blue-white and turns a grey color when exposed to air. **Mercury** is a silver-white, heavy, and odorless liquid. **Nickel** is a shiny silver metal. **Tin** is a silvery-white solid or a grey-green powder.

Do you work with them?

Metals are used in electronic, garment, and shoe industries. **Cadmium**, **chromium hexavalent**, **copper**, and **lead** are used in electronics and in dyes in garments and shoes. **Mercury**, **nickel**, and **tin** are used in electronics. **Nickel** is also used in metal buttons on jeans, buckles, zippers, and clasps.

When they come in contact with your body

Skin: They can irritate your skin. **Copper**, **mercury**, and **nickel** cause rashes and itching. **Mercury** might discolor your skin grey or brown. See First Aid on page 175.

Eyes: They irritate the eyes. **Chromium hexavalent** can damage the eyes. See First Aid on page 175.

(continued)

Metals *(continued)*

Nose/lungs: They can irritate your nose, throat, and lungs, causing coughing, wheezing, and difficulty breathing. Breathing **chromium hexavalent** can cause a burning sensation. Inhaling fumes can cause dizziness and headaches. They can also create a buildup of fluid in the lungs, called lung edema. Inhaling fumes may cause "metal fume fever," which feels like a short-lived flu. **Lead** can cause severe irritability, chest pain, reduced memory, disturbed sleep, and mood and personality changes. Severe **mercury** poisoning results in shaking, memory loss, difficulty concentrating, weight loss, personality changes, and hallucinations. See First Aid on page 174.

Mouth/belly: They can damage the gastrointestinal tract and stomach. Some signs include loss of appetite, nausea, vomiting, diarrhea, and abdominal pain. Increased salivation and metallic taste are also signs of exposure to **metals**. See First Aid on page 176 and seek medical attention.

When you are exposed over time:

All metals can harm your liver, kidneys, bones, and lungs.

Cadmium and **lead** can cause hypertension (high blood pressure). **Cadmium** can also cause bronchitis, anemia, loss of the sense of smell, and discolored teeth. It can damage the baby in the womb and damage men and women's reproductive systems. It can cause kidney, prostate, and lung cancer.

Chromium hexavalent can cause lung cancer. It can damage the respiratory tract causing nose sores and nose bleeds. It can cause skin blisters and ulcers.

Copper can cause discoloration of the skin, hair, and teeth, and may reduce fertility in men and women.

Lead may cause birth defects and harm the baby in the womb. It may reduce fertility in men and women. It can cause lung, stomach, brain, and kidney cancers.

Mercury causes permanent psychological and neurological problems. It may cause miscarriages, reduce fertility in men and women, and harm the baby in the womb.

Nickel may cause lung cancer.

Tin damages the nervous system, causing shaking and tremors.

If you are at risk of exposure:

Use silver shield or latex inner gloves, and nitrile or neoprene outer gloves with long cuffs (see pages 262 to 265).

Use a respirator that can filter **metal** dust and fumes (see pages 266 to 270).

Noble gases

Noble gases are very stable chemicals that do not react easily with other chemicals and are not flammable. Many noble gases are normally found in the air. This means you breathe in small amounts of noble gases every day.

Noble gases are used in electronics. They are used in light bulbs for computer screens, televisions, and projectors. They are mixed with halogens (chlorine and fluorine) to make ultraviolet lasers that are used to make integrated circuits. The gases come in either compressed gas or liquid and gas form. You might work with noble gases in gas from, but a leak from a container can be liquid or gas.

These gases are not very toxic but they can be harmful in large amounts. Noble gases are asphyxiants. Asphyxiant gases replace oxygen in the air so there is less of it to breathe. Without oxygen you can die. Before entering a room with large amounts of noble gas, make sure that there is enough oxygen in the room or have a respirator mask with its own air supply.

The charts include only some of the noble gases that exist. See pages 178 to 184 and page 464 for how to find information about other noble gases. See the Index of chemical names on page 467 to find alternative names for noble gases.

Prevent or reduce exposure:

- Use ventilation systems that remove fumes and dilute the air (see chapter 17: Ventilation).

- Wear gloves. Wear correct respirators that fit you. All protective clothing should be clean, available each day, put on before work, and never taken homen with you (see chapter 18: Personal protective equipment).

- Have an emergency plan that includes first aid treatment and protective equipment for spills, splashes, and accidental exposures. Keep necessary emergency supplies at the work site well stocked and accessible to workers.

- Work areas where noble gases are used, stored, and mixed need to be controlled for heat and monitored for concentration of fumes and vapors.

Noble gases

Krypton (Kr) – CAS No. 7439-90-9

Neon (Ne)– CAS No. 7440-01-9

Xenon (Xe) – CAS No. 7440-63-3

What are they?

Noble gases are colorless gases that have no smell or taste. However, all noble gases (with the exception of **radon**) produce a bright colorful light when electric current is passed through a gas-filled space such as a tube. They are used to create light.

Do you work with them?

Noble gases are used to fill lamp bulbs in projectors and tubes in the electronics industry. They help light up electronic screens such as plasma televisions and plasma computer monitors. A gas mixture is placed between two glass sheets, one of which is the front screen. When the device is turned on, electricity passes through, interacts with the gas, and creates a visible picture on the screen. **Noble gases** are also found in ultraviolet lasers that are used to make circuit boards.

When they come in contact with your body

Skin: They may cause discomfort to your skin. In gas form they are not toxic to the skin, but if a liquid form touches you, it will burn quickly, but the skin will feel cold and numb. Treat it quickly as a chemical burn. See First Aid on page 175.

Eyes: They may cause discomfort to your eyes. In gas form, they are not toxic to the eyes, but a liquid form can cause severe eye burns. See First Aid on page 175.

Nose/lungs: The fumes can cause dizziness, headache, weakness, confusion, and suffocation. **Noble gases** take the place of oxygen in the room. Without enough oxygen, you can lose consciousness and die very quickly. Make sure there is enough oxygen before entering a room with noble gases present. See First Aid on page 174.

Mouth/belly: This is not a common way of coming into contact with **noble gases**.

When you are exposed over time:

Noble gases are not known to have dangerous long-term health effects.

If you are at risk of exposure:

Use cold-insulating gloves, an apron, and eye/face protection when handling cylinders in which gases are stored (see chapter 18: Personal protective equipment).

Use a supplied-air respirator (see pages 268 to 270).

Phthalates

Phthalates are oily, thick, colorless liquid chemicals. They are called "plasticizers" and added to plastic shoe soles, rubber material, and electronic cables to make them more bendable and soft.

Plastics such as polyvinyl chloride (PVC, see page 512) contain phthalates.

Phthalates get in your body and interfere with hormones. They harm the person in contact with them, but they also harm the person's future children. Daughters of people who come in contact with phthlates have an increased chance of developing breast cancer. Your future children, both sons and daughters, may develop fertility problems if you are exposed to phthalates.

The charts include only some of the phthalates that exist. See pages 178 to 184 and page 464 for how to find information about other phthalates. See the Index of chemical names on page 467 to find alternative names for chemicals.

Prevent or reduce exposure:

- The most harmful route of exposure is through your mouth. Wash your hands very carefully before eating, drinking, and smoking to prevent any ingestion of phthalate particles.
- Phthalates do not evaporate as easily as some other liquid chemicals. But you should still have ventilation systems that extract fumes and dilute the air (see chapter 17: Ventilation).
- Do not mix or pour phthalates by hand.
- Wear gloves and other protective equipment when handling phthalates (see chapter 18: Personal protective equipment).
- Have an emergency plan that includes first aid treatment and protective equipment for spills, splashes, and accidental exposures. Keep necessary emergency supplies at the worksite, well stocked, and accessible to workers.

Phthalates

Butyl benzyl phthalate (BBP) – CAS No. 85-68-7

Di(2-ethylhexyl)phthalate – CAS No. 117-81-7

Dibutyl phthalate (DBP) – CAS No. 84-74-2

Diethyl phthalate (DEP)– CAS No. 84-66-2

Dimethyl phthalate (DMP) – CAS No. 131-11-3

Dioctyl phthalate (DOP) – CAS No. 117-84-0

What are they?

Phthalates are colorless, oily, thick liquids. Some may have a very slight sweet smell. Others have no smell at all.

Do you work with them?

Phthalates are used in the shoe industry to make soles softer and more flexible. **Dioctyl phthalate** is used to make rubber. **Phthalates** are added to glues and, in electronics, the plastic used to cover wires.

When they come in contact with your body

Skin: They can irritate and burn your skin. See First Aid on page 175.

Eyes: They can irritate your eyes. See First Aid on page 175.

Nose/lungs: They can irritate your nose, throat, and lungs, causing coughing, wheezing, and shortness of breath. You may also become dizzy and lightheaded. See First Aid on page 174.

Mouth/belly: If they get into your mouth and belly, they can cause nausea, vomiting, and diarrhea. See First Aid on page 176 and seek medical help.

When you are exposed over time:

All phthalates may harm your kidneys and liver, and can damage the nervous system causing weakness and numbness in the hands and feet.

Butyl benzyl phthalate, dibutyl phthalate, di(2-ethylhexyl)phthalate, and **dimethyl phthalate** may reduce fertility in men and women and may damage the baby in the womb. **Dioctyl phthalate** may damage the baby in the womb.

Butyl benzyl phthalate and **dibutyl phthalate** may cause cancer. **Di(2-ethylhexyl) phthalate** can cause cancer.

(continued)

Phthalates *(continued)*

If you are at risk of exposure:

Use elbow-length, butyl rubber, nitrile rubber or polyvinyl alcohol gloves and eye/face protection (see chapter 18: Personal protective equipment).

Use a respirator with a full face mask and air filter (see pages 266 to 270.

Safer substitutes:

Some alternative chemicals are **citrate esters**, **adipates** and **phosphates**. But many chemicals in these groups can also cause harm. **Dioctyl terephthalate** is a safer, phthalate-free alternative although its name might make you think it contains phthalates.

Polymers

Polymers are made of many chemicals called "monomers" that are linked together. A polymer is like chain of paperclips. Each paperclip represents one monomer. Different polymers are made of different monomers and are linked in different ways. Things made from polymers can be rubbery like shoe soles, sticky like glue, or hard like plastic.

Polymers are often used in electronics, shoes, and textiles.

Polymers are not as toxic as the monomers that link together to make them. But a polymer can break down into individual toxic monomers that can harm you. Also, before a polymer becomes a hard plastic, strong rubber, or sticky glue, a worker may use many harmful chemicals to mold and cure the polymer into the desired shape or form.

The name of the polymer often contains the names of the monomers linked together to make it. The chart includes only a few of the many polymers that exist. See pages 178 to 184 and page 464 for how to find information about other polymers. See the Index of chemical names on page 467 to find alternative names for chemicals.

Prevent or reduce exposure:

- Use ventilation systems that remove fumes and dilute the air (see chapter 17: Ventilation).
- Enclose operations whenever possible.
- Do not mix or pour polymers by hand.
- Use gloves when handling polymers. Wear correct respirators that fit you. All protective clothing should be clean, available each day, put on before work, and never taken home (see chapter 18: Personal protective equipment).
- Have an emergency plan that includes first aid treatment and protective equipment for spills, splashes, and exposures. Keep necessary emergency supplies at the work site well stocked and accessible to workers.
- Work areas where polymers are used, stored, and mixed need to be controlled for heat and monitored for concentration of fumes and vapors. The work areas should also have alarms, fire extinguishers, and a fire emergency plan (see chapter 11: Fire).

Polymers

Ethylene vinyl acetate (EVA) – CAS No. 24937-78-8

Phenol formaldehyde (PF) resin – CAS No 9003-35-4

Polyurethane (PU) – CAS No. 9009-54-5

⊘ **Polyvinyl chloride (PVC) – CAS No. 9002-86-2**

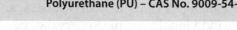

What are they?

Polymers come in both liquids and solids. **Ethylene vinyl acetate** comes as white powder that smells like wax, while its monomer, **Vinyl acetate**, is a clear liquid with a strong, sweet smell. **Phenol formaldehyde resin** is a liquid with a slight pleasant smell. **Polyurethane** comes as liquid or solid, while its monomer, **Urethane**, is a white flour-like powder or sand-like crystal. **Polyvinyl chloride** comes as white powder or pellets, while its monomer, **Vinyl chloride**, is a colorless gas with a sweet smell, but it is used as a liquid under pressure.

Do you work with them?

Polymers are used to make rubber in shoe soles. They are used to make plastics and textiles. **Phenol formaldehyde** is a resin used in photoresist in electronics and in textiles to prevent wrinkles. **Polymers** are also used in glues.

When they come in contact with your body

Skin: They irritate your skin. You may develop a skin rash, redness, dryness, and blisters. Your skin might start peeling, itching, and cracking. See First Aid on page 175.

Eyes: They irritate your eyes. See First Aid on page 175.

Nose/lungs: The vapors and dusts irritate your nose, throat, and lungs, causing congestion, coughing, sneezing, and shortness of breath. They can cause dizziness, confusion, and headaches. See First Aid on page 174.

Mouth/belly: If they get into your mouth and belly, they can cause nausea, stomach pain, vomiting, and diarrhea. See First Aid on page 176 and seek medical attention.

When you are exposed over time:

Polymers are not as toxic to people as the monomers they contain. But when cut, heated, or manipulated, polymers and their byproducts can release dangerous dust and vapors.

Vinyl acetate in **EVA** may affect the heart, nervous system, and liver. It may reduce fertility in men. It may cause cancer.

(continued)

Polymers *(continued)*

Phenol formaldehyde resin releases **formaldehyde**, which can damage your lungs, cause bronchitis and asthma, and may damage a baby inside the womb and reduce fertility in women. See **Formaldehyde** on page 496.

Urethane in **Polyurethane** can damage kidneys, liver, brain, and bone marrow. It may cause cancer. It may damage and cause cancer in a baby inside the womb.

Vinyl chloride in **PVC** can damage the liver, nervous system, and lungs. It may damage a baby inside the womb, reduce fertility in men, and cause miscarriages. It can cause liver, brain, lung, and other cancers. In electronics, workers using **PVC** are often exposed to **lead** and **cadmium** (see pages 503 to 505), and **phthalates** (see pages 508 to 510).

If you are at risk of exposure:

Use ethylene vinyl alcohol gloves and eye/face protection (see chapter 18: Personal protective equipment). Do not heat or work with large amounts of polymers at once.

Use a respirator, especially when there is a lot of dust or vapor, when working with large surfaces, or when heating polymers. See Respirators on pages 266 to 270.

Safer substitutes:

Alternatives to **phenol formaldehyde resin** are **glyoxal resin** and **polymeric carboxylic acid**. A safer alternative to **PVC** is **polyethylene**. The best alternative is not to use **polymers** at all and to use metal or glass instead.

Radiation

Radiation is a form of energy that travels as invisible waves through air away from the radiation source. Radiation used in electronics includes radiofrequency (RF) radiation, ultraviolet (UV) light, and x-rays. A lot of radiation comes from the sun or elements in the earth around us. This type of radiation is called natural radiation. Other radiation is man-made, such as that used in manufacturing.

Some types of radiation are more dangerous than others. The higher the amount of energy, the more dangerous the radiation. X-rays are more dangerous than UV light, but UV light is more dangerous than RF radiation.

You can be exposed to a large amount of radiation all at once or to smaller amounts over a long period of time. Whole-body exposure to radiation is more damaging than if only a small part of your body comes in contact with radiation.

Prevent or reduce exposure:

- Distance, time and shielding are the main ways to reduce radiation exposure. Placing yourself far away from the radiation source, spending less time near the source, and shielding yourself behind a radiation-proof barrier will help control exposure to harmful radiation.
- Enclose machines with a radiation-proof shield.
- Avoid contact with machines. Use a remote control to operate them.
- Avoid looking directly at a radiation source.
- Wear protective equipment and clothing (see chapter 18: Personal protective equipment).
- Always turn off a machine that could give off radiation when it is not in use. Turn off, tag out, and lock out the machine for repairs.
- Warning signs and radiation level monitors should be posted around work areas. Workers in the area should wear radiation monitoring badges.

Radiation

Radiofrequency (RF) radiation	
Ultraviolet (UV) light	
X-ray	

What are they?

Radiation is an invisible form of energy. You need special equipment to detect and measure radiation. If you are close to an **RF radiation** heater and feel that your skin is getting warmer and your body temperature increases, you are being exposed to harmful **RF radiation**. But even if you don't feel warm, radiation can go through your skin and cause harm.

Do you work with them?

Radiation is mostly found in the electronics industry. **RF radiation** is used in heaters for dry etching and for dopant deposits on wafers. **X-rays** are produced from dopant deposits on wafers. **UV light** is used during the photolithography process in chip production. In the shoe industry, **RF radiation** is used to heat or melt rubber and glue, and in the garment industry to dry textile webs.

When they come in contact with your body

Skin: They severely burn your skin. **UV light** causes reddening and darkening of the skin.

Eyes: They severely burn your eyes. **UV light** causes photokeratitis and conjunctivitis. Signs of photokeratitis are pain, watery eyes, and blurred vision. It feels like you have sand in your eyes. Signs of conjunctivitis are watery eyes and discomfort. High levels of **RF radiation** and **UV light** causes eye cataracts. Signs of cataracts are clouded and blurred vision, sensitivity to light, difficulty seeing at night, and fading of colors. If exposed to large amounts of **RF radiation** and **UV light**, you may become blind.

Nose/lungs: Inhaling the dust of a material exposed to radiation damages your respiratory tract and causes harm over time.

Mouth/belly: Ingesting the dust of a material exposed to radiation may damage your digestive tract and cause more harm over time.

When you are exposed over time:

All radiation can harm your organs and damage your immune system.

RF radiation may harm your nervous system and affect your reflexes and heart rate. It can cause miscarriages, affect the menstrual cycle, and decrease breastmilk in nursing women. It may reduce fertility in men. It can harm a baby in the womb.

UV light can cause skin cancer.

X-rays can cause all types of cancer. **X-rays** can reduce fertility in men and women. They are also very damaging to the baby in the womb.

(continued)

Radiation *(continued)*

If you are at risk of exposure:

Use radiation-proof suits, gloves, and goggles. When working with **UV lights** use nitrile gloves and wear a long-sleeved shirt . For **RF radiation**, electrically insulating gloves can protect against **RF** burns. For **X-ray radiation**, use lead-lined gloves.

Wear a radiation monitoring badge.

Solvents

Solvents come in liquid form and are used as cleaners, added to glues to make them stronger or quicker to dry, and are part of many mixes of chemicals in shoe, garment, and electronics industries.

Most solvents quickly burn and explode when exposed to heat. They also release more vapors and fumes when heated.

There are many "families" of solvents. Solvents that are similar share many qualities, and are often used in the same processes. In some families, there are several chemicals that are more dangerous than other chemicals in the same family. Some entire families of solvents are dangerous to people's health, for example, aromatic hydrocarbons (see page 522) and chlorinated hydrocarbons (see page 524). The best way to protect workers who use solvents is to ban the most dangerous solvents and find less dangerous substitute solvents.

The charts include only some of the solvents that exist. See pages 178 to 184 and page 464 for how to find information about other solvents. See the Index of chemical names on page 467 to find alternative names for chemicals.

Prevent or reduce exposure:

- Use ventilation systems that remove fumes and dilute the air (see chapter 17: Ventilation).
- Enclose operations whenever possible.
- Do not mix or pour solvents by hand.
- Use gloves when workers are handling solvents directly (cleaning). Wear correct respirators that fit you. All protective clothing should be clean, available each day, put on before work, and never taken home (see chapter 18: Personal protective equipment).
- Have an emergency plan that includes first aid treatment and protective equipment for spills, splashes, and accidental exposures. Keep necessary emergency supplies at the work site well stocked and accessible to workers.
- Work areas where solvents are used, stored, and mixed need to be controlled for heat and monitored for concentration of fumes and vapors. The work areas should also have alarms, fire extinguishers, and a fire emergency plan (see chapter 11: Fire).

Alcohol solvents

Ethyl alcohol (ethanol) – CAS No. 64-17-5

Isopropyl alcohol (IPA) – CAS No. 67-63-0

Methyl alcohol (methanol) – CAS No. 67-56-1

What are they?

Alcohol solvents are colorless liquids. **Ethanol** smells a little like wine. **IPA** smells musty. **Methanol** has a slightly sweet odor.

Do you work with them?

Alcohol solvents are used as cleaners. They are used to make rubber for shoes, to spot clean fabric, to electroplate, and in printed circuit boards. **IPA** and **methanol** are the most common.

When they come in contact with your body

Skin: They irritate your skin. After continued or repeated exposure to alcohols, you may develop a skin rash, redness, and dryness. Your skin might start peeling, itching, and cracking. See First Aid on page 175.

Eyes: They irritate, burn, and can cause permanent damage to the eyes. **Methanol** will blur your vision and can cause blindness. See First Aid on page 175.

Nose/lungs: The fumes can irritate your nose and throat, causing coughing and wheezing. Breathing the vapors can make you feel weak, dizzy, lightheaded, short of breath, and even pass out. **IPA** can slow down your pulse and lower your blood pressure, and at high levels it can cause hallucinations. See First Aid on page 174.

Mouth/belly: They can lead to loss of appetite, nausea, vomiting, and diarrhea. Larger amounts could cause loss of consciousness. See First Aid on page 176 and seek medical attention.

When you are exposed over time:

All alcohols can harm your liver, kidneys, and nervous system. **Alcohols** can enter into a mother's milk and pass to a baby through breastfeeding.

Ethanol can cause miscarriages, birth defects, and other problems. It may cause cancer of the liver, esophagus, breast, prostate, and colorectum.

Isopropyl alcohol may damage a baby in the womb.

Methanol may damage a baby in the womb.

(continued)

Alcohol solvents (continued)

If you are at risk of exposure:

Use butyl gloves. Polyvinyl alcohol (PVA) gloves will not protect you from **alcohol solvents**. If you're working with **alcohols** as liquids, use indirect-vent, impact- and splash-resistant goggles (see chapter 18: Personal protective equipment).

If there is no ventilation installed, or if you are doing maintenance work and you do not know the level of alcohol in the air, use a respirator that can filter **solvents**.

Aliphatic hydrocarbon solvents (petroleum distillates)

2,2-Dimethylbutane (neohexane) - CAS No. 75-83-2

2-Methylpentane - CAS No. 107-83-5

Cyclohexane - CAS No. 110-82-7

Heptane - CAS No. 142-82-5

Hexane - CAS No. 110-54-3

What are they?

Aliphatic hydrocarbon solvents are colorless liquids. **Hexane** and **heptane** have a mild, gasoline-like smell. **Cyclohexane** has a strong, sweet smell.

Do you work with them?

Aliphatic hydrocarbon solvents are used in glues for shoes and as cleaners in electronics. They are used in surface coatings and adhesives. **Cyclohexane** is used to make nylon.

When they come in contact with your body

Skin: They can irritate and burn your skin. If they get on your skin repeatedly, your skin will become dry, cracked, and red and you might develop a rash. See First Aid on page 175.

Eyes: They can irritate the eyes. See First Aid on page 175.

Nose/lungs: Inhalation of these solvents can lead to irritation of the nose and throat. . Breathing the vapors can cause you to feel weak, dizzy, lightheaded, and short of breath, and even pass out. See First Aid on page 174.

Mouth/belly: They can lead to loss of appetite, nausea, vomiting, and diarrhea. See First Aid on page 176 and seek medical attention.

When you are exposed over time:

All **aliphatic hydrocarbons** can affect your brain, causing headaches and dizziness.

2,2-dimethylbutane can cause irregular heartbeat.

Cyclohexane may permanently damage the liver and kidney. It can cause headaches, convulsions, and other problems with the nervous system.

Heptane can cause damage to the nervous system, causing reduced coordination and personality changes, fatigue, and reduced memory and concentration.

(continued)

Aliphatic hydrocarbon solvents *(continued)*

Hexane can damage the nervous system, causing problems with coordination, memory and concentration, personality changes, and fatigue. It may damage the testes. High doses can be fatal.

If you are at risk of exposure:

Use nitrile or viton gloves and eye/face protection (see chapter 18: Personal protective equipment).

Use a respirator that can filter organic **solvents** (see pages 266 to 270).

Safer substitutes:

Heptane is less toxic than **hexane**.

Aromatic hydrocarbon solvents

⊘ **Benzene** – CAS No. 71-43-2

⊘ **Styrene** – CAS No. 100-42-5

Toluene – CAS No. 108-88-3

Xylene – CAS No. 1330-20-7

What are they?

Aromatic hydrocarbon solvents are clear, colorless to light yellow liquids that have sweet odors.

Do you work with them?

Aromatic hydrocarbon solvents are found in garment, shoe, and electronics factories. **Toluene** is a common additive for glues in shoes, and **styrene** is found in resins that reinforce plastics in electronics.

When they come in contact with your body

Skin   They irritate your skin and lead to dermatitis, which results in skin rash, dryness, redness, and a burning feeling. **Benzene** can cause blisters. See First Aid on page 175.

Eyes: They irritate your eyes. **Benzene** can make you blind. See First Aid on page 175.

Nose/lungs: The fumes can irritate your nose and throat, causing coughing and wheezing. Breathing the vapors can cause headaches, drowsiness, dizziness, confusion, nausea, weakness, and loss of consciousness. **Benzene** can cause bronchitis, lung edema, and pneumonia. It can cause problems with the heart. Breathing a lot of benzene (20,000 ppm) can kill you in 10 to 15 minutes. **Toluene** affects the nervous system, causing difficulty thinking, slow reflexes, dilated pupils, anxiety, and weakness. See First Aid on page 174.

Mouth/belly: **Benzene** and **xylene** can cause nausea, vomiting, and abdominal pain. **Benzene** can cause rapid heart rate, difficulty breathing, chest tightness, and respiratory failure, all of which can be fatal.   See First Aid on page 176 and seek medical attention.

When you are exposed over time:

All aromatic hydrocarbons can damage your liver, kidneys, brain, and the nervous system.

Benzene can cause problems with the blood and destroy blood cells. This can cause aplastic anemia. It may cause birth defects. It can cause leukemia (cancer of the blood).

Styrene may cause birth defects and other reproductive health problems. It may cause lung cancer.

Toluene may cause birth defects.

Xylene may cause birth defects. It may cause cancer. Higher exposures can cause coma.

(continued)

Aromatic hydrocarbon solvents *(continued)*

If you are at risk of exposure:

Use polyvinyl alcohol (PVA), silver shield, or viton gloves. If you work with **aromatic hydrocarbons** as liquids, use indirect vent, impact- and splash-resistant goggles. If you are exposed to fumes, gas, or vapor forms of these solvents, use non-vented, impact-resistant goggles (see chapter 18: Personal protective equipment).

Use a respirator that can filter **solvents** (see pages 266 to 270.)

Safer substitutes:

Toluene has been used as a safer alternative to **benzene**. However, **toluene** is still toxic.

Chlorinated hydrocarbon solvents

⊘ **Carbon tetrachloride - CAS No. 56-23-5**

Dichloropropane (DCP) - CAS No. 78-87-5

Methyl chloroform - CAS No. 71-55-6

Methylene chloride (DCM) - CAS No. 75-09-2

Tetrachloroethylene (PERC) - CAS No. 127-18-4

⊘ **Trichloroethylene (TCE) - CAS No. 79-01-6**

What are they?

Chlorinated hydrocarbon solvents are colorless liquids that contain chlorine. They have a mild, sweet smell.

Do you work with them?

Chlorinated hydrocarbon solvents are used as cleaners. They are used to make rubber for shoes, degreasers in electroplating, and as agents in wafer production and semiconductor cleaning.

When they come in contact with your body

Skin: They can irritate your skin. **Carbon tetrachloride** can burn your skin. **TCE** might make you allergic, and you will have a reaction even at low exposure levels. See First Aid on page 175.

Eyes: They can irritate and burn the eyes. **Carbon tetrachloride** can make you blind if it gets in your eyes. See First Aid on page 175.

Nose/lungs: The fumes can irritate your nose and throat. Breathing the fumes can cause you to feel weak, dizzy, lightheaded, short of breath, and to pass out. Often you will also have poor equilibrium, lack of coordination, mental confusion, and numb and tingling limbs. Inhaling **Dichloropropane** and **PERC** fumes can create a buildup of fluid in the lungs, called lung edema. See First Aid on page 174.

Mouth/belly: They can lead to loss of appetite, nausea, vomiting, and diarrhea. See First Aid on page 176 and seek medical attention.

When you are exposed over time:

All **chlorinated hydrocarbons** can damage the liver and kidneys.

Carbon tetrachloride can lead to coma. It may damage a baby in the womb and reduce fertility in men. It may cause cancer.

(continued)

Chlorinated hydrocarbons *(continued)*

Dichloropropane can cause liver cancer.

Methyl chloroform may cause miscarriages and birth defects. It also may cause liver and kidney cancer.

Methylene chloride may cause lung, liver, and breast cancer.

PERC may damage a baby in the womb, decrease fertility in men and women, and cause miscarriages. It can cause many types of cancer including liver, esophagus, bladder, lung, and leukemia (cancer of the blood).

TCE can lead to irregular heartbeat. It can cause birth defects and it can cause liver, kidney, and lung cancer.

If you are at risk of exposure:

Use gloves. If you are working with these chemicals in liquid form, use indirect-vent, impact- and splash resistant goggles. If you are exposed to fumes, gas, or vapors, use non-vented goggles (see chapter 18: Personal protective equipment).

Use a respirator that can filter **solvents** (see pages 266 to 270).

Safer substitutes:

Bromopropane has been used as a safer substitute for **TCE**. But it can cause cancer so it is not a real solution.

Ester solvents

Butyl acetate - CAS No. 123-86-4

Ethyl acetate - CAS No. 141-78-6

Isobutyl acetate - CAS No. 110-19-0

What are they?

Ester solvents are colorless liquids with a pleasant, fragrant, fruity odor. **Butyl acetate** smells like bananas.

Do you work with them?

Ester solvents are used in garments, shoes, and electronics as glues, surface cleaners, and to make plastic materials.

When they come in contact with your body

Skin: They can irritate and burn your skin. If they get on your skin repeatedly, your skin will become dry, cracked, and red and you might develop a rash. See ""First Aid"" on page 175.

Eyes: They can irritate and burn the eyes. See First Aid on page 175.

Nose/lungs: The fumes can irritate your nose and throat. Breathing the vapors can cause you to feel weak, dizzy, lightheaded, short of breath, and to pass out. See First Aid on page 174.

Mouth/belly: They can lead to loss of appetite, nausea, vomiting, and diarrhea. See First Aid on page 176 and seek medical attention.

When you are exposed over time:

Butyl acetate may damage a baby in the womb. **Butyl acetate** can irritate your lungs and damage your nervous system. You may develop bronchitis along with coughing, phlegm, and shortness of breath.

Ethyl acetate may damage liver and kidneys. It may decrease fertility in men.

If you are at risk of exposure:

Use neoprene or butyl rubber gloves and eye/face protection (see chapter 18: Personal protective equipment).

Use respirator that can filter organic **solvents** (see pages 266 to 270).

Glycol ether solvents

ETHYLENE-BASED GLYCOL ETHERS
These are more toxic and have "ethanol" or "ethylene" in the name.

Ethylene glycol butyl ether (EGBE) – CAS No. 111-76-2

Ethylene glycol ethyl ether (EGEE) – CAS No. 110-80-5

⊘ Ethylene glycol methyl ether (EGME) – CAS No. 109-86-4

PROPYLENE-BASED GLYCOL ETHERS
These are less toxic and have "propanol" or "propylene" in their name.

1-Methoxy 2-propanol – CAS No. 107-98-2

2-Methoxy 1-propanol – CAS No. 1589-47-5

What are they?

Glycol ether solvents are colorless liquids. They have a mild, pleasant smell or no smell at all.

Do you work with them?

Glycol ether solvents are used as cleaners, dyes, and coatings in shoe, garment and electronics factories. They are often ingredients of proprietary mixes.

When they come in contact with your body

Skin: They irritate and burn your skin. You may develop a skin rash, redness, and dryness. Your skin might start peeling, itching, and cracking. See First Aid on page 175.

Eyes: They irritate and burn your eyes. See First Aid on page 175.

Nose/lungs: Some glycol ethers evaporate quickly and can easily be inhaled. Their fumes can irritate your nose and throat, causing coughing, wheezing, and shortness of breath. Breathing the vapors can cause you to feel weak, dizzy, lightheaded, disoriented, and tired. See First Aid on page 174.

Mouth/belly: They can lead to loss of appetite, nausea, vomiting, and weight loss. See First Aid on page 176 and seek medical attention.

When you are exposed over time:

All **glycol ethers** can harm your liver, kidneys, and nervous system, causing trembling and weakness. **Glycol ethers** can enter mother's milk and pass to a baby through breastfeeding.

(continued)

Glycol ether solvents *(continued)*

Ethylene-based glycol ethers can cause anemia by damaging red blood cells and bone marrow. Some **ethylene-based glycol ethers** can decrease fertility in women and men and damage the baby in the womb.

Ethylene glycol butyl ether may cause liver cancer.

Ethylene glycol ethyl ether is slightly less toxic, but can also decrease fertility in women and men and harm the baby in the womb.

Ethylene glycol methyl ether can cause changes in personality, memory loss, and chronic headaches. Breathing large amounts may damage the spleen and produce bloody urine. It can decrease fertility in women and men, damage the testes, and is extremely toxic to the baby in the womb.

Propylene-based glycol ethers are less dangerous than ethylene-based glycol ethers.

2-methoxy, 1-propanol can damage the baby in the womb.

If you might come in contact with them:

Use butyl rubber gloves. If these are not available, use neoprene or nitrile gloves. Use eye/face protection (see chapter 18: Personal protective equipment).

Use a respirator that can filter **glycol ether** fumes (see pages 266 to 270).

Safer substitutes:

Glycol ethers such as **propyl ether, isopropyl ether,** and **phenyl ether** are less harmful to the reproductive organs and baby inside the womb. **Propylene-based glycol ethers** are safer than **ethylene-based glycol ethers.**

Ketone solvents

Acetone – CAS No. 67-64-1

Methyl butyl ketone (MBK) – CAS No. 591-78-6

Methyl ethyl ketone (MEK) – CAS No. 78-93-3

Methyl isobutyl ketone (MIBK) – CAS No. 108-10-1

What are they?

Ketone solvents are colorless liquids that have a pleasant, sweet or mint-like smell.

Do you work with them?

Ketone solvents are added to glues for shoes. They are used in surface coatings on electronics, as adhesives for PVC pipes, and as cleaners in shoes, garments, and electronics. **MIBK** is added to the rubber in shoes.

When they come in contact with your body

Skin: They can cause skin irritation. If they get on your skin repeatedly, your skin will become dry, cracked, and red and you might develop a rash. See First Aid on page 175.

Eyes: They can irritate and burn the eyes. See First Aid on page 175.

Nose/lungs: The fumes can irritate your nose and throat, causing coughing and wheezing. Breathing the vapors can cause you to feel weak, dizzy, light-headed, short of breath, and to pass out. See First Aid on page 174.

Mouth/belly: They can lead to loss of appetite, nausea, vomiting, and diarrhea. See First Aid on page 176 and seek medical attention.

When you are exposed over time:

All **ketones** can damage the nervous system causing weakness and poor coordination in the hands and feet. They can damage the liver and kidneys.

MBK and **acetone** may reduce fertility in men. **Acetone** may cause miscarriages.

MEK may cause birth defects.

MIBK may cause cancer.

If you are at risk of exposure:

Use butyl rubber gloves and eye/face protection (see chapter 18: Personal protective equipment).

Use a respirator that can filter for organic **solvents** (see pages 266 to 270).

Resources

Organizing for safe work

International organizations

Asia Monitor Resource Center

Independent organization that supports Asian labor movements and workers' rights, equality, and occupational safety and health. Many online resources.

Flat 7, 9th Floor, Block A, Fuk Keung Industrial Building, 66-68 Tong Mi Road, Kowloon, HONG KONG
T: +852 2332-1346
Website: amrc.org.hk

Clean Clothes Campaign

An international alliance of trade unions and NGOs dedicated to promoting better working conditions and supporting garment factory workers.

Postbus 11584
1001 GN Amsterdam, NETHERLANDS
T: +31 (20) 412-2785
Website: cleanclothes.org

Maquiladora Health and Safety Support Network

A network of occupational safety and health professionals who provide technical assistance, information, and training to workers on the USA-Mexico border, in Central America, and Asia.

P.O. Box 124
Berkeley, CA 94701, USA
T: +1 (510) 558-1014
Website: mhssn.igc.org

Solidarity Center

The outreach arm of the US labor movement provides training and support to labor unions internationally on issues of wages and working conditions, organizing and bargaining skills, and gender equality.

888 16th Street NW, Suite 400
Washington, DC 20005, USA
T: +1 (202) 974-8383
Website: solidaritycenter.org

Worker Rights Consortium

An organization dedicated to monitoring labor rights, conducting investigations, and reporting on working conditions.

5 Thomas Circle NW, 5th Floor
Washington, DC 20005 USA
T: +1 (202) 387-4884
Website: workersrights.org

Books and materials online

Barefoot Research: A Worker's Manual for Organising on Work Security

This manual helps workers learn to conduct surveys and workplace inspections, and to discuss problems in the workplace as a group, providing them with ways to identify dangers and take action.

International Labour Organization (ILO)
Website: ilo.org/public/english/
protection/ses/info/publ/2barefoot.htm

Made in LA

Videos with comprehensive discussion and training guide for garment industry workers (in 12 languages).

Garment Worker Center
Website: madeinla.com

Organising at Work: Building stronger unions in the workplace

A guide to help unions increase participation and union effectiveness.

Trades Union Congress
Website: tuc.org.uk/sites/default/files/
OrganisingAtWork.pdf

The Factory Floor Guide to Corporate Accountability: Seeking Redress for Labour Rights Violations in Global Supply Chains

Step-by-step processes for preparing and carrying out legal campaigns and complaints about labor rights and standards.

Oxfam
Website: policy-practice.oxfam.org.uk/
publications/the-factory-floor-guide-to-
corporate-accountability-seeking-redress-
for-labour-296875

The Global Workplace: A Manual for Trade Union Activists

Promotes workers' and unions' understanding of globalization's effects on workers' conditions and rights. Information on how unions can launch international campaigns, get involved with NGOs, and approach international institutions like the ILO.

War on Want
Website: tinyurl.com/o48kllk

No Choice But to Fight

The story of Chinese women battery workers' struggle for health.

Globalization Monitor
P.O. Box No. 70065K
Kowloon Central Post Office, HONG KONG
T: +852 6187 3401
website: http://www.globalmon.org.
hk/content/%E2%80%9Cno-choice-
fight%E2%80%9D

Websites and apps

Cambodian Labour Law Guide, Better Factories Cambodia

Mobile phone app is a labor law guide with links to training modules. English, Mandarin, and Khmer.

ILO Better Factories
Website: betterfactories.org/?p=7267

International Labour Rights Conventions of the ILO

ILO conventions by name and number.

Website: ilo.org/global/standards/lang--
en/index.htm

United Nations (UN) conventions

UN conventions by name and date.

Website: treaties.un.org

International unions

IndustriALL Global Union

54 bis. Route des Acacias
Case Postale 1516
1227 Geneva, SWITZERLAND
T: +41 (22) 308-5050
Website: industriall-union.org

International Trade Union Confederation

Boulevard du Roi Albert II, 5, Bte 1
1210 Brussels, BELGIUM
T: +32 (0) 2224-0211
Website: ituc-csi.org

UNIGLOBAL

8-10 Ave Reverdil
1260 Nyon, SWITZERLAND
T: +41 (22) 365-2100
Website: uniglobalunion.org

NGOs working with business

BIZNGO

Business and environmental groups
working together for safer chemicals
and sustainable materials.

310 Broadway, Suite 101
Somerville, MA 02144, USA
T: +1 (781) 391-6743
Website: bizngo.org

Business for Social Responsibility

Works with companies to improve
labor and environmental issues.
HERProject trains women workers on
basic health concepts.

88 Kearny Street, 12th Floor
San Francisco, CA 94108, USA
T: +1 (415) 984-3200
Website: bsr.org

VERITÉ

Works with companies to improve
labor issues. Publishes reports and
guides for employers on workplace
improvement.

44 Belchertown Road
Amherst, MA 01002, USA
T: +1 (413) 253-9227
Website: verite.org

Industries

Electronics

GoodElectronics

International network promoting
human rights, labor rights, and
sustainability in the electronics
industry.

Website: goodelectronics.org

Health Hazards in Electronics: A Handbook

Tom Gassert's classic handbook on
work-related illness and injuries
in electronics and how to prevent
illness, injuries, and environmental
contamination in the workplace and
surrounding communities.

Asia Monitor Resource Center
Website: http://amrc.org.hk/content/
health-hazards-electronics-handbook

International Campaign for Responsible Technology (ICRT)

Dedicated to promoting sustainable
electronics, focusing on global
electronic industry impacts on health,
the environment, and workers' rights.

Website: icrt.co

Garment

Garment Industry Supply Chains: A Resource for Worker Education and Solidarity

This pack of materials is designed for educating and organizing with garment workers, primarily but not only women.

Women Working Worldwide
Website: women-ww.org/documents/
www_education_pack.pdf

Sewing and Related Procedures: Ergonomics

A workers' ergonomic guide for sewing, scissor work, working with bulk fabric, and other tasks. Also available in Spanish.

US Department of Labor, Occupational Safety and Health Administration
Website: osha.gov/SLTC/etools/sewing/
index.html

Shoes

Improving safety, health and the working environment in the informal footwear sector: Participatory action training for informal sector operator's manual

International Labour Organization (ILO)
Website: ilo.org/public/libdoc/
ilo/2002/102B09_419_engl.pdf

Work dangers

General dangers

Canadian Centre for Occupational Health and Safety (CCOHS)

CCOHS offers education, training, information, and health and safety programs.

135 Hunter Street East
Hamilton, ON L8N 1M5, CANADA
T: +1 (905) 572-2981
Website: ccohs.ca

Hazards Magazine

Includes resources on organizing, strain injuries, chemicals, compensation, sickness, young workers, women and work dangers, and unions.

Website: hazards.org/resources/index.htm

Encyclopedia of Occupational Health and Safety

Topics include health care, general work dangers, accidents and safety management, and chemicals. Also has chapters for each industry.

International Labour Organization (ILO)
Website: ilo.org/oshenc

Labor Occupational Health Program (LOHP)

Does research, and develops curricula and action-oriented trainings for workers. Also works with employers. Offers materials in Spanish, Tagalog, and other languages.

2199 Addison St., 4th Floor,
Berkeley, CA 94720-5120, USA
T: + 1 (510) 642-5507
Website: lohp.org

LaborDoc Website

Search for documents in the International Labour Organization database. Contains non-ILO materials and is in multiple languages.

Website: ilo.org/public/libdoc/ilo/1930/30B09_1_engl_V.1.pdf

Labor Occupational Safety and Health Program (LOSH)

Conducts research, outreach, and trainings on health and safety.

Peter V. Ueberroth Building
10945 Le Conte Avenue, Suite 2107
Los Angeles, CA 90095-1478, USA
T: +1 (310) 794-5964
Website: losh.ucla.edu

Industrial Health Resource Group

Supports organizing through training and materials on occupational safety and health.

Princess Christian Home
Rondebosch, Private Bag X3
Cape Town 7701, SOUTH AFRICA
Website: ihrg.org.za

OSHwiki

Developed by EU-OSHA, a growing, searchable, online collection of articles on occupational safety and health information and best practices.

EU-OSHA
website: oshwiki.eu

Organising for Health and Safety: A Guide for Trade Unions

Training material and data sheets.
Industrial Health Resources Group
Website: tinyurl.com/l2zkjw6

World Health Organization (WHO)

Content on occupational health.

Website: www.who.int/occupational_health/en/

Your Health and Safety at Work

Guide with 12 modules on OSH.

International Labour Organization (ILO)
Website: ilo.org/safework/info/instr/WCMS_113080/lang--en/index.htm

Ergonomics

Ergonomic Checkpoints: Practical and easy-to-implement solutions for improving safety, health and working conditions

International Labour Organization (ILO)
Website: ilo.org/wcmsp5/groups/public/@ed_protect/@protrav/@safework/documents/instructionalmaterial/wcms_178593.pdf

Chemicals

See discussion and list of helpful websites on pages 463 to 464.

Machine injuries

Safety and Health in the Use of Machinery

Guidelines for workers and employers.

International Labour Organization (ILO)
Website: ilo.org/safework/info/standards-and-instruments/codes/WCMS_164653/lang--en/index.htm

Electricity

Safety and Health for Electrical Trades: A Student Manual

A NIOSH publication for workers.

NIOSH
Website: cdc.gov/niosh/docs/2009-113/
pdfs/2009-113.pdf

Noise

Noise at work

Training module that includes health effects of noise, and how to measure and control noise.

International Labour Organization (ILO)
Website: ilo.org/public/libdoc/
ilo/1996/96B09_331_engl.pdf

Ventilation

General Ventilation in the Workplace: Guidance for Employers

An accessible guide for employers and workers on implementing good ventilation systems.

Health and Safety Executive
Website: ucu.org.uk/media/pdf/f/g/
HSG202_-_Ventilation.pdf

Social dangers

Wages

Asia Floor Wage Alliance

International alliance of trade unions and labor rights activists working to achieve a living wage for garment workers in all of Asia.

Website: cleanclothes.org/livingwage/
asia-floor-wage-alliance

Home-based work

Self-employed Women's Association (SEWA)

Women's trade union comprised of self-employed women workers. Their program HomeNet represents, organizes, and supports home-based workers around the world to improve working and living conditions.

Opp. Victoria Garden, Bhadra,
Ahmedabad - 380 001, INDIA
T : +91 (79) 2550-6444
Website: sewa.org

Women workers and women's health

Health and safety for women and children

Basic information on how work affects women and children. Special focus on reproductive and developmental health.

International Labour Organization (ILO)
Website: ilo.org/public/libdoc/
ilo/1996/96B09_338_engl.pdf

Promoting Gender Equality: A Resource Kit for Trade Unions

6 booklets on gender equality in unions, including collective bargaining and organizing for women workers' rights.

International Labour Organization (ILO)
Website: workinfo.com/free/links/gender/
cha_0.htm

Working for Life: Sourcebook on Occupational Health for Women

Covers occupational health, safety, and welfare issues of working women in all industries.

Isis International
Website: amrc.org.hk/content/working-life-sourcebook-occupational-health-women

Migration

Guide to Labor and Employment Laws for Migrant Workers in North America

Covers labor laws, resources for migrants, and on-the-job safety and health for Canada, Mexico, and the United States. Available in English, Spanish, and French.

Commission for Labor Cooperation
Website: naalc.org/migrant/english/pdf/guide_en.pdf

The Migrating Women's Handbook

Information and practical tips about travel documents, visa requirements, residency, work permits, wages, and how to protect your rights.

GAATW International Secretariat
Website: gaatw.org/books_pdf/migrating_woman_handbook.pdf

Child labor

Trade Unions & Child Labor: A Guide to Action

Set of 7 booklets on child labor laws, how to draft proposals, run campaigns, and use ILO standards.

International Labour Organization (ILO)
Website: ilo.org/actrav/projects/WCMS_112597/lang--en/index.htm

Access to health

Occupational health: A manual for primary health care workers

This WHO book trains health workers to identify and treat workplace health issues. 12 modules include ergonomics, stress, and first aid.

World Health Organization (WHO)
Website: who.int/occupational_health/publications/emhealthcarework/en/

Reproductive and sexual health

Male and female reproductive health hazards in the workplace

Background information on how occupational dangers affect the reproductive health of men and women.

International Labour Organization (ILO)
Website: ilo.org/public/libdoc/ilo/1996/96B09_337_engl.pdf

Violence

Guidelines on Sexual Harassment Prevention at the Workplace

Handbook defines harassment and outlines how workers and employers can prevent it and respond to complaints.

International Labour Organization (ILO)
Website: betterwork.org/in-labourguide/wp-content/uploads/2012/05/L-GUIDE-2011-Guidelines-on-Sexual-Harassment-Prevention-at-the-Workplace-MoMT-LG.pdf

How to respond to rape and other gender-based violence: A guide for survivors and activists

Covers personal care and filing legal charges. Also provides guidelines for community action, campaigns, and activities.

Treatment Action Campaign (TAC)
Website: tac.org.za/sites/default/files/
publications/2012-11-28/Gender-based-
violence-book-web.pdf

Stop sexual harassment and violence at work: Smart guide for workers

A guide to recognizing and preventing sexual harassment and violence at work.

International Labour Organization (ILO)
Website: ilo.org/public/libdoc/
ilo/2014/114B09_41_engl.pdf

HIV and AIDS

COSATU Booklet on the Campaign Against HIV/AIDS

Explains AIDS and HIV, its transmission and prevention. Addresses workplace conditions and outlines union responses in developing HIV policies for the workplace.

COSATU
Website: cosatu.org.za/show.php?ID=1474

HIV/AIDS and the World of Work

ILO Global Program on HIV/AIDS

Website: ilo.org/aids

Workplace action on HIV/AIDS: Factsheets 1 to 6

International Labour Organization (ILO)
Website: ilo.org/public/libdoc/
ilo/2006/106B09_308_engl.pdf

TB (tuberculosis)

Guidelines for Workplace TB Control Activities

Information about TB, and education and training materials for employers and workers.

Website: weforum.org/pdf/Initiatives/
GHI_Guidelines_WHO_TB.pdf

TB Treatment Brochure

Treatment Action Campaign (TAC)
Website: tac.org.za/publications/tb-
treatment-brochure

Environment

A Community Guide to Environmental Health

Offers information, stories, and activities to develop simple health technologies and introduces a wide variety of environmental health issues including water, sanitation, food security, pollution, and others.

Hesperian Health Guides
Website: en.hesperian.org/hhg/A_
Community_Guide_to_Environmental_
Health

Index

This index lists topics covered in the book in the order of the alphabet.
Chemical names that begin with numbers appear first, before the letter A.

1 2 3 4 5 A B C D E F G H I J K L M N O P Q R S T U V W X Y Z

Page numbers in **bold** (for example **527–528**) are the main page numbers for information about chemicals.

E

Notes

Other Titles from Hesperian Health Guides:

Where There Is No Doctor, by David Werner, Carol Thuman and Jane Maxwell, is the most widely used health manual in the world with information on how to diagnose, treat and prevent common diseases, emphasizing prevention and the importance of community mobilization. 512 pages.

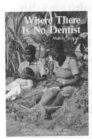

Where There Is No Dentist, by Murray Dickson, shows how to care for teeth and gums at home, and in community and school settings. Detailed, illustrated information on dental equipment, placing fillings and pulling teeth, teaching hygiene and nutrition, and HIV and oral health. 248 pages.

A Community Guide to Environmental Health, by Jeff Conant and Pam Fadem, helps urban and rural health promoters, activists and community leaders take charge of environmental health from toilets to toxics, watershed management to waste management, and agriculture to air pollution. Includes activities, how-to instructions, and stories. 640 pages.

Health Actions for Women, by Melissa Smith, Sarah Shannon and Kathleen Vickery, was field tested by 41 community-based groups in 23 countries and provides a wealth of clearly explained and engagingly illustrated activities, strategies and stories that address the social obstacles and practices that prevent women and girls from enjoying healthy lives. 352 pages.

Where Women Have No Doctor, by A. August Burns, Ronnie Lovich, Jane Maxwell and Katharine Shapiro, combines self-help medical information with an understanding of the ways poverty, discrimination and cultural beliefs limit women's health and access to care. Clearly written and with over 1000 drawings, this is an essential resources for any woman who wants to improve her health. 600 pages.

Helping Health Workers Learn, by David Werner and Bill Bower, is an indispensable resource that makes health education fun and effective. Includes activities, techniques, and ideas for low-cost teaching aids, and presents strategies for community involvement through participatory education. 640 pages.

A Book for Midwives, by Susan Klein, Suellen Miller and Fiona Thomson, is an invaluable training tool and practical reference for midwives and anyone concerned about care for women in pregnancy, birth and beyond. This book discusses preventing, managing and treating obstetric complications, covers HIV in pregnancy, birth and breastfeeding, and has extensive information on reproductive care. 544 pages.

A Health Handbook for Women with Disabilities, by Jane Maxwell, Julia Watts Belser and Darlena David. This handbook provides groundbreaking advice and suggestions from women with disabilities worldwide, and helps women with disabilities improve their health, self-esteem, and ability to care for themselves and participate in their communities. 416 pages.

Disabled Village Children, by David Werner, covers most common disabilities of children, giving suggestions for rehabilitation and explaining how to make a variety of low-cost aids. Emphasis is placed on how to help children with disabilities find a role and be accepted in the community. 672 pages.

Helping Children Who Are Deaf, by Darlena David, Devorah Greenstein and Sandy Niemann, aids parents, teachers, and other caregivers to help deaf children learn basic communications skills and language. Includes simple methods to assess hearing, develop listening skills, and explore community support for deaf children. 256 pages.

Helping Children Who Are Blind, by Sandy Niemann and Namita Jacob, aids parents and caregivers of blind children from birth to age 5 develop all their capabilities. Topics include: assessing how much a child can see, preventing blindness, moving around safely, teaching common activities, and many others. 200 pages.

hesperian
health guides

1919 Addison St., #304
Berkeley, CA 94704 USA

All our books are available in multiple languages. See **www.hesperian.org** for details.

To purchase books:
tel: (510) 845-4507
toll free in the USA: (888) 729-1796
fax: (510) 845-0539
email: bookorders@hesperian.org
online: store.hesperian.org